Donald B. Ly[...]
The Arith. Tea[...]
<u>III</u> 3: 119-12[...]

<u>percentage-board</u>

<u>acoustic t.l.</u>

ARITHMETIC

Its Structure and Concepts

ARITHMETIC

Its Structure and Concepts

FRANCIS J. MUELLER

Chairman, Department of Mathematics
Maryland State Teachers College
Towson, Maryland

PRENTICE-HALL, INC.

Englewood Cliffs, N. J.

1956

PRINTED IN THE UNITED STATES OF AMERICA

04601

To my wife

PREFACE

It is my belief that much of the difficulty that learners have with arithmetic can be traced to a lack of understanding on the part of students—and often of teachers—of the basic concepts which underlie arithmetic. Thus this book has been written as a guided approach to arithmetic as a system of thought, as a rationale, rather than as a set of arbitrary rules to be mechanically applied.

Obviously such an understanding as this book aims at has an importance which is of value to anyone who is in any way concerned with the field of basic mathematics, vocationally or avocationally. As a consequence, it is expected that not only teachers in training and in service, but students in pre-freshman refresher courses, persons in adult education courses, even certain high school students, as well as the lone reader bent on self-improvement may derive various measures of benefit from these pages.

The adaptation of this book to any of its several possible uses is, I believe, made easier by the arrangement of its material into short and interchangeable units, providing for considerable flexibility of content and order. For example, should it be felt desirable to place less emphasis on the material which deals with number scales other than the decimal (Units 5, 6, 9, 11, 14), or assign these units as extra work, or omit them entirely, one may do so without disrupting the mainstream of discussion; also the units on fractions (Units 19–26) may be introduced earlier and developed concurrently with those dealing with whole numbers. The algebraic parallels which are interjected from time to time for the benefit of the better prepared reader may be studied or omitted without loss of continuity.

While this text assumes no previous mathematical background on the part of the reader, its discussions are pitched at a mature level. The problems which follow each unit are of the same level and are designed to provoke thought as well as to test mastery of computation.

I am especially grateful to Dr. Harold Moser, of State Teachers College, Towson, Maryland, who supplied the initial impetus to this work as well as helpful suggestions along the way; to Mr. Phineas P. Wright, also of the Towson faculty, who diligently criticized and anglicized these writings; to my father, Mr. Frank Mueller, and to Miss Jean Wastler for their typing; and to my wife, Charlotte, who by serving as both father and mother to our brood made possible the many hours necessary in the preparation of this book.

F. J. M.

CONTENTS

approximate numbers, *256*. 4. Multiplication with approximate numbers, *257*. 5. Division with approximate numbers, *260*. 6. Multiplication and division when one number is exact, *262*.

FOREWORD

IN RECENT YEARS a radical change has been occurring in the teaching of arithmetic. The old school of thought, happily in the descendancy, held that arithmetic is little more than a mechanical skill, something like typing; and that there was no real need for one to *understand* what he was learning any more than a typist needs to understand why the letters have been so arranged on the keyboard of a typewriter: the fact that things work better that way is reason enough.

The new school of thought which looks upon arithmetic as a rational process, a system for *thinking*, holds that the truths of arithmetic can be more effectively taught and better retained when the meanings of the processes are stressed. Otherwise the teaching of arithmetic is little more than training someone in the memorization of nonsense syllables. Adherents of this latter point of view are the promoters of *meaningful mathematics*.

Dr. Brownell, in a study of meaningful *vs.* mechanical learning, has in relatively few words contrasted the positions of these two schools of thought particularly well. He says,*

[There is] . . . genuine doubt on the part of some students of arithmetic instruction that children need to understand what they learn. For them it is enough if children develop high degrees of skill, no matter how devoid of meaning. Ballard stated their position thirty years ago: ". . . for pure practical efficacy it is better that the rationale should not at the actual time of working be thought of at all. The pupil should confine his efforts to a rigid application of the rule." The "intelligence" afforded by rationalization is only a "temporary illumination." To take time to engender understanding is wasteful, and the effect may be merely perplexity on the part of learners. If rationalization is provided at all, it should come some time (years) after initial instruction. The best methodology, therefore, is to give children at the outset the procedure we want them to have, and then to furnish an abundance of practice . . .

During the last twenty years or so, students of arithmetic in increasing numbers have been taking a different position in the matter of meaning or understanding. Admittedly, they can point to little research in arithmetic

* Brownell, William A. and Moser, Harold E., *Meaningful vs. Mechanical Learning: A Study in Grade III Subtraction.* Duke University Research Studies in Education, No. 8. Durham, North Carolina: Duke University Press, 1949, pp. 19–20.

to support them (not more than a score or two of studies). For the most part they have had to rely upon arguments, two of which are mentioned here. One argument is negative: mechanical instruction in arithmetic, which has dominated American schools for the last generation and longer, has not produced the kind of quantitative competence which is demanded by modern society. (This is not the place to assemble the evidence for this statement, but there is plenty of it.) In other words, the argument goes, since mechanical learning gets nowhere, a change is called for, and the logical change (or what is apparently the logical change) is a shift to meaningful learning.

The second argument is based upon educational research (other than in arithmetic) and, much more importantly, upon psychological research in which it has been unmistakably shown that meaning facilitates learning. For example, Lyon, reporting in 1914, stated that his subjects required, on the average, 93 minutes to learn 200 nonsense syllables, 85 minutes to learn 200 digits, 24 minutes to learn 200 words of prose, and 10 minutes to learn 200 words of poetry. And Reed found that it took his subjects, college students, an average of 111.25 seconds to learn nine lines of simple prose narrative, while it took them an average of 261.25 seconds to learn the same amount of material from Hume's *The Origin of Ideas* (which assumedly was less meaningful to them). In a retention test his subjects recalled an average of 49 ideas of the total of 67 in the simple narrative as compared with an average of 11.5 of the 67 ideas in a passage of the same length from Hume.

So consistent is the evidence in psychological research respecting the contribution of meaning to learning that McGeoch in his scholarly summary of data on human learning states: "It is probable, on the basis of available data, that there is a very high positive correlation, and perhaps a perfect one when other things are equal, between meaning and rate of learning."

From this it follows that if one is to impart arithmetic in a meaningful way to others he needs first to understand the subject that way himself. Simply knowing the skills of arithmetic (and there are precious few adults and college students who do know even that) while necessary is by no means sufficient qualification. However, this adventure into arithmetic which we are about to begin is intended to help considerably in meeting such a qualification; the extent to which it is successful depends largely upon the reader. Its plan is to teach or reteach, as the case may be, the "hows," or skills, of the subject through its "whys," or meanings.

The pursuit of our subject will be at a mature level and is designed to impress a thinking adult. Thus it is not a course in methods **for** teaching at specific grade levels. The philosophy of this approach holds that first and foremost the teacher must have complete control of the subject he teaches; only after that can he profit from a study of the psychological ways of imparting this knowledge at the various levels, which is method. Taking first things first, our task is the former; other texts will provide for the latter.

Chapter 1

NUMBER

Unit 1: Beginnings of Number

1. *Introduction*. Arithmetic is a system of thought, the product of thinking men. Through the centuries its concepts have been originated, shaped, and improved upon by man to aid him in his struggle with the quantitative problems posed by his environment.

Fundamental to arithmetic is the concept of number. Whether man is born with a number sense, as some believe, or whether number came to him originally by insight, or both, is for us an unsettled question. However it did begin, it should be clearly understood that number is not found *in* things; it is imparted *to* things by the observer as he attempts to generalize, to make less vague his experience. The fact that the frame of reference is within man, rather than external to him, is significant. It accounts for the fact that different men at different times and at different levels of civilization have produced different methods for coping with the quantitative situations of reality. As might be expected, some of these various approaches have proved to be more effective than others.

One notable feature of the civilizing process is the ability to profit from the experiences of others. Thus we shall witness the growth, from meager beginnings, of intricate systems of number and even more intricate and complex systems of computations with these numbers. And it is important to note that in every case such systems are entirely the product of man's mind. In no instance are they the product of some God-given revelation or the necessary reflection of some natural law. Mathematically, at least, man is the measure of all things.

2. *One-to-One Correspondence*. Recognition of the advantages of acquiring possessions is one important stage in the civilizing process.

Now if it is wise to acquire things, it is equally wise to keep track of these things. When one's possessions are few, no intricate system of accounting is necessary. A flock of three sheep hardly presents a problem in accounting for its owner; simply a glance will serve to tell whether or not there is one or more missing. But it is a different matter when the flock reaches the size of ten or twelve. Perhaps here the accounting function might be taken care of by giving to each sheep a name or descriptive title, like "Blackie" or "Whitey" or "Limp-ear." The Biblical passage concerning the Good Shepherd saying, "I know mine and mine know me" is not entirely metaphor. Even so, the limitations of such a system are evident.

How then, for example, might a shepherd of a large flock account for his sheep? There is ample historical evidence that primitive man frequently hit upon a rather ingenious device, one which is basic to much of our modern-day mathematics. It is the principle of one-to-one correspondence. By matching each sheep in his herd with an item in a collection of objects, such as pebbles, sticks, or knots in a thong, the shepherd provided himself with an accurate accounting record, one that was entirely independent of a counting *system*.

Of course, such a technique had its limitations, too. It treated total quantity only in a relative way, in terms of more, less, or equal to. Should the shepherd find in the evening when matching returning sheep with his pile of stones that there was an excess of stones, he was immediately aware that some of his sheep were still out on the hillside. Exactly how many, or which ones, he could not tell. Even today, when we are primarily interested in the question of majority or deficiency we frequently use this technique. Tabulating ballots in a club election or checking the empty seats when marking roll in the classroom are illustrations.

Now the transition from relative number of this sort to specific number is not too great a one. In fact, it seems that a natural extension of this one-to-one matching was the formulation of *model groups*. This technique utilized certain well-known items from one's immediate environment to symbolize or serve as a model for a given collection. Such symbolizing was not too abstract, at least not in the beginning, for each item was chosen because of some characteristic which was typical of the given *model group*. Thus the wings of a bird might symbolize *two*, leaves of clover *three*, legs of a certain animal *four*, the hand *five*, and so on. To anthropologists one measure of the degree of civilization which has been attained by a tribe is the extent to which that tribe has developed number words. Even today, for some primitive tribes the total number vocabulary consists only of *one, two,* and *many.*

In order to characterize the size of a given collection by this model-group method, one had to test the collection member by member against his models until the right one was found. Used in proper context the *names* of these models would then convey the same information as an appropriate pile of pebbles. With increased use, these model names underwent gradual and further changes; in some languages certain number names can actually be traced back to such realistic origins. Thus we have an example of a very familiar historical pattern, the gradual retreat from concreteness toward abstraction in the interest of certain economies. The vocabularies of all of us contain countless abstract words which in their beginnings were beautifully descriptive and incisively meaningful. Later we shall see that similar situations abound in the study of arithmetic. The computations which we all perform today have been considerably mechanized and organized through the years in the interests of time and space. Today they are such a far cry from their meaningful origins that there is small wonder that most children and many teachers have little appreciation of what they are doing in arithmetic beyond following a certain routine.

3. *Counting.* The advent of model groups, though a major step in the direction of counting, did not in itself constitute counting. Here was recognition of number in its *cardinal* (how many) sense only. No array of models, regardless of extent, in itself constitutes counting. The essence of counting lies in its system, and system implies order. Not until man has arranged his models in a certain order, and what is even more important, not until he is fully aware of the principle underlying this order, does he have a counting *system.*

We might surmise that once man had set up these model groups, it would not have taken him long to notice a natural succession, or sequence, among his models. Investigations into primitive cultures do not support this conclusion. The time lapse between the use of models and recognition of some principle for ordering these models was considerable. This bears out the fact that ability to detect order and sequence is not an inborn trait, but one that must be acquired.

For teachers this point is significant, for it follows that there is little likelihood that children will come to a full appreciation of the number *system* by haphazard experiences with model groups. In other words, while it is true that by manipulating groups of five blocks, bundles of five straws, or piles of three stones, clusters of three soldiers, the child will gradually gain an appreciation of "fiveness" and "threeness," these and similar experiences will not in themselves lead to an understanding of our number *system*. The task of developing in the student a consciousness of the systematic aspects of number rests heavily upon the teacher. Number, arithmetic, and all of mathematics beyond must be approached as the *system of thought* which it is. To look upon it as a hodgepodge of accepted facts, which somehow the student must swallow whole while in school so that they may be regurgitated in equal wholes later on when practical circumstances require, is largely wasted effort.

Once man has cleared this hurdle of arranging his set of models in accordance with some ordering principle (increase by one) he has at his disposal a counting set which possesses both cardinal (how many) and ordinal (which one) features. These we call the *natural numbers*.

To determine now the size of one's herd, that is, its cardinal number, one no longer needs to test various models to find the appropriate one; instead a person counts to it. Further, ordering one's models in this way makes it possible for one to differentiate among particular members of a group, to note position in a series. House numbers, dates, telephone numbers, serial numbers are a few examples of our use of number in this sense. These are referred to as *ordinal* numbers.

It is interesting to note that although most of the problems of arithmetic are concerned with the "how many" (cardinal) aspect of a situation, basic to computation is the ordinality of the system, which is to say that it is always possible to move from one number to its successor. The fact that number always has a systematic successor, which is itself a number and which in turn has another number for its successor, is a concept that over the years has challenged the best of men's minds. While we will avoid a discussion of infinity here, plainly this circumstance does result in problems for the creator of a counting system. For if man's environment were such as to present him with no problems involving number beyond seven, seven models (or their symbolic representations) properly ordered would be sufficient. Or if today nature somehow ordained that groups would never exceed twenty-six, then the letters of our alphabet, with their present arrangement (A = one, B = two, C = three, . . . , Z = twenty-six), would serve adequately. For the face of a clock which marks the time of day, the number system need never exceed twelve.

But reality is not so restricted. In fact reality in its quantitative phases races well beyond man's ability to invent and retain in proper sequence an adequate set of models. So man counters with increased systematization within his counting system. Subsequently we shall investigate certain systems of notation which have been developed by man in different cultures in an attempt to maintain pace with reality. Some, as implied earlier, proved to be better systems than others. Of more than just casual interest, however, they offer the reader an excellent opportunity to learn by contrast. The study of the results of these attacks upon the problem of counting, the appraisal of their respective weak points and strong points, the ferreting out of the basic principles which make a particular system tick, should further one's ability to criticize and understand his own.

PROBLEMS SET 1

1. Give five instances in which the technique of one-to-one correspondence is used.

2. In the instances given in Question 1, compare the advantages and disadvantages of counting over the technique of one-to-one correspondence.

3. Look up the following words in a good standard collegiate dictionary; choose what you think to be the most appropriate definition for the term as it is used in our particular context:

> cardinal   model   system
> count   ordinal

4. Develop a series of models taken from familiar surroundings today to represent groups from one through six.

5. Identify the following as illustrations of cardinal or ordinal number:

(a) Henry VIII
(b) 60 apples
(c) 7-day week
(d) CEntral 6-3205
(e) March 21
(f) Fifth Symphony
(g) Seven Liberal Arts

(h) License Number CE-62-82
(i) Failures: 0
(j) 100-page book
(k) Page 37
(l) A class of 35 pupils
(m) Team mascot with jersey number "0"

6. Give five additional examples of number used in a cardinal sense; number used in an ordinal sense.

7. Give three examples in which the number has both ordinal and cardinal properties.

8. How might the letters of our alphabet be made to represent number concepts beyond twenty-six?

Unit 2: Egyptian System of Notation

1. *Introduction*. We introduce in this and the next unit, as illustrations, three systems of number notation. Though they are the product of man's thought in different eras and in different cultures, they are not intended to demonstrate interrelationships or evolutionary trends. They are presented here, first, to show that at other times in an effort to meet the quantitative situations of his environment, man has developed systems of counting radically different from our own; and second, to provide for the reader a certain variety of background which will be helpful when he tackles an analysis of his own system, that familiar number notation known as the Hindu-Arabic system.

2. *Principles and Accidentals*. While studying these unfamiliar systems, the reader will do well to concentrate on their respective *principles*, for these constitute the essence of the system. From the principles the system derives its structure and organization, which in turn directly influences its application.

The symbols chosen by these various people for their systems are perhaps of passing interest, but other than that, they bear little consequence to the system itself. These symbols and the choice of compounding point (point at which new sizes or denominations are introduced) might be referred to as some of the *accidentals* of the system. Accidentals are things which are not fundamentally necessary to the system for it to function; they do, however, provide the vehicle by which the principles manifest themselves. It follows that should we change the accidentals (and we shall do so later when we introduce other bases and other symbols) the system itself remains unaffected. On the other hand, to change the principles is to change the system itself. In order fully to understand a system (which is our intent) it is necessary that the reader clearly distinguish in his investigations between that which is essential to the system and that which is only accidental to it, namely, those things which without detriment to the system *could have been otherwise.*

An illustration may be helpful in pointing up this distinction between principles and accidentals. Objects in motion exhibit certain patterns of behavior, obeying the laws of motion first expressed by Sir Isaac Newton. These laws of motion are three in number: (1) A body in motion tends to remain in motion in a straight line and a body at rest tends to remain at rest unless otherwise acted upon. (2) The acceleration of a body is directly proportional to and takes the direction of the force acting upon it. (3) For every action there is an equal and opposite reaction.

In terms of our definitions, these three laws can be thought of as the basic principles which underlie all motion. Should such motion involve the flight of an airplane, the dropping of a coin, the bounce of a basketball, or the movement of a planet, in each case one or a combination of these fundamental principles is reflected. And furthermore, whether or not the moving objects are airplanes or birds, coins or rocks, basketballs or footballs, large planets or small planets is a matter of complete indifference to the actual principles in operation. Therefore we term these latter things, these qualifiers, the accidental aspects of motion. Notice that a principle cannot manifest itself without the presence of the accidentals which clothe it, modify it, and give it substance. Principles, the essence of the matter, are by nature intangible, while the accidentals are tangible; the accidentals are the things which we perceive, the principle we learn either by abstraction or revelation. But once the principle is grasped, we have control of something which is worth more than ten thousand specific illustrations. Thus the unswerving aim of this book: *a comprehension of the principles which underlie the whole of arithmetic.* Some of these principles we shall learn by revelation (statements by the text or instructor) while others we shall discover by the more self-satisfying method of abstraction. Like the laws of motion, the principles of arithmetic are relatively few. And once they are understood, these principles are like so many passkeys, readily available to open up the countless locks of arithmetical problems.

3. *The Egyptian System of Notation.* The ancient Egyptians had attained a high degree of civilization many centuries before the time of Christ. Among their various accomplishments was a form

of picture writing known as hieroglyphics. Included in this, to satisfy their number requirements, was a set of numerical symbols. Undoubtedly at one time the choice of these symbols was significant, for in effect they represented model groups. The Egyptians did not set up a model group for each quantity; instead they evolved a system of compounding which permitted coverage of a wide range of values with a limited symbolism. These symbols are given in Table I. Note the systematic way in which new symbols were introduced (powers of ten).

In its operation this system followed a simple pattern. The symbol for one was the stroke I, the symbol for two was one written twice II, three III, and so on to nine IIIIIIIII. Up to this point the system was hardly more than a tally method of one-to-one correspondence. At ten a compounding took place and the heel bone symbol ∩ replaced what would have been ten strokes. As the Egyptian counted on toward higher values, his notation grew by accretion. Thus what we call twelve was ∩II, eighteen ∩IIIIIIII, twenty ∩∩, forty-three ∩∩∩∩III, etc. At the hundred a new symbol, the scroll ⊙, was introduced for what otherwise would have been ten heel bones. Essentially the value of any Egyptian number was precisely the sum of its parts. In this light we say that the

TABLE I. EGYPTIAN NUMBER SYMBOLS OR NUMERALS

Hindu-Arabic	Egyptian Symbol	Description
1	I	Vertical stroke
10	∩	Heelbone
100	⊙	Coil of rope, scroll
1,000	⚘	Lotus flower
10,000	⌐	Bent line
100,000	↶	Burbot
1,000,000	𓀠	Man in astonishment

Egyptian system of notation was governed by the principle of *addition*.

The second principle upon which this system was based has already been observed: *repetition*. Repeating the basic symbols usually took care of cases of multiplicity for the Egyptians, except in those instances where a new symbol was substituted for ten of a lower order. Here are the expressions of several numbers in both our Hindu-Arabic system of notation and the Egyptian.

$$2,664 = \text{⌓⌓ ⌒⌒⌒ IIII}$$

$$3,702 = \text{⌓⌓⌓ ⌒⌒⌒⌒ II}$$

$$10,082 = \text{⌐ ⌒⌒⌒⌒ II}$$

Would you say that both systems operate in accordance with the **principle** of addition? What about the principle of repetition?

4. *The Abacus.* It is pertinent here to introduce the most ancient form of computing machine, the abacus. In its operation the basic principles of the Egyptian system, repetition and addition, are forcefully illustrated. Furthermore, when it is looked at from a slightly different point of view, the abacus demonstrates with specific clarity the basic principles of our own system of notation, the Hindu-Arabic. But first consider the forerunner to the abacus, man's fingers.

Suppose a man is faced with the problem of putting a group of objects into one-to-one correspondence with his fingers. He will start by ticking off fingers and objects in successive pairs until he has exhausted all his fingers. If there are still more objects to be counted, he is faced with the following alternatives: (1) stop counting and characterize the group of objects as "more than ten," or (2) find more fingers (what about toes?), or (3) somehow record the fact that the ten fingers have been used once and are now released for further duty. The latter is by far the most ingenious of the possible solutions, though it is at best only a temporary one. For if his objects are sufficiently numerous, the man will soon exhaust his fingers again. Faced with this obstacle he may see that that which worked once may well work again, record the fact that two full hands have been counted, and go on. Theoretically there is no limit to this approach, save the availability of means of recording tens. He might realize an economy in this direction, however, should he extend his trick of recording "tens of ones" to "tens of tens" also. This very thing the Egyptians did with their symbols *heel bone* and *scroll.* The abacus accomplishes it with different strands of beads.

Figure 1 shows a simplified version of the abacus. There are ten beads, called unit-beads, on the first strand at the right. These correspond to man's ten fingers and to the Egyptian's unit strokes. In order to count a collection of objects, the beads of the units-strand are (by sliding them up) placed in one-to-one correspondence with the objects until beads or objects are exhausted. To record the fact that the ten unit-beads have been used once, one bead in the second column is slid to the top, and the ten unit-beads are then slid back down to their "zero" position, ready for future use. The abacus now records one ten (which equals ten ones) and no units. To record the eleventh, twelfth, and thirteenth objects, this system would call for, respectively, one, two, and three beads at the top in the company of the one ten-bead (see Figure 2). Eventually there will be ten beads again at the top in the unit column; here again one bead in the second column is slid to the top to replace the ten unit-beads, making once more the ten unit-beads available for action. Thus the "one ten and ten ones" is replaced by "two tens and no ones." Should our counting take us on beyond the hundred, the

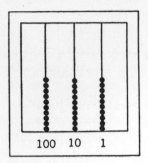

Figure 1. Abacus in zero state.

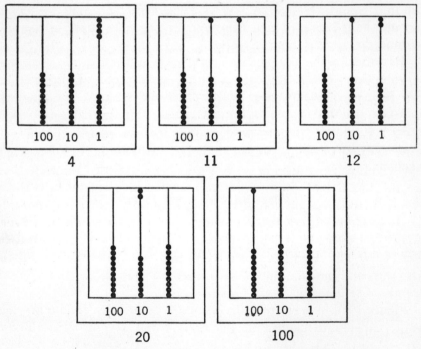

Figure 2. Abaci recording 4, 11, 12, 20, and 100.

second column will eventually possess ten beads at the top. This calls into action the beads in the third column, each of which is intended to record "tens of tens." Thus ninety-nine would be recorded as nine beads up on the unit-strand and nine beads up on the tens-strand. Adding one more, the hundredth, on the unit-strand would make ten there and call for a substitution of one bead on the tens-strand. But this means ten beads are up on the tens-strand, which in turn may be substituted for by one on the next strand to the left, the hundreds-strand. Thus one hundred would be recorded as one bead up on the third strand and none up on the second and first (see Figure 2). Notice the resemblance here between our Hindu-Arabic symbol for one hundred and the position of the beads on the abacus.

To save time manipulating the beads at the substitution or compounding points, a modified version of the abacus might contain only nine beads on each strand. To count by ones on this form of the abacus we have: one—one unit-bead up; two—second unit-bead up; three—third unit-bead up . . . nine—ninth unit-bead up; ten—nine unit-beads *down*, first ten-bead up, etc. Similarly, one hundred would be recorded by pushing *down* the nine ten-beads and nine unit-beads (which recorded the previous ninety-nine) and pushing up the first hundred-bead.

Historically the abacus has been found in a multitude of forms, varying somewhat with local conditions and systems of numeration. The Roman counting board, the Japanese *soroban*, the Chinese *suan-pan* are but three of its variations. Furthermore, teachers today are finding this ancient device a real aid in the elementary classroom, for there is much that can be taught by this simple machine.

PROBLEMS SET 2

1. Look up the following words in a good standard collegiate dictionary; choose what you think to be the most appropriate definition for the term as it is used in our particular context:

        accidental   compound   principle
        base   notation

2. Discuss briefly either the Ten Commandments or the Constitution of the United States in terms of principles and accidentals.

3. Using the Egyptian system of notation, write the symbols for num-

bers from one to twenty-five; from eighty-eight to one hundred four; from nine thousand nine hundred ninety-six to ten thousand twelve.

4. Translate the following numbers from the given Hindu-Arabic symbolism to Egyptian symbolism.

234	780	82,024
425	1,300	340,322
562	1,403	999,999
604	2,007	1,000,001

5. What explanation can we give for the fact that the Egyptian failed to include among his number symbols a symbol for zero?

6. If the Egyptians had to contend, as we do today, with values of tens of millions, billions, and even trillions, how do you suppose they would have handled it in their system of notation?

7. Make simple sketches showing the bead arrangement on a nine-bead abacus of the numbers of Question 4.

8. Suppose the Egyptians had been born with a total of *five* fingers instead of ten. Develop for them a system of notation, guided by the same principles of addition and repetition, which would be effective for numbers up to at least three thousand. (*Hint:* use the same symbols I, ∩, etc., with newly defined values.) Write the numbers in such a system from one to thirty.

9. Using pennies, nickels, and quarters, and lines drawn on a sheet of paper, develop a variation of the abacus that will work in conjunction with the system developed in Question 8. Demonstrate on this abacus the following values:

three	twenty
seven	twenty-four
nine	twenty-five
ten	twenty-six
twelve	eighty
fourteen	one hundred six
fifteen	one hundred twenty-four
sixteen	

10. Compare the abacus arrangements for the values under thirty in Question 9 with the symbolic representation for these same values as found in Question 8.

Unit 3: Greek and Roman Systems of Notation

1. *The Greek System of Notation.* The ancient Greeks had three important number notation systems, the oldest of which we shall consider here. For symbols the Greeks used the twenty-four letters of their alphabet and three obsolete forms borrowed from an earlier alphabet. They were assigned values as shown in Table II.

TABLE II. GREEK NUMERALS WITH HINDU-ARABIC EQUIVALENTS

1	α	alpha	10	ι	iota	100	ρ	rho	1,000	$\prime\alpha$
2	β	beta	20	κ	kappa	200	σ	sigma	2,000	$\prime\beta$
3	γ	gamma	30	λ	lambda	300	τ	tau	3,000	$\prime\gamma$
4	δ	delta	40	μ	mu	400	υ	upsilon	4,000	$\prime\delta$
5	ϵ	epsilon	50	ν	nu	500	ϕ	phi	5,000	$\prime\epsilon$
6	ς	vau*	60	ξ	xi	600	χ	chi	6,000	$\prime\varsigma$
7	ζ	zeta	70	o	omicron	700	ψ	psi	7,000	$\prime\zeta$
8	η	eta	80	π	pi	800	ω	omega	8,000	$\prime\eta$
9	θ	theta	90	P	koppa*	900	λ	sampi*	9,000	$\prime\theta$

* Obsolete symbols.

As in the Egyptian system of notation, the principle of *addition* was applied in the evaluation of Greek numbers below ten thousand. For instance,

$\tau\mu\epsilon$ where $(\tau = 300) + (\mu = 40) + (\epsilon = 5)$
$= 300 + 40 + 5 = 345$

$\prime\beta\chi\zeta$ where $(\prime\beta = 2,000) + (\chi = 600) + (\zeta = 7)$
$= 2,000 + 600 + 7 = 2,607$

When numbers appeared in context, an accent sign or a line drawn above the symbol usually distinguished letters used as numerals from letters used as words. For numbers greater than ten thousand, however, a special multiplying technique was employed. A twenty-eighth symbol, M, was introduced to represent ten-thousand. When one of the other symbols was written above the M, this compounded symbol then stood for ten-thousand times the upper symbol. Thus

$\overset{\beta}{\mathrm{M}} = 20,000$ (two ten-thousands)

$\overset{\epsilon}{\mathrm{M}} = 50,000$ (five ten-thousands)

$\overset{\delta}{\mathrm{M}}\tau\mu\epsilon = 40,345$ (four ten-thousands plus three hundred
plus forty plus five)

Thus we see illustrated the second principle used in the Greek system of notation, the principle of *multiplication*.

What the Greeks were able to accomplish with their system was an over-all economy of symbolism which could not be matched by the Egyptian system, or for that matter, by our own. This conciseness of notation, however, was achieved at the expense of memory burden. Whereas the Egyptian needed to learn only three symbols to record values less than a thousand, the Greek needed to master twenty-seven. In the Hindu-Arabic one needs to know all ten of its symbols to accomplish this same end.

The Greek system of notation, shown in Table II, like the Egyptian, has also a *base of ten*, but it differs in that specific symbols are assigned first to each of the units, then to each decade (10^1), then to each hundred (10^2), then to each thousand (10^3) and finally to the ten thousand (10^4). Unlike the Egyptian system the Greek system does not involve the principle of repetition.

In all, the Greek system of notation was a particularly cumbersome one, and even less conducive to computation than either the Egyptian or Roman which we shall see below. The Greeks were not unique with their alphabet numerals, for the Hebrews and the Syrians too used their alphabet symbols in a similar dual capacity.

2. *Roman System of Notation*. Before the invention of the printing press, letters and symbols had a habit of changing over the years. We will ignore the instances of this in the Roman system of notation and discuss the essentials of this system in terms of the more modern symbols I, V, X, etc.

TABLE III.   ROMAN NUMERALS

1	I
5	V
10	X
50	L
100	C
500	D
1,000	M

Like the Egyptian and Greek, the Roman system of notation employed the principle of *addition*. That is, the value of any given number is equal to the sum total of its parts. Similarly, it may be characterized as a decimal scale, leaning more toward the Egyptian type than the Greek. Special symbols, mostly unused relics of the

Grecian alphabet, represented certain powers of ten: I = units, X = tens (10¹), C = hundreds (10²), M = thousands (10³). An economy of symbolism was effected by the Roman system with the introduction of mid-values in each of these orders. Thus V = five (mid-ten), L = fifty (mid-hundred), and D = five hundred (mid-thousand). The principle of *repetition* was utilized with respect to the basic ten-power symbols of I, X, C, and M to form other numbers. For example:

III = three   CCCXXIII = three hundred twenty-three
XXXII = thirty-two   MMCCII = two thousand two hundred
                                two

To handle the larger numbers, a third principle, *multiplication*, met previously in the Greek system, was put into use. A bar drawn over portions of the number indicated that those symbols covered were to be multiplied by one thousand, then added to the remaining symbols of the number expression to effect its total value. So

$\overline{\text{XXXII}}$ = twenty thousand twelve (20,012)
$\overline{\text{XXXV}}$ = thirty-five thousand (35,000)
$\overline{\text{MMMD}}$ = three million, five hundred thousand (3,500,000)

Still a fourth principle, that of *subtraction*, came into being at a later date. It is claimed by some historians that this was an invention of the early clockmakers, who were hard pressed for space on the faces of their clocks. Whatever the case, by substituting IV for IIII and IX for VIIII a more economical notation was certainly achieved. Had this contraction been restricted only to the specific values of four and nine, however, we would not have a principle but merely a special case. In today's version of Roman notation we do see in effect the principle of subtraction. It operates specifically with respect to the *fours and nines of each order*. Thus

IV = four   XL = forty   CD = four hundred
IX = nine   XC = ninety   CM = nine hundred

But this saving in symbolism produces in turn a new problem. Heretofore, in each of the systems considered, the value of the number expression was not materially affected by the sequence in which the symbols were written. And while undoubtedly there existed in the various systems certain standard procedures or techniques which governed the writing of numbers, still the Egyptian could realize twenty-three from ∩II∩I, as could the Greek from a mixed-up γκ. But here in the Roman system coupling I and V, for instance, could mean either six or four, depending upon whether the addition or subtraction principle was to operate. Thus we see as a necessary adjunct to the principle of subtraction a rule of right order. For the Roman system it is this: symbols are to be written from left to right in order of decreasing value, and the principle of addition applies; the only exceptions to this order are the pairs I before V or X, X before L or C, and C before D or M, in which case the subtraction of the left numeral from the right is indicated.

This rule has been interpreted by some as a sort of forerunner of the principle of place value which is so important to the Hindu-Arabic system of notation. It must be admitted that there is a certain amount of logical overlap, though historically there seems to exist no relationship.

Great as the Romans were as conquerors, builders, and engineers, it can be safely stated that they did not accomplish these glorious triumphs through a superior system for counting and computing. Rather, it might be said to their credit that they accomplished these marvelous feats in spite of what they had. The Romans produced a system which was more concise than that of the Egyptians and less burdensome to the memory than that of the Greeks, though more complex in structure than either (witness its four principles as opposed to the others' two). Like the others mentioned, the Romans also found the need for an abacus of sorts in order to perform computations beyond the very simplest. Recognition of both the fact and the degree to which these ancients must have been hampered by the lack of what is so commonplace today —a really workable system of numerical notation—certainly adds significantly to the monumental stature of their achievements, especially in engineering.

PROBLEMS SET 3

1. Using the Greek symbolism, write the numbers from one to forty; from ninety to one hundred seven. Do likewise in the Roman system of notation.

2. Translate the following numbers written in our familiar Hindu-Arabic notation to equivalent number expressions in: (a) the Greek system of notation, (b) the Roman system of notation.

234	1,000	8,409
449	1,492	82,024
562	1,703	340,322
780	4,006	760,004

3. Translate the following Greek numbers to their equivalents in the Hindu-Arabic system.

$$νθ \qquad φλα \qquad \overset{β}{\mathrm{M}ρλ}$$

$$ωπη \qquad {}_{\prime}βιβ \qquad \overset{ε}{\mathrm{M}}{}_{\prime}βσπδ$$

$$τγ \qquad {}_{\prime}θχ \qquad \overset{κδ}{\mathrm{M}φγ}$$

4. Generally speaking, the Greek system realized an economy of symbolism superior to our own. Cite four specific examples of numbers in which fewer symbols are required in the Hindu-Arabic expression than in the equivalent Greek expression.

5. Translate the following Roman numbers to their equivalents in the Hindu-Arabic notation.

XXIX	CMLVIII	M̄CDXI
XLVI	CMXLIX	CD̄XIII
LXXVIII	MCMLVI	L̄X̄CXVIII
CCII	MDCXLVI	M̄DIX

6. Why do you suppose the Romans and Greeks, like the Egyptians, failed to include a symbol for zero among their numerals?

7. So far we have discussed four principles: repetition, addition, subtraction, and multiplication; which if any would you say apply to the Hindu-Arabic system?

8. Using four pennies, one nickel, four dimes, and one half-dollar, and lined paper, make an abacus which would serve the Roman system of notation for values up to one hundred. Demonstrate on this abacus the following values.

three	forty-six
eight	fifty-two
fifteen	sixty-seven
twenty-one	eighty-eight
forty-four	ninety-one
forty-five	ninety-nine

Unit 4: Our System of Notation

1. *The Hindu-Arabic System.* Historians are at odds concerning the specific origins of the Hindu-Arabic system of notation. Actually it was not until the close of the nineteenth century that scholars were fully aware of the fact that the numerals of our system were of Hindu origin. The Arabs, a highly nomadic people, had at an early date come into contact with the Hindu notation, picked it up without using it generally, and transmitted it to the Europeans. This system, first noted by European scholars in Arabian works, was presumed Arabian in origin, and thenceforth referred to as Arabic. Only much later were the Hindu influences discovered and proper credit given. Though it was known in Europe as early as the thirteenth century A.D., the advantages of this "heathen system" were not immediately appreciated, with the result that it was not until the sixteenth century that the Hindu-Arabic succeeded in overcoming the inertia of the old Roman system. It is significant indeed that the eventual general acceptance of this new method of notation, with its computational advantages, coincided with the early developments in modern scientific study.

The Hindu-Arabic system of notation, like the Greek system, is nonrepetitive; that is to say, a new and different symbol is assigned for each of the early numbers. But whereas the Greek system continues to introduce new symbols well beyond nine, the Hindu-Arabic at this point has introduced all of its symbols except one— the all-important zero. A similarity with the Egyptian system can be noted in that there is a significant compounding at each power of ten, but there is no limit to the number of compounding points possible. Thus the Hindu-Arabic system is also one of scale ten (decimal). Finally, in the Hindu-Arabic system as in the Roman, position of the symbols or numerals is important for proper interpretation of a number's value.

In summary, we might characterize the Hindu-Arabic system of notation as one based upon two principles: the first, common to each of these three foregoing systems, is the principle of *addition;* the second, which was unique, is the principle of *place value.*

2. *Hindu-Arabic Numerals.* Although the exact date and place of origin of the Hindu-Arabic numerals is unknown, it is believed that they had been used as early as five or six centuries before the time of Christ. In its earliest stages, the Hindu-Arabic system of notation did not contain the zero character; without it this system

was no better off than some of the others which we have discussed. The earliest known use of the Hindu-Arabic zero occurs in an Indian inscription, dated at 876 A.D. The unquestioned superiority of the Hindu-Arabic system of notation over all others stems directly from the invention and use of this null symbol, the zero.

The basic characters employed in the Hindu-Arabic system of notation are the 0, 1, 2, 3, 4, 5, 6, 7, 8, 9. These ten characters are generally referred to as *digits* and comprise all the necessary symbolism required of this system of notation. Each of these digits is a cardinal number in its own right, a representative, as it were, of a model group. For example, the symbol 1 conveys the concept of singleness or oneness, the symbol 3, the concept of tripleness, the symbol 0, absence or emptiness, and so on. This characteristic we shall refer to as the "face value" of a numeral.

In order to extend the Hindu-Arabic system beyond nine, that point at which all the basic symbols have been expended, the necessity of some sort of compounding becomes evident. Whereas other systems had met this problem by merely introducing some new symbol, the Hindus hit upon one of the most ingenious ideas of all times: that of place value.

Under such a scheme, each numeral operates in a dual capacity, one with respect to its "face" value, and the other with respect to its "place" or location value. Taken at "face" value, the symbol 3 represents three of something; the symbol 7 represents seven of something; the symbol 1, a single something; the symbol 0, absence of something; and so on. "Place" value establishes whether this "something" is units, tens of units, tens of tens of units (hundreds), tens of tens of tens of units (thousands), and so on. These "somethings" are known technically as *orders* and turn out, in the decimal scale, to be consecutive powers of the base, ten.

With the aid of the principle of addition, the compounding scheme of the Hindu-Arabic system of notation becomes possible. To express the next natural or counting number beyond nine (the point at which all our original symbols had been used up) we write 10, which readily signifies to those who understand the system "one ten and no units." The next natural number after ten is eleven, which is symbolized as 11, and signifies "one ten and one unit"; the next is twelve, 12, which signifies the sum (principle of addition) of "one ten and two units" (principle of place value). After all pairs of the basic numerals (except 0 in the tens place) have been so utilized, we find ourselves at ninety-nine, faced with the necessity of pressing three-digit combinations into service. Thus

$$100 = 1 \text{ hundred } + \text{ no tens } + \text{ no units}$$
$$= (1 \times 10^2) + (0 \times 10^1) + (0 \times 1) = 100 + 0 + 0$$
$$387 = 3 \text{ hundreds} + 8 \text{ tens } + 7 \text{ units}$$
$$= (3 \times 10^2) + (8 \times 10^1) + (7 \times 1) = 300 + 80 + 7$$

Later, four-digit combinations must be called upon:

$$1{,}406 = 1 \text{ thousand} + 4 \text{ hundreds} + 0 \text{ tens } + 6 \text{ units}$$
$$= (1 \times 10^3) + (4 \times 10^2) + (0 \times 10^1) + (6 \times 1)$$
$$= 1{,}000 + 400 + 6$$

and so on. There being no limit to the number of places which are theoretically possible under such a scheme, it follows that there is no limit to the number of natural numbers which may be expressed symbolically in this system.

3. *Exponential Notation.* As the topic of "powers of the base," already occasionally met with, will arise frequently hereafter, it will be advantageous to discuss the matter of exponential notation. In the following chapter we shall discuss multiplication as a case of repeated addition of the same number: for example, $2 + 2 + 2 + 2 = 4 \times 2 = 8$. In like manner, "raising to a power" may be considered as repeated multiplication of the same number. Thus $2 \times 2 \times 2 = 2^3 = 8$; $3 \times 3 \times 3 \times 3 = 3^4 = 81$.

Descartes, the great French philosopher and mathematician, is usually credited with introducing this particular type of shorthand notation, known as exponential notation. It simplifies writing out the product of identical factors such as $N \times N \times N \times N \times N$ by expressing the typical factor (known as the *base*) and then attaching to it a number (known as the *power* or the *exponent*) which tells how many times the factor is repeated.

$N = N^1$ $4 \times 4 \times 4 = 4^3$
$N \times N = N^2$ $7 \times 7 \times 7 \times 7 \times 7 \times 7 = 7^6$
$N \times N \times N \times N = N^4$ $10 \times 10 \times 10 \times 10 \times 10 = 10^5$
$N \times N \times N \times N \times N \times N = N^6$ $32 \times 32 \times 32 \times 32 \times 32 \times 32 = 32^6$

In practice, the more-frequently used second and third powers have taken on a somewhat special terminology. Specifically, N^2, which can be read generally as "N raised to the second power," is more often read as "N-squared," and N^3, which would generally be read as "N raised to the third power" is more often expressed as "N-cubed." Thereafter, N^4 simply becomes "N raised to the fourth power" (or "N to the fourth"), N^5 is "N raised to the fifth power" (or "N to the fifth"), and so on.

However, exponential notation has values beyond economy of number expression. It is also a computational form. While it is not within our province to investigate this form of computation, there do exist laws and rules which govern it. A study of these is usually found in algebra, but since one phase of its use offers an alternative approach to two operations which are clearly within the province of arithmetic—multiplication and division—we shall at least state two of its laws without proof:

When numbers are expressed in exponential form with the same base:

1. *they may be multiplied by adding the exponents;*
2. *they may be divided by subtracting the exponent of the divisor from the exponent of the dividend.*

To illustrate these "laws," we have

(a) $6^3 \times 6^2 = 6^{3+2} = 6^5$. This seems reasonable, since $6^3 = 6 \times 6 \times 6$ and $6^2 = 6 \times 6$. Then

$$6^3 \times 6^2 = (6 \times 6 \times 6) \times (6 \times 6) = 6 \times 6 \times 6 \times 6 \times 6 = 6^5$$

(b) $5^7 \div 5^3 = 5^{7-3} = 5^4$. This can be verified by recognizing that

$$5^7 = 5 \times 5 \times 5 \times 5 \times 5 \times 5 \times 5 \quad \text{and} \quad 5^3 = 5 \times 5 \times 5$$

Then

$$5^7 \div 5^3 = \frac{5^7}{5^3} = \frac{\not5 \times \not5 \times \not5 \times 5 \times 5 \times 5 \times 5}{\not5 \times \not5 \times \not5} = 5^4$$

Before we end this brief discussion on exponential notation, let us analyze what N^0 (N to the zero power) would be. In light of the foregoing, N^0 could have come about either as the result of a multiplication or a division. Had it been multiplication, the factors must have been $N^0 \times N^0$, since only zeros will add to zero (assuming only positive exponents) and this sheds no light at all on the nature of N^0. But if N^0 had been the result of division, then there are any number of cases which could have produced such a result. For instance,

$$N^1 \div N^1 = N^{1-1} = N^0 \qquad N^8 \div N^8 = N^{8-8} = N^0$$
$$N^5 \div N^5 = N^{5-5} = N^0 \qquad N^k \div N^k = N^{k-k} = N^0$$

Note, however, that the only way in which one can get a zero in subtraction is to subtract a number from itself; hence the exponent of the dividend and the divisor must be alike if N^0 is to result. Moreover, since the base (N) must also be the same for each term, it follows that both divisor and dividend must be the same number. And since dividing a number by itself invariably results in a quotient of 1, it follows that *any number, whose exponent is zero, equals one.* Thus

$$N^1 \div N^1 = N^{1-1} = N^0 \quad \text{or} \quad \frac{N}{N} = 1$$

$$N^4 \div N^4 = N^{4-4} = N^0 \quad \text{or} \quad \frac{N \times N \times N \times N}{N \times N \times N \times N} = 1$$

$$N^a \div N^a = N^{a-a} = N^0 \quad \text{or} \quad \frac{N \times N \times \ldots \times N \ (a \text{ times})}{N \times N \times \ldots \times N \ (a \text{ times})} = 1$$

By implication, also: $2^0 = 1$, $10^0 = 1$, $(37\frac{1}{2})^0 = 1$, $x^0 = 1$, etc.

4. *The Abacus and Hindu-Arabic Notation.* As was stated earlier, the abacus can be particularly helpful in visualizing the place value aspect of our Hindu-Arabic system. Recall that in Unit 2 we discussed a modified version of this device which consisted of strands each containing nine beads. To adapt this instrument to our system would require only that we interpret the various strands from right to left as ascending powers of ten, and to each bead on each strand from top to bottom we assign distinct values of 1 through 9.

To count we start with the bead in the right (units) column and mark each count by sliding one bead to the top half of the rack. After nine (all nine unit-beads at the top), ten is shown by the presence of the first (1-bead) at the top in the second column (the tens column) and none at the top in the units column. Thus we see that when the denomination lines are clearly drawn, the zero symbol is not necessary: the absence of unit-beads at the top speaks for

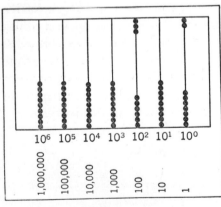

Figure 3. Abacus showing 302.

itself. In the Egyptian, Greek, and Roman systems denomination lines were clearly drawn through different symbols. Take the number "three hundred two" as an example. On the abacus it would be shown as in Figure 3, in the Egyptian system 999ΙΙ, in Greek $\tau\beta$, and the Roman CCCII. The fact that there was no ten present was stated indirectly by an absence of the ten character ($\cap$; ι, κ

etc.; X) from the number expression. So long as orders or denominations are clearly evident, no special symbol for absence is necessary.
But in the Hindu-Arabic system where specific denomination mark-
ings are stripped away except for relative location of the symbols,
some kind of null place holder or spacer becomes a necessity. The
choice here was the now familiar oval character, 0, called by us the
zero or *cipher*. In fact these two words come to us from the Arabic
sifr (*zero* via the Italians) which was a translation of the Sanskrit
word *sunya*, meaning "vacant." Thus our number three hundred
two would be written in the Hindu-Arabic as 302. Without such a
spacer 3 2 could easily be confused with the symbol representing
thirty-two.

The expression of larger numbers on the abacus clearly illustrates
the principle of addition, as well as the grouping concept of number.
An appreciation of this will be necessary for understanding the
computations which we perform with these symbols, the content
of the next several chapters. To further illustrate, picture six hundred twenty-five on the abacus: six beads up on the hundreds
column, two on the tens column and five in the units column. In
symbols it is 625. The thirteen beads, each according to its respective denomination, contribute to the total of six hundred
twenty-five. Similarly the symbol 625 implies a total of "thirteen
somethings": *six* hundreds, *two* tens, and *five* units—total six hundred twenty-five.

5. *An Algebraic Approach.* Though a knowledge of algebra is not
needed to follow the mainstream of discussion in this text, there is
no denying that such a knowledge would materially aid the under-
standings which one may derive from these discussions. So, we shall
introduce from time to time, wherever it is deemed helpful, the
algebraic parallel for the benefit of those who might profit from it.
After all, algebra is nothing more than generalized arithmetic, and
seeing the general case often aids in appreciating the specific.

Algebraically any whole number can be expressed as a polynomial of the form

$$N = a_n x^n + a_{n-1} x^{n-1} + a_{n-2} x^{n-2} + \ldots + a_2 x^2 + a_1 x^1 + a_0 x^0$$

Thus $7{,}627 = N$

where $x = 10$ and $a_n = a_{n-1} = \ldots = a_4 = 0; a_3 = 7; a_2 = 6; a_1 = 2; a_0 = 7$

$$7{,}627 = (7)(10^3) + (6)(10^2) + (2)(10^1) + (7)(10^0)$$
$$= (7 \times 1{,}000) + (6 \times 100) + (2 \times 10) + (7 \times 1)$$

and $82,009 = N$
where $x = 10$ and $a_n = a_{n-1} = \ldots = a_5 = 0; a_4 = 8; a_3 = 2; a_2 = a_1 = 0; a_0 = 9$.
$$82,009 = (8)(10^4) + (2)(10^3) + (9)(10^0)$$
$$= (8 \times 10,000) + (2 \times 1,000) + (9 \times 1)$$

6. *Numeration.* A practical requirement for any system of notation is a technique for expressing its numbers in words. This is known as numeration. Its convenience depends heavily upon consistency and simplicity, which it draws in large measure from the notational system itself. Nevertheless, numeration is arbitrary, could have been otherwise, and therefore is one of the accidental aspects of any system of notation. As a matter of fact, certain large numbers, such as 632,497,688,502,437, would be read quite differently in each of the two English-speaking countries, the United States and Great Britain.

As has already been demonstrated, in the Hindu-Arabic system each digit contributes to the over-all value of the number in accordance with both its symbolic (face) value and its location (place) value. The "faces" are limited to ten in number, but the "places" are unlimited. These places are reckoned from the right to the left in successively higher powers of the base, ten. Single-digit numbers are said to be of the first order and are called units. Two-digit numbers involve two places, tens and units, and are spoken of as second-order numbers. Three-digit numbers involve three places, hundreds, tens, and units, and are referred to as third-order numbers, and so on. To read a single-digit number we merely pronounce its name: three, five, eight. To read a two-digit number, such as 63, we say "sixty-three," a contraction of a more descriptive "six tens and three." This is consistent for all two-digit numbers from twenty (two-tens) and beyond. The 'teens, from 13 to 19 inclusive, follow a slightly different pattern of contraction: for example, "thirteen" is a shortened "three and ten" and "eighteen" a modified "eight and ten." Eleven and twelve came into our language from the old Teutonic *ainlif* and *twalif*, which are literally "one left over [after counting ten]" and "two left over [after counting ten]." It might be noted that a conscious study of numeration, besides its immediate practical values, offers the reader still another viewpoint on the basic structure of his notational system.

Third-order or three-digit numbers are all characterized by the presence of the word "hundred" in their verbalization. "Hundred" is the English term associated with the concept of ten tens, or exponentially 10^2. Fourth-order numbers are referred to as "thousands," which means ten tens of tens, or 10^3. Thereafter, new names are introduced every third power, or period: million, 10^6; billion, 10^9; trillion, 10^{12}; etc. A *period*, in the United States, is a group of three digits, starting with the units place and working left. Periods are set off by commas and are treated in the reading of a number in much the same manner as a complete phrase is treated in a sentence. Proper numeration technique in this country calls for the reading of a number by periods, starting at the left or greatest period. Each period is subdivided into hundreds, tens, and units. Thus (a) in Table IV would be read: six hundred four trillion, five hundred eighty-seven billion, six hundred thirty-nine million, five hundred two thousand, six hundred seventy-eight (units understood).*

TABLE IV. NUMERATION SCHEME (UNITED STATES)

←	10^{18}	10^{17}	10^{16}	10^{15}	10^{14}	10^{13}	10^{12}	10^{11}	10^{10}	10^9	10^8	10^7	10^6	10^5	10^4	10^3	10^2	10^1	10^0
	Quintillions	Hundred-quadrillions	Ten-quadrillions	Quadrillions	Hundred-trillions	Ten-trillions	Trillions	Hundred-billions	Ten-billions	Billions	Hundred-millions	Ten-millions	Millions	Hundred-thousands	Ten-thousands	Thousands	Hundreds	Tens	Units (ones)
(a)					6	0	4	5	8	7	6	3	9	5	0	2	6	7	8
(b)												3	2	0	0	0	2	7	5

Sometimes periods are skipped, as in (b) of Table IV. Zero spacers are of course needed in writing the number symbolically, but in reading it absent periods are simply by-passed in the same way the Romans, Greeks, and Egyptians did in writing theirs. In this manner, (b) would be read as thirty-two million, two hundred seventy-five.

The opportunities for reading numbers in excess of fifteen digits (trillions) are somewhat rare. Still the systematic pattern of nomenclature for successively higher periods is worthy of note. The names for the period beyond the million are a combination of the Latin number stem followed by -illion. Historically, the word million (a thousand thousands) was invented by the Italians of the fourteenth century to signify a "big thousand" (*mille*-thousand, *on*-big). Shortly thereafter the words billion, trillion, quadrillion, quintillion,

---

* Note the lack of the word "and" in reading a whole number. Strictly speaking, and with good reason, the use of the word "and" is limited to separating the whole and fractional part in the reading of a mixed number. This will be better appreciated later in Chapter 5, after we have discussed fractions and decimals.

sextillion, etc., were introduced. These denoted successive powers of the million:

$$(1,000,000)^2 = \text{billion } (10^{12})$$
$$(1,000,000)^3 = \text{trillion } (10^{18})$$
$$(1,000,000)^4 = \text{quadrillion } (10^{24}), \text{ etc.}$$

This numeration was eventually adopted by Germany and England about the eighteenth century and is in use today in these countries.

However, the French around the middle of the seventeenth century began the practice of dividing their number expressions into periods of three digits, rather than six, while keeping the same sequence of names for successive periods beyond the million. Thus the words billion, trillion, quadrillion, quintillion, etc., were in effect redefined to mean 10^9, 10^{12}, 10^{15}, 10^{18}, etc., respectively. Along with many of the countries of Southern Europe, the United States has adopted this French variation. The number (a) in Table IV, which was read in the United States style in an earlier paragraph, would be read by the English as six hundred four billion, five hundred eighty-seven thousand six hundred thirty-nine million, five hundred two thousand six hundred seventy-eight.

7. *Alternative Expressions of Number.* An interesting and important extension of the numeration scheme is worthy of consideration here. Generally speaking, when a number is given such as 82,465, units is implied in the absence of any mention of another denomination. In other words, 63 is sixty-three of whatever one (the unit) is. But this does not prohibit the expression of a number in terms of other denominations when they are specifically mentioned. Thus the number 4,000 (units implied) has the following equivalent expressions: 4 thousands, 40 hundreds, 400 tens. A glance at the chart of Figure 4 makes this obvious. An everyday illustration of this interchange is our decimal money scale and its two chief denominations, the dollar and the cent. Thus 3,600 units (cents) = 36 hundreds (dollars). Also 3,600 units (cents) = 360 tens (dimes). Later on when this system of notation is extended to fractional values and the decimal point is

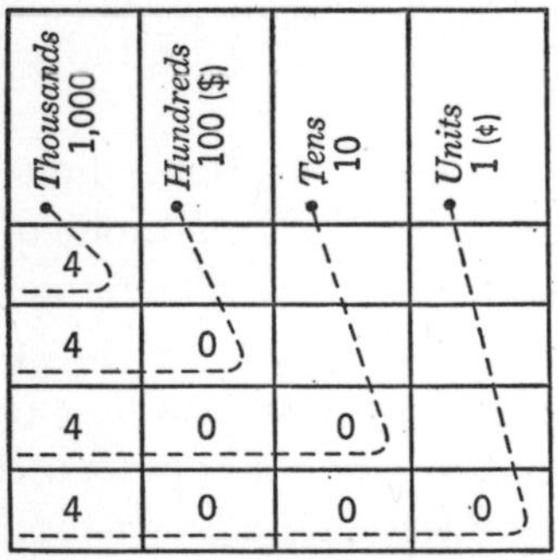

Figure 4. Equivalent expressions of same number.

introduced as a designator of the basic denomination, this concept will have further developments and values. Meanwhile a working knowledge of the interrelationships which exist among the various denominations (orders) for integral values (whole numbers) will be of considerable immediate aid to the reader in several of the units which follow.

PROBLEMS SET 4

1. Compare in as many ways as possible the Hindu-Arabic system to the notational system used by the Egyptians, Greeks, and Romans. Compare the four systems as to their difficulty in teaching.

2. Express exponentially:
    (a) $6 \times 6 \times 6 \times 6$
    (b) $10 \times 10 \times 10 \times 10$
    (c) $3 \times 4 \times 3 \times 4 \times 3 \times 4$
    (d) $2 \times 5 \times 2 \times 5 \times 2 \times 5 \times 2$
    (e) $2 \times 4 \times 8 \times 16$

3. Solve the following exponentially:
    (a) $3^7 \times 3^3$ (f) $M^a \div M^b$
    (b) $5^4 \div 5^3$ (g) $3^8 \div 3^8$
    (c) $10^5 \div 10^2$ (h) $6^4 \times 6^0$
    (d) $27^3 \div 27^2$ (i) $3^3 \times 3^4 \div 3^2$
    (e) $k^a \times k^b$ (j) $2^4 \times 2^6 \div 2^{10}$

4. Sketch pictures of an abacus showing the following numbers.

    36, 306, 603, 427, 32 tens, 43 hundreds, 304 tens, 60 hundreds

*5. Identify the elements $(a_n x^n)$ of the following numbers when expressed as an algebraic polynomial.

$$36,827, \quad 4,032, \quad 46, \quad 201, \quad 3$$

6. Write in words the following numbers:
    (a) 3,642,307   (e) 4,000,000,003
    (b) 8,633,333   (f) 4,000,362,000
    (c) 42,362,857   (g) 6,300,000,027
    (d) 463,872,921,683   (h) 42,000,000 thousands

7. Write in symbols as one number:
    (a) Three hundred seven million, four thousand, sixty-eight
    (b) Four million, three hundred seventy thousand, two hundred four
    (c) Seven and a quarter thousand
    (d) One and a half million

* For those who understand the algebraic parallels.

(e) Sixteen and three-quarter billion

(f) Fifty-two trillion, seven

8. Write in words Question 6(e, f, g) and Question 7(e, f) as the English would.

9. Convert the following to denominations of tens, hundreds, thousands.

(a) 4,000,000 units

(b) 632,000 units

(c) 8,720 hundreds

(d) 6,072 millions

(e) 4,362,500 units

10. Show how the integral linear measurements of the metric system (meter, dekameter, hectometer, kilometer) use the interrelationship of denominations to advantage in converting from one measure to another. Compare this with our English system of measure (inch, foot, yard, mile).

11. How many complete (a) thousands, (b) hundreds, (c) tens are there in the following?

$$6,327,498, \quad 52,437,625, \quad 24,621, \quad 328$$

12. Write the largest four-digit number possible; the smallest four-digit number possible; the largest six-digit number possible; the smallest six-digit number possible.

13. Assume a stack of 500 sheets of paper is 1 in. high. From among the following choices pick the three measurements you think best describe the height of: (a) a million sheets of paper; (b) a billion sheets of paper; (c) a trillion sheets of paper.

(a) 50 ft

(b) 50 yd

(c) 1,000 yd

(d) 1 mile

(e) 30 miles

(f) 1,000 miles

(g) more than once around the world at the equator

Check your choices by working the problem out.

Units 5, 6:   Other Scales of Notation

1. *Choice of Base.* The selection of ten as a base or compounding point of our system of notation was more a physiological accident of nature than a rational choice. Actually the choice has little to commend it. Either eight or twelve would have made better selections because of their greater divisibility. On the other hand, when the system is extended into the realm of fractions, there are distinct advantages favoring prime numbers, such as seven or eleven, for a base, for then all systematic fractions would be irreducible and thus free of equivalences. For example, in our present decimal system, whose base is neither prime nor highly divisible, the decimal fraction

.64 actually stands for $\frac{64}{100}$, $\frac{32}{50}$, and $\frac{16}{25}$ simultaneously; such situations can not arise when the base is itself a prime number, because all the numerators will of necessity be relatively prime (lacking a common divisor) to the denominator which is a power of the base. But the die was cast when man was born with ten fingers—and probably for all eternity, too, despite the strong and forthright arguments of the Duodecimal Society of America, an organization actively dedicated to the replacement of ten by twelve as the base for our system of notation. In regard to this whole matter, Tobias Dantzig's words seem appropriate: "Those who see the hand of Providence in everything will have to admit that Providence is a poor mathematician."

Yet there are advantages to be gained from speculation on what might have been had man actually been born with, say, eight, or perhaps twelve fingers instead of his ten. Such conjecture leads to new scales of notation and offers an excellent opportunity to learn more about our own system by contrast. For in such instances, things which are essential to our system, the principles, remain invariant, while those things which are only accidental to the system, the details, differ from scale to scale. Moreover, consideration of these new scales carries an additional value for teachers in that they pose striking parallels to many of the difficulties which a young child encounters as he attempts to gain control over what is for him an equally strange system: the decimal system. Later on we shall expand our knowledge of other bases, permitting us to continue to parallel the path of the child as he moves with his number system into the arithmetic processes. If we learn nothing else from such an adventure, we shall certainly discover that the principles which underlie our arithmetic processes are not peculiar to base ten alone.

2. *Other Scales of Notation.* Let us now build up a few scales of notation involving a *radix* (base) other than ten. These scales will be designed to follow in accordance with the principles of addition and place value, characteristic of the Hindu-Arabic system of notation. Instead of ten distinct symbols, however, we shall sometimes need more, sometimes less, but the ever-necessary symbol for absence or nullity must always be among them. The compounding point will of course vary with the base selected. Actually we might introduce a brand new set of symbols for each new scale, but that would only complicate matters needlessly. After all, the symbols are merely arbitrary figures which represent certain concepts, and

are applicable in any scale. So we shall continue to use the familiar Arabic numerals 0, 1, 2, 3, 4, 5, 6, 7, 8, 9, augmenting this set or eliminating from it whenever necessary. In the beginning this may confuse the reader, but it should clear up easily once he gains a precise appreciation of what these symbols really are.

To keep matters straight in our ensuing discussions, it will be well to make a conscious distinction between the number-word, which represents a certain invariant quantitative concept, and its symbolic representation, which changes with each system of notation. Since the English language and the decimal scale of notation are used everywhere around us, we tend to pair the number-word and the symbol inextricably. Actually they are quite independent of each other. We tend to think, for example, of the word "seventeen" as always being expressed symbolically as 17, and 17 as always meaning "seventeen." Ordinarily we are not conscious of a tacit assumption operating here, namely, that the 1 stands for one group of ten ones and the 7 for seven individual ones, and that collectively in that context they represent seventeen. Suppose now it was agreed that the digit on the left should represent groups of a dozen rather than ten, and the digit on the right the usual units. Then 17 in this context would stand for a dozen ones and seven more, or nineteen all together. In just such a way we often speak of a person's height as, say, "five-six," tacitly implying that the first digit stands for feet (dozens of inches) and the other individual inches. Number expressions mean nothing unless the frame of reference is known, either stated or implied.

So, to repeat because it is important, number concepts and number expression are independent of each other; *number concept* is defined here to be a specific, invariant property of a thing or situation, much the same as its color or texture, while a *number expression* is but one way of characterizing that property. For example, the number property of the stars of the Big Dipper is invariant at seven; yet for primitive man his number expression for this concept of sevenness would have been his model group for seven. The Roman would have given it expression with his VII, the Greek ζ (zeta), the Egyptian |||||||, the Hindu-Arabic (base ten) 7, and the electronic calculator (base two) 111. Here we see six distinct *number expressions* all conveying the same basic *number concept* seven.

It follows then that since the number concept remains invariant despite its symbolism, we need an invariable means of communicating that concept. This we do by appropriating from the English language its counting terms. It is granted that these terms have grown directly out of our base ten system, but for purposes of our discussion we shall look upon them when used within the context of "other bases" merely as specific names for model groups. Thus to characterize a collection as being twenty in number, we mean only that there are precisely enough things in the collection to put them into one-to-one correspondence with the following set of terms: one, two, three, four, . . . , eighteen, nineteen, twenty. Only in one scale, the decimal, would the number twenty appear in the familiar form 20. In base twelve, the dozens scale, the appropriate numerical expression for twenty would be 18.

In the Hindu-Arabic system, it will be recalled, each digit contributes to the total value of the number in relation to its face and place value. Since we shall continue to use the Arabic symbols, the face values will be immediately understood, except in cases where the base exceeds ten. Here additional symbols must be defined, which we shall do at the time they are needed. In the matter of place value it will be further recalled that there existed a relationship between place and power of ten, the base. In other scales of notation this relationship between place and power of the base will remain invariant, an essential feature (principle) of the system; on the other hand, the choice of base, an accidental, will vary. This is to say that whereas the places from right to left in base ten are successive powers of ten—units, tens, hundreds, thousands, etc.—in base five, for instance, they would be successive powers of five— units, fives, twenty-fives, one hundred twenty-fives, etc. Similarly in base three they would be successive powers of three—units, threes, nines, twenty-sevens, etc.

Let us now investigate base five. For basic symbols we are going to need separate symbols for the number concepts absence, one, two, three, and four. These will be 0, 1, 2, 3, and 4, respectively. The quantity five is of course expressed as 10 (one base group of five, plus no units), and six as 11 (one base group of five, plus one unit), seven as 12 (one group of five plus two units), etc. In base three, another scale of notation, the number concept three would be expressed as 10, so separate symbols are needed only for absence, one, and two. All other number concepts beyond these are expressible as compoundings involving the basic digits and the principle of place value. In general the number of distinct symbols required, including zero, is always equal to the base. Thus in base six, six symbols are required: 0, 1, 2, 3, 4, 5, with the value six expressed

TABLE V. NUMBERS EXPRESSED IN VARIOUS SCALES OF NOTATION

Base ten	Base twelve	Base eight	Base five	Base three	Number-word (concept)
1	1	1	1	1	one
2	2	2	2	2	two
3	3	3	3	10	three
4	4	4	4	11	four
5	5	5	10	12	five
6	6	6	11	20	six
7	7	7	12	21	seven
8	8	10	13	22	eight
9	9	11	14	100	nine
10	T	12	20	101	ten
11	E	13	21	102	eleven
12	10	14	22	110	twelve
13	11	15	23	111	thirteen
14	12	16	24	112	fourteen
15	13	17	30	120	fifteen
16	14	20	31	121	sixteen
17	15	21	32	122	seventeen
18	16	22	33	200	eighteen
19	17	23	34	201	nineteen
20	18	24	40	202	twenty
21	19	25	41	210	twenty-one
22	1T	26	42	211	twenty-two
23	1E	27	43	212	twenty-three
24	20	30	44	220	twenty-four
25	21	31	100	221	twenty-five
26	22	32	101	222	twenty-six
27	23	33	102	1000	twenty-seven
28	24	34	103	1001	twenty-eight
29	25	35	104	1002	twenty-nine
30	26	36	110	1010	thirty
40	34	50	130	1111	forty
60	50	74	220	2020	sixty
70	5T	106	240	2121	seventy
125	T5	175	1000	11122	one hundred twenty-five
307	217	463	2212	102101	three hundred seven

as 10; in base ten: 0, 1, 2, 3, 4, 5, 6, 7, 8, 9, with the value ten expressed as 10; in base twelve: 0, 1, 2, 3, 4, 5, 6, 7, 8, 9, T (ten), E (eleven), with twelve expressed as 10. Table V gives the expressions in the various bases for number concepts one through thirty, plus a few more, in bases three, five, eight, ten, and twelve.

Numeration, it will be recalled, is the technique for reading numbers. According to Table V the number concept twenty-three takes on the following expressions: 212 (three), 43 (five), 27 (eight), 23 (ten), and 1E (twelve). In order to avoid confusion in both thought and action, it is suggested here that we read the above stated number expressions as "two-one-two, base three"; "four-three, base five"; "two-seven, base eight"; "two-three, base ten"; and "one-E, base twelve," much the same as we often read decimals (e.g., .62 as "point-six-two").

For a moment let us consider a type of abacus which would fit some of these scales. Since there were nine beads on each strand in the base ten system (no bead was necessary for zero), by extension, each strand of a base five abacus would require four beads; seven beads would be required for a base eight model, eleven beads for one of base twelve, and so on. (Recall Question 9, Problems Set 2.) Furthermore, since the principles of our system when applied to other bases have remained totally unchanged, basic abacus operations should also remain invariant. Actually the only change involves the number of beads one must go through per strand before a substitution (compounding) becomes necessary—an unimportant feature as far as the principles or essence of the "system" is concerned. This implies that not only are we able to record numbers using other scales, but we can also actually compute with such expressions.

3. *Algebraic Interpretation.* In the previous unit it was noted that any number N could be expressed in accordance with the Hindu-Arabic principles as

$$N = a_n x^n + a_{n-1} x^{n-1} + \ldots + a_2 x^2 + a_1 x^1 + a_0 x^0$$

where x equaled ten and $a_n \ldots a_0$ ranged over the single-digit symbols from 0 to 9 inclusive.

Other scales of notation differ from base ten in the value of x in the polynomial N and the range of single-digit values for $a_n \ldots a_0$. Thus the aforementioned 212 (three) for the number twenty-three would be

$$N = 212 \text{ (three)} = 2x^2 + 1x^1 + 2x^0$$

Since $x = $ three, we have

$$2 \text{ (three)}^2 + 1 \text{ (three)}^1 + 2 \text{ (three)}^0,$$

which is

$$2 \text{ (nine)} + 1 \text{ (three)} + 2 \text{ (one)} = \text{twenty-three}$$

Consider two hundred fifty-nine $= 197$ (twelve):

$$N = 1x^2 + 9x^1 + 7x^0 \quad \text{where } x = \text{twelve}$$
$$= 1 \text{ (twelve)}^2 + 9 \text{ (twelve)}^1 + 7 \text{ (twelve)}^0$$
$$= 1 \text{ (one hundred forty-four)} + 9 \text{ (twelve)} + 7 \text{ (one)}$$
$$= \text{two hundred fifty-nine}$$

4. *Change of Base.* In studying Table V we might conclude that
any given number ultimately will find some expression in each of
the bases. Take seventy, for instance. In base eight it is 106,
in base five, 240, in base twelve, 5T. In base ten, seventy is of
course 70. Since these are all symbolic representations of the same
thing, there must exist some relationship among them; and it should
be possible to translate numerical values from the decimal scale to
other scales and vice versa.

It will be advantageous to look upon these various numerical
expressions of a given number in the light of a packaging operation.
For instance, if we have twenty-four apples and wish to package
them for sale, we have a variety of possibilities. Packing them by
dozens will produce two packages of apples; by half dozens, four
packages; by eights, three packages, or if by tens, two full packages
of ten and four loose, individual apples. Or perhaps we should want
to package them by sixteens and fours, with the result of one package of sixteen and two packages of four. In any case, the total
number of apples involved, *whatever the packaging plan*, remains
invariant at twenty-four.

When we express a number in the decimal scale we assume a
packaging design in terms of units, tens, and powers of ten (units,
tens, hundreds, thousands, etc.). For each possible number (concept)
this design will render a unique minimum set of packages. Thus
the number seven thousand, four hundred sixty-eight produces this
unique minimum set: 7 thousands, 4 hundreds, 6 tens, and 8
individual units.

Furthermore, the fact that a given group of objects can be
packaged according to one design does not preclude other packaging

designs. The same seven thousand, four hundred sixty-five above could have equally well been packaged by units, dozens, gross, and great gross, namely four great gross, three gross, ten dozens, and four units—a design following twelves and powers of twelve. Thus by the principles of place value and addition:

$$N = \text{seven thousand, four hundred sixty-eight}$$
$$= 7,468 \text{ (ten)}$$
$$= 43T4 \text{ (twelve)}$$

Similarly, base five involves nothing more than a packaging design where the groups are units, fives, and powers of five. *In general any base B involves grouping by units, groups of B, and powers of B.*

From this evolve two practical problems: (1) How might we convert a number expressed in another base to one in base ten, and (2) How might we convert a base ten number to one in some other base? The remaining possibility of converting from a base other than ten to another base other than ten in effect can be considered a combination of these two problems.

Consider the first case. Suppose we are asked to find the decimal equivalent of 236 (seven). The packaging plan here is seven and powers of seven (namely units, sevens, forty-nines, three hundred forty-threes, etc.). Thus 236 (seven) means 2 forty-nines, 3 sevens, 6 units. Converting to decimal equivalents and computing we get

$$(2 \times 49) + (3 \times 7) + (6 \times 1) = 125 \text{ (ten)}$$

Another: convert T6E (twelve) to its equivalent number expression in the decimal scale.

$$T6E = (T \times \text{twelve-squared}) + (6 \times \text{twelve}) + (E \times \text{one})$$

In decimal terms,

$$T6E\text{(twelve)} = (10 \times 144) + (6 \times 12) + (11 \times 1)$$
$$= 1,523 \text{ (ten)}$$

The second case, that of converting from base ten to another base, is easily understood in terms of this packaging analogy. Suppose the problem is to change 1,523 (ten) to its equivalent expression in base twelve. This involves determining the minimum package arrangement when the packages are to follow powers of twelve: great gross, gross, dozens, units. We proceed as follows:

How many great gross (1,728) in 1,523? Answer: *none.*
How many gross (144) in 1,523? Answer: *ten* and 83 left over.

How many dozens (12) in the remaining 83? Answer: *six* and eleven left over.

Thus,

$$1,523 \text{ (ten)} = \text{(ten gross)} + \text{(six dozen)} + \text{(eleven units)}$$
$$= \text{(T} \times \text{twelve-squared)} + \text{(6} \times \text{twelve)} + \text{(E units)}$$
$$= \text{T6E (twelve)}$$

Another illustration: Convert 42 (ten) to a number in scale five. The package denominations here are powers of five: units, fives, twenty-fives, one hundred twenty-fives, etc. Performing the computations in the familiar decimal scale, it is obvious there are no 125's in 42. There is one 25, however, which when removed leaves a remainder of 17. In the seventeen there are three of the next smaller denomination, fives. When they are removed, two units remain. Thus we can see that while 42 (ten) = $(4 \times 10) + (2 \times 1)$, it can also be reorganized to $(1 \times 25) + (3 \times 5) + (2 \times 1)$, which in turn is expressible as 132 (five).

There is an alternative method whereby numbers in base ten can be translated into corresponding numbers of another base. This approach, by repeated division, based upon a rationale of repeated regrouping, has the advantage of less computation. To explain it, let us again proceed by analogy. Suppose we had four hundred twenty-nine pennies and set out to convert them to the smallest number of coins possible. For purposes of the problem we restrict ourselves to the following denominations: pennies, nickels, quarters, and a new coin: the "buck-and-a-quarter." Let this latter be defined as the equal of one hundred twenty-five pennies. Perhaps the significance of the choices of denominations is apparent to the reader at this point (powers of five).

Applying first our previous method of removal (continued subtraction) to this problem we arrive at the following distribution:

> 3 buck-and-a-quarters
> 2 quarters
> no nickels
> 4 pennies

For convenience in demonstrating the second approach (repeated division), all computations are done in the familiar decimal scale.

1. Divide the 429 pennies into groups of five pennies each. Result: 85 groups of five-pennies (nickels) and 4 pennies left over.
2. Then divide the 85 nickels into groups of five nickels each (quarters). Result: 17 quarters exactly, no nickels left over.

3. Now divide the 17 quarters into groups of five quarters each (buck-and-a-quarters). Result: 3 buck-and-a-quarters and 2 quarters left over.

Summarizing the result of this repeated regrouping process, we find that we have transformed the original pennies into

> 3 buck-and-a-quarters (five-cubed)
> 2 quarters (five-squared)
> 0 nickels (five)
> 4 pennies (units)

And as before, expressing this arrangement in scale five notation, we have 3,204 (five) = 429 (ten).

In review, this repeated division approach required in this problem three distinct computations (divisions):

$$\begin{array}{r} 85 \\ 5\overline{)429} \end{array}$$ Remainder 4 (pennies)

$$\begin{array}{r} 17 \\ 5\overline{)85} \end{array}$$ Remainder 0 (nickels)

$$\begin{array}{r} 3 \\ 5\overline{)17} \end{array}$$ Remainder 2 (quarters)

Since the quotient of one step becomes the dividend of the next, a more abbreviated arrangement is possible.

$$\begin{array}{r} 5\overline{)429} \\ 5\overline{)85} \\ 5\overline{)17} \\ 3 \end{array}$$

5)429
5)85 Remainder 4 (pennies)
5)17 Remainder 0 (nickels)
 3   Remainder 2 (quarters)
Result: 3,204 (five) = 429 (ten)

Three more illustrations are given below which employ the repeated division approach.

1. Change 125 (ten) to its equivalent in scale seven:

7)125
7)17 R 6
 2 R 3   *Ans.:* 125 (ten) = 236 (seven)

2. Change 1,523 (ten) to its equivalent in base twelve:

12)1523
12)126 R 11(E)
10(T) R 6)   *Ans.:* 1,523 (ten) = T6E (twelve)

3. Change 29 (ten) to its equivalent in base two:

$$2\underline{)29}$$
$$2\underline{)14} \ \text{R} \ 1$$
$$2\underline{)7} \ \ \text{R} \ 0$$
$$2\underline{)3} \ \ \text{R} \ 1$$
$$\quad \ 1 \ \ \text{R} \ 1$$

Ans.: 29 (ten) = 11,101 (two)

5. *Algebraic Interpretation of Changing Bases.* So as to make more concrete the algebraic parallel for changing bases, we shall demonstrate it side by side with some specific case. First we shall show a change in base from one other than ten to the decimal scale, and second, a change from the decimal scale to one other than ten.

1. Since any integer can be expressed as a polynomial:

$$N = a_nx^n + a_{n-1}x^{n-1} + a_{n-2}x^{n-2} + \ldots + a_4x^4 + a_3x^3 + a_2x^2 + a_1x^1 + a_0x^0$$

then the job of changing a number expression such as 6,325 (eight) to an expression in base ten simply requires an appraisal of it in terms of the polynomial; in this case we have N above, where x = eight and $a_n = a_{n-1} = \ldots = a_4 = 0$, and $a_3 = 6$, $a_2 = 3$, $a_1 = 2$, and $a_0 = 5$. Hence

$$\begin{aligned} 6,325 \ (\text{eight}) &= N \ (\text{ten}) \\ &= a_3x^3 + a_2x^2 + a_1x^1 + a_0x^0 \\ &= 6 \ (8)^3 + 3 \ (8)^2 + 2 \ (8)^1 + 5 \ (8)^0 \\ &= (6 \times 512) + (3 \times 64) + (2 \times 8) + (5 \times 1) \\ &= 3,185 \ (\text{ten}) \end{aligned}$$

2. The situation of converting a number (say 334) expressed in the decimal scale to some other scale of notation is expressed algebraically thus:

$$334(\text{ten}) = a_nx^n + a_{n-1}x^{n-1} + \ldots + a_5x^5 + a_4x^4 + a_3x^3 + a_2x^2 + a_1x^1 + a_0x^0$$

where the value of x has been decided (the base we are to change to, in this case five). The problem which remains is that of evaluating the coefficients a_n, a_{n-1}, $\ldots$, a_1, a_0. If we divide 334 by 5 we get a quotient of 66 and a remainder of 4. If we divide its polynomial equivalent by x we get

$$Q_1 = a_nx^{n-1} + a_{n-1}x^{n-2} + \ldots + a_5x^4 + a_4x^3 + a_3x^2 + a_2x^1 + a_1$$

and remainder a_0. Hence $Q_1 = 66$ and $a_0 = 4$.

If we divide 66 by 5, we get 13 and a remainder of 1. If we divide Q_1 by x we get

$$Q_2 = a_nx^{n-2} + a_{n-1}x^{n-3} + \ldots + a_5x^3 + a_4x^2 + a_3x^1 + a_2$$

and remainder a_1. Hence $Q_2 = 13$ and $a_1 = 1$.

If we divide 13 by 5 we get 2 and a remainder of 3. If we divide Q_2 by x we get

$$Q_3 = a_n x^{n-3} + a_{n-1} x^{n-4} + \ldots + a_5 x^2 + a_4 x^1 + a_3$$

and a remainder of a_2. Hence $Q_3 = 2$ and $a_2 = 3$.

If we divide 2 by 5 we get 0 and a remainder of 2. If we divide Q_3 by x we get

$$Q_4 = a_n x^{n-4} + a_{n-1} x^{n-5} + \ldots + a_5 x^1 + a_4$$

and a remainder of a_3. Hence $Q_4 = 0$ and $a_3 = 2$.

But if $Q_4 = 0$, this means that all the remaining coefficients $a_n = a_{n-1} = \ldots a_5 = a_4 = 0$. Thus the polynomial expression for 334 (ten) is

$$2x^3 + 3x^2 + 1x^1 + 4$$

where $x = $ five or 2,315 (five).

PROBLEMS SET 5

1. Make a table similar to Table V to show the counting numbers from one to thirty in the following scales: two, four, seven, eleven, and thirteen. Use the Arabic symbols wherever possible, and invent others when necessary.

2. Sketch an abacus of four strands (orders) which would be appropriate for the following scales: seven, eight, twelve, two. What number concept would be expressed when there is one bead at the top of each of the four strands?

3. Make a sketch of abaci showing representations of the following numbers.

(a) Six, nine, twelve—scale two

(b) Fourteen, twenty-four, fifty—scale five

(c) Seventy-six, three hundred seven, one hundred ninety-six, one thousand five hundred twenty-three—scale twelve

(d) Numbers of (c)—scale thirteen

(e) Numbers of (b)—scale four

4. Given the following symbols and their number concept equivalents:
$\triangle$ = absence, $-$ = one, $<$ = two, $\leq$ = three, $\square$ = four.

(a) What would be the base of a scale which would employ all these number symbols?

(b) Build a system of notation which employs these symbols and follows the principles of the Hindu-Arabic system; count to thirty with it.

5. Under the conditions established in this Unit, is a "base one" scale of notation possible?

6. How many single-digit symbols would be necessary in a system where the first compounding occurs at: (a) nine; (b) sixteen; (c) thirty-four? In each of these cases, respectively, what would be the number expression for: (d) nine; (e) sixteen; (f) thirty-four? In each of these cases, respectively, what would be the number expression for: (g) ten; (h) seventeen; (i) thirty-five?

7. Had we been born with a thumb and three fingers on each hand, we would undoubtedly be using a base eight system of notation today. What changes would be necessary in the mileage indicator (odometer) of your car under a base eight system?

PROBLEMS SET 6

1. Change the following number expressions to their equivalents in the decimal scale.

(a)	32	(four)	(f)	432	(eight)	(k) 5T6	(twelve)
(b)	321	(four)	(g)	10,010	(two)	(l) 4EE	(twelve)
(c)	405	(six)	(h)	2,222	(three)	(m) 107	(twenty)
(d)	327	(twelve)	(i)	4,021	(five)	(n) 461	(thirteen)
(e)	500	(six)	(j)	376	(nine)	(o) ETE	(twelve)

2. State what is wrong with these number expressions.

$$463 \text{ (five)} \qquad 405 \text{ (five)} \qquad 4{,}070 \text{ (six)}$$

3. Transform 341 (base n) to its decimal equivalent, when n takes on values five; six; seven; . . . ; twelve.

4. Find the equivalent number expression for 341 (ten) when the scale is five; six; . . . ; twelve.

5. Convert the following decimal expressions to the required base:

(a) 387 (ten) = ? (five)	(e) 995 (ten) = ? (twelve)
(b) 427 (ten) = ? (seven)	(f) 2,071 (ten) = ? (five)
(c) 363 (ten) = ? (six)	(g) 1,727 (ten) = ? (twelve)
(d) 42 (ten) = ? (two)	(h) 2,468 (ten) = ? (two)

6. In what scale would

(a) $3 + 2 = 11$	(c) $10 - 4 = 3$	(e) $4 \times 5 = 12$
(b) $3 \times 3 = 10$	(d) $12 - 5 = 6$	(f) $4 \times 5 = 32$

7. In what scale or scales would 53 be an even number? In what scales would 75 be an odd number? (Even numbers are those which are divisible by two without a remainder.)

Unit 7: Work with Numbers Study

1. *Introduction.* Up to this point our discussions have centered upon ways and means of characterizing the number property of a single group. We shall turn now to group situations which involve either the actions of several groups or the interactions within groups and attempt to characterize the number property of the results of this activity. Specifically we are interested in those instances in which groups combine, an activity which we shall term *synthesis;* situations in which a group breaks apart, which we shall term *analysis;* and finally, means of comparing groups, whether they be wholes or fragments, which we shall call *comparison.**

In the types of action classified under synthesis we start with several groups and end with one single group, while those actions classified under analysis start with a single group and end with several groups. These two actions are said to be *inverses* of each other. Reality and our daily life are full of inverses or reverse actions. We dress in the morning and undress at night; we go downstairs to breakfast and upstairs to bed; we tie our shoestrings at one time, untie them at another; a doorway is an entrance for one direction and an exit for the other; and so on. Those already familiar with other areas of mathematics will readily recognize such inverse relationships as exist between logarithms and antilogarithms, sines and arc sines, powers and roots, differentiation and integration.

Since the end product of both synthesis and analysis is always a group or groups, the number property of the resultant group in every case might be found by the simple process of counting. While this constitutes a perfectly valid approach, computation by counting, except for the simplest cases, presents rather monumental practical limitations. Evidence of this can be seen in the fact that in the various ancient cultures wherever work with numbers exceeded the most elemental levels, the abacus or some form of it invariably was pressed into service. The computer was not freed from dependence upon such mechanical aids until the advent of the Hindu-Arabic system, a system which involved computations by the use of the *symbols themselves.* Under this system the computer would write down the numbers of the problem, then following some sort of ritual or pattern, ultimately emerge with the correct solution.

---

* The terms *synthesis* and *analysis* are adopted here with the full knowledge that they are used with various meanings in the disciplines of science and philosophy; in mathematics alone the term *analysis* has at least four other distinct meanings. None the less, these terms have been chosen for their aptness in light of their etymologies: *synthesis*—a putting together; *analysis*—a taking apart.

These patterns of procedure were known as *algorisms* (named after one of the early great Arabic mathematicians, Al-Khowarizmi), and the users of such techniques were called *algorists*. The algorisms of course were actually by-products of the Hindu-Arabic system of notation and as a consequence were closely related and dependent upon that system.

There was never much question that the algorisms of the Hindu-Arabic system offered a far superior approach to computation than did counting, and for that matter, offered many advantages over previously used mechanical devices. Yet its victory in Europe over the prevailing Roman system was by no means sudden and sweeping. Even though the Hindu-Arabic system was known in Europe in the thirteenth century, the adherents to the old Roman system of notation, notably the scholars and theoreticians, resisted these methods with a strenuous vigor. The foothold gained by the Roman notation over the centuries, the prevailing attitude in the early days of the Renaissance of near-reverence for all that was old Roman, and the fact that this upstart system was of pagan origins, made the Roman system a stern adversary for its fundamentally superior foe. Indeed frequent and spirited were the contests in which a medieval abacist competed against an opponent algorist on a problem field of battle. But along with the ever-rising tide of mercantilism and its attendant need for practical and speedy calculations, Europe by the sixteenth century had become fairly well converted to the Hindu-Arabic system and its algoristic approach.

2. *Arithmetic Today.* Today elementary arithmetic is looked upon as that body of knowledge which embraces both number and the commonplace activities with number. These activities in the main are specifically guided by algorisms which may be classified as processes or operations. Traditional arithmetic recognizes *four processes* with their attending activities: addition, subtraction, multiplication, and division. Our approach in this book to this same body of knowledge involves a basic shift in emphasis: we recognize as fundamental *three activities* with their attending processes. These activities, with their attending processes in parentheses are:

I *Synthesis:*
  (1) Combining groups of any sizes (addition)
  (2) Combining groups of equal size (multiplication)

II *Analysis:*
  (1) Separating a group into subgroups of any size (subtraction)
  (2) Separating a group into subgroups of equal size (division)

III *Comparison:*
  (1) Relationship in terms of deficiency or excess (subtraction)
  (2) Relationship in terms of measurement or ratio (division)

It is not recommended that this departure from the usual treatment and sequence of elements in arithmetic be carried directly to elementary school classrooms. Any effect there will have to be indirect, for we must not lose sight of the fact that our approach is designed for maximum impact upon mature minds which already have had varying degrees of experience and training in arithmetic. Restructuring the subject in this way offers to such a mature learner a somewhat different standpoint from which to view a familiar area—in fact an all too familiar area. Yet this approach is not without its applications for the elementary classrooms, for the trend in the teaching of arithmetic today is decidedly away from the passive (mechanical memorization of "handy facts" and processes) and toward the active (learning through discovery and activity) type of learning. Consequently our present approach, which is organized around one's *actions with number*, is not without value for the teacher.

3. *Organization of Future Units.* The over-all arrangement of topics which follow will be according to the synthesis, analysis, and comparison classification. Along the way, each of the fundamental processes or algorisms (addition, subtraction, multiplication, and division) will be explored and analyzed in terms of its basic ingredients—principles and number facts. This will be done first with respect to integers and then later with respect to fractions. Once the rationales of the four basic operations are understood and applied to situations involving synthesis and analysis, their extension into the realm of comparisons should be accomplished with minimum effort and maximum understanding. As in our dealing with systems of notation, considerable emphasis will be placed upon the principles which are involved in these various operations. These invariant elements lie at the very root of meaning and will be found reflected consistently in these operations, whether they deal with integers, common fractions, decimals, digits under radical signs, or the abstract quantities of algebra. The principles are the keys to understanding and appreciation; without them unification and consolidation of the subject is impossible.

4. *Various Concepts of Number.* Number is a multipurpose item. Essentially number is an attribute, like color, or texture, or honesty.

No one has ever been able to capture a pure three or isolate a six in a test tube, in the same sense that no one has ever seen a quantity of pure green or the attribute of pure honesty. What we do perceive is *three* apples, *six* dogs, *green* shirts, or *honest* people. Number, color, taste, and the like are characteristics of things and are non-existent apart from things; they can be appreciated only in abstraction. Digits such as 6 or 4 are but symbols for these abstractions, the same as "red" is the language symbol for a certain color. When the concept of number is specifically associated with a concrete object, such as 7 houses, 316 men, $19, 27 cats, we call them *concrete numbers*. When numbers are associated with some specific unit of measure, such as 8 feet, 6 pounds, 3 seconds, we call them *denominate numbers*. When concrete or denominate numbers agree in terms of their "somethings" we have *like* numbers. For instance, 7 *houses* and 13 *houses*, 4 *inches* and 8 *inches*, 17 *dozen apples* and 3 *dozen apples* are paired illustrations of like numbers.

We are aware that certain generalizations about numbers can be made, such as when 6 of something is combined with 3 of the same thing, the result is a total of 9 of that thing. Stripping away the specifics, this generalization is usually stated merely as $6 + 3 = 9$, without further qualification. In such cases the number symbols have been employed to convey a generalization which is an abstraction. Appropriately enough, numbers used under such circumstances are referred to as *abstract numbers*. Though practically all our arithmetic problems have roots in concrete situations, most of our computation is carried out using these unencumbered *abstract* numbers. Distinguishing between the two concepts of numbers is important for a teacher, particularly in applying the educational maxim "Begin teaching with the concrete and work toward the abstract," that level at which greatest efficiency can be achieved.

5. *Number as Discrete and Continuous.* The distinction between the cardinal (how many) concept of number and the ordinal (which one) has already been made. Similarly a distinction is made between numbers as applied to discrete (separate, unconnected) situations and numbers applied to continuous situations. So far practically our whole consideration of number has been limited to the former concept, the number property of groups of discrete objects. Although historically number was first conceived as *counting numbers*, there is nevertheless another important concept of number, the continuous or geometric concept, which stems from the ordinality

of number in our system. Here all number is looked upon as a continuum, with each specific number (whether an integer or a fraction or both) being a unique measurement from a basic zero point. The continuum is best pictured as a *number line* starting with the zero point at the left and extending infinitely to the right. The natural numbers are shown below on such a line—each a specific and unique distance from the zero point.

In the field of physics there is to be found an interesting parallel to these two concepts of number. In the days of Newton the universe was held explainable in terms of the whole being equal to the sum of so many discrete parts. This was the atomistic point of view. Later it was held that reality was best understood as a continuum, and the wave theory replaced the old corpuscular theory. Now in fairly recent years, with the discoveries of Planck and his quantum, there is reason to believe that the atomic point of view is by no means completely discredited. All of which leads to considerable debate among physicists, and for those who must have an either/or explanation this situation presents a real dilemma. Meanwhile others take a more realistic attitude and say, "Admittedly some things in our universe are more adequately explained atomically, while other things certainly make better sense to our finite minds when comprehended in terms of the wave theory. So in the absence of definite proof or disproof, both theories may be tolerated."

In the field of arithmetic the computations and algorisms usually taught in the schools are principally paper and pencil methods. The rationales behind these methods are perhaps best understood from an atomic point of view; that is, number should be thought of as being made up of so many discrete packages. For instance, the number 647 can be thought of as a whole equal to the sum of the following parts: 6 hundreds, 4 tens, 7 units. When we add to it, say, 321, we add the units together, the tens together, and the hundreds together for a total of 9 hundreds and 6 tens and 8 units. This final collection is our answer, 968. The algebraic concept of number, which looks upon each number as a polynomial, illustrates with particular clarity this "discrete" idea (see Unit 4, Section 5).

On the other hand, the rationale behind the most frequent type of mental computation is perhaps better appreciated in terms of the continuum or the number line. To add 62 to 36, most of us would think, "62 (a point on the number line) and 30 more is 92 and 6 is 98." Thus:

Figure 5. 62 + 36 on the number line.

Note that when mentally computing in this way we usually work from the left to right with the digits of the numbers, while with the paper and pencil algorisms we invariably work from right to left. Reasons for this difference will become clear as we explore the thinking behind these two approaches.

Returning for a moment to the algorisms, it may be helpful to think of them as a type of labor saving machine. By systematically breaking the whole problem into easily handled subparts, they offer the user both a wider range and an added facility of operation which otherwise could not have been accomplished mentally. Our system of notation, we have seen, is constantly concerned with what have been referred to as "face" and "place" values, or number of parts and size of the part (denomination or order). What the algorism accomplishes for its user is relief from any concern about "place," since its routine automatically takes care of this item, permitting full concentration upon getting the correct "face" values. But like any machine, the algorism is not without its drawbacks. Concentration on only one half of the picture, and a half which consists wholly of accidentals at that (the memory facts), often results in a loss of meaning in the interest of these more immediate economies. Too, like any machine, the algorism possesses a certain amount of inflexibility. For instance, the algorism would attack a multiplication problem like 25 × 36 in the very same way that it would 23 × 37. In the second instance the usual algorism provides the most satisfactory method, but in the case of 25 × 36, dividing 36 by 4 and multiplying the result by 100 would have been far simpler and speedier. Thus the machine, constructed in the interest of wider scope, is not sufficiently sensitive to recognize special cases and short cuts. In later units, as each process is treated individually, the effects of these distinctions will be better appreciated.

Since most of our daily dealings with numbers are of a relatively simple variety, the ability to compute mentally is a tremendous

asset and should be encouraged. Yet there is a definite limit, varying with individuals, to those problems which are workable mentally, so one dare not slight the more far-reaching paper and pencil
methods. Thus in subsequent units the algoristic point of view will
be stressed, recognizing that that approach has the widest application and receives the greatest attention in the schools. However,
this will by no means be to the complete exclusion of the geometric
or continuum approach. The important thing at this point is first,
that the reader appreciate the distinction between the two concepts,
and second, that he be conscious of the areas in which each is of
maximum benefit.

PROBLEMS SET 7

1. Using a collegiate dictionary, find the definitions of the following
terms.

(a) abstract	(f) continuum
(b) algorism	(g) denominate
(c) analysis	(h) discrete
(d) comparison	(i) inverse
(e) concrete	(j) synthesis

2. Give five illustrations of inverse relationships.

3. Give three illustrations for each of (a) concrete numbers, (b) abstract
numbers, (c) denominate numbers.

4. Make a number line for the first twenty counting numbers in the
scale of (a) seven, (b) twelve, (c) four, (d) six.

5. Add the following, using the number lines which you have drawn in
Question 4.

   Scale seven:
   (a) six plus eight
   (b) four plus twelve
   Scale twelve:
   (a) six plus eight
   (b) four plus twelve
   Scale four:
   (a) three plus seven plus four
   (b) six plus eight plus four
   Scale six:
   (a) two plus four plus six plus six
   (b) four plus twelve plus one.

6. Add $3.04 + $6.25 mentally; write down the sequence or thought
pattern which you followed in arriving at your answer.

Chapter 2

SYNTHESIS

Unit 8: Addition

1. *Introduction.* Synthesis is the first of our three basic arithmetical activities, that of putting groups together. The underlying assumption here is that any group, which is the resultant of joining together several other groups, has one or more properties which are similar to and determined by the properties of the constituent groups—for instance color, size, material, type, and of course number. The problem in synthesis is to ascertain the number property of the resultant group when the number properties of the constituent groups are known.

The simplest approach to the solution of this problem is that of counting. Since the items in each group determine its number property (which may be ascertained by counting), and since the resulting

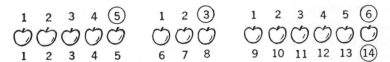

Figure 5. Addition by counting.

group will contain all the items of the constituent groups, then by counting all the items of all the groups in one sequence, we shall arrive at the number property of the resultant group. For example, suppose we wish to know the number property of the group resulting from putting together groups of five apples, three apples, and six apples. In Figure 5 above the numbers above the apple symbols identify the number property of the respective constituent groups, while those below refer to that of the resultant group. The circled

48

final counting number characterizes the number property of that particular group. Thus five apples and three apples and six apples collectively form a new group of fourteen apples.

Despite the absolute effectiveness of this approach in arriving at the correct solution of such problems, its slowness is obvious. Imagine the time it would take to determine the total population of this country, or for that matter even of its ten largest cities, by this method. No, a shorter process must be found, and in the operation of addition we have it.

2. *Addition.* While perhaps not sufficiently rigorous to satisfy the higher mathematician, a definition of addition adequate for our needs is now stated:

> *Addition is the process of finding, without counting, the number property of a group which is formed by the combination of two or more groups.*

The constituent groups are referred to as the *addends*, and the resultant group as the *sum*.

The process of addition is based upon three fundamental principles and a considerable number of memory facts. Full and effective use of this process demands a thorough knowledge of both.

Principle A-1: *Only like numbers can be added.*

This *principle of likeness* is directly related to the fact that a group is a group because of some common unifying characteristic. Several individual groups can merge into a new group if each item of each group possesses at least one common characteristic, whether quantitative or qualitative. Thus four quart bottles and two quart bottles, regardless of their shapes, color, etc., may be combined to form a new group of six quart bottles, because each element in each of the constituent groups possesses the same quantitative (quart) characteristic. Similarly, three apples and four apples may be combined to form a new group of seven apples because of the common qualitative characteristic "appleness." In this same sense, however, we cannot form a new group with a group of three apples and a group of five lemons because "appleness" and "lemonness" are not the same quality. But by choosing a more general characteristic, such as "fruitness," they may be grouped and the result is "eight pieces of fruit."

Among the far-reaching effects of this principle of likeness is the specific alignment which we normally give to the digits in the addition algorism; also, it is reflected when we seek a common denominator in adding certain fractions.

Principle A-2: *The sum of an addition is unaffected by the sequence or order of its addends.*

This principle is known as the *commutative law with respect to addition.* Here again we have a rather subtle law also with far-reaching effects. For instance, whenever we check an addition by again adding the digits, but in reverse order, we are operating under this law. Interpreting this generally, for addends a and b, we have $a + b = b + a$ (although the addends need not be restricted to two). Note the reflection of the commutative law in the following example.

$$6 + 3 + 2 + 4 = 4 + 2 + 3 + 6$$
$$= 3 + 6 + 4 + 2 = 15$$

These and a few other basic laws form the ultimate pillars upon which the whole rationale of arithmetic computation is built. Still, far-reaching as they may be, they are not so fundamental as to pervade all of reality. For example, in the chemistry laboratory, to add sulfuric acid to water is harmless, while to add water to sulfuric acid can be disastrous. Thus water and sulfuric acid certainly cannot be said to be commutative with respect to addition.

Principle A-3: *The sum of an addition is unaffected by combinations or groupings of the addends.*

This is known as the *associative law with respect to addition.* In symbols, it states that $(a + b) + c = a + (b + c)$.

The person who, when adding a column of figures, adds to tens whenever possible reflects an assurance guaranteed by this law. To illustrate: suppose you are to add $6 + 3 + 7 + 4 + 8$. Perhaps you see tens in

$$\boxed{6} + \widehat{3} + \widehat{7} + \boxed{4} + 8$$

and add by these grouped values: $10 + 10 + 8 = 28$. In effect the associative law provides that we can add by subgroups without fear of arriving at a distorted solution. To see that this law too lacks universality we have only to consider that favorite circus or ballgame refreshment, a soft drink and a hot dog laden with mustard. Consider a regrouping of these elements from [soft drink + (hot dog + mustard)] to [(soft drink + mustard) + hot dog]. Would you say either combination would be equally tasty?

3. *The Addition Algorism.* The algorism of addition is based upon the exercise of certain number memory facts in accordance with the basic principles of addition (A-1, A-2, and A-3). The memory facts are known as the *primary* addition combinations.

TABLE VI. PRIMARY ADDITION COMBINATIONS
(Decimal Scale)

	0	1	2	3	4	5	6	7	8	9
0	0	1	2	3	4	5	6	7	8	9
1	1	2	3	4	5	6	7	8	9	10
2	2	3	4	5	6	7	8	9	10	11
3	3	4	5	6	7	8	9	10	11	12
4	4	5	6	7	8	9	10	11	12	13
5	5	6	7	8	9	10	11	12	13	14
6	6	7	8	9	10	11	12	13	14	15
7	7	8	9	10	11	12	13	14	15	16
8	8	9	10	11	12	13	14	15	16	17
9	9	10	11	12	13	14	15	16	17	18

Specifically these are the respective sums of all pairs of single digit numbers. In the decimal scale these would number one hundred, including the zero combinations. Table VI shows an array of all the primary combinations for the decimal scale. In order to employ the modern algorism of addition, these must be committed to memory. However, a couple of generalizations will help reduce the task considerably. For instance, the sum of any number and zero (nothing) is that number; and the commutative law applied to a knowledge of, say, 6 + 3 = 9 gives automatically the sum of 3 + 6.

Once the primary combinations have been committed to mem-

ory, it is possible to broaden the scope of our operation by taking
on such combinations as 23 + 42. Here we look at the group of 23
in terms of its component parts, 2 tens and 3 units, and the group
of 42 as 4 tens and 2 units. Putting these two groups together
(following the principle of likeness, A-1) we get a new group of
6 tens and 5 units, which, in accord with the principle of place
value, may be written as 65. Thus 23 + 42 = 65.

But what happens when one tries to add, say, 27 and 35 in a
similar fashion? Following the initial breakdown, we operate in
accordance with Principle A-1 and our knowledge of the primary
combinations to get

$$\begin{array}{r} 2 \text{ tens} + 7 \text{ units} \\ 3 \text{ tens} + 5 \text{ units} \\ \hline 5 \text{ tens} + 12 \text{ units} \end{array}$$

But in the Hindu-Arabic system we cannot express 5 tens and 12
units as we did 6 tens and 5 units. So an intermediate reorganizing
step is necessary: the 12 units may be thought of as exchanged for
1 ten + 2 units. Then applying the associative law (A-3), we have

$$\begin{aligned} 5 \text{ tens} + 12 \text{ units} &= 5 \text{ tens} + (1 \text{ ten} + 2 \text{ units}) \\ &= (5 \text{ tens} + 1 \text{ ten}) + 2 \text{ units} \\ &= 6 \text{ tens} + 2 \text{ units} \\ &= 62 \end{aligned}$$

This exchange or reorganizing step is known technically as a
reduction. By definition, a reduction of a number expression involves *only a change in form without any change in value*. Note by
this definition there is no restriction upon a reduction's direction;
that is, the ultimate result of a reduction is *not* necessarily a simpler
expression or even a more abbreviated one. For that reason some
writers prefer the less widely accepted but less ambiguous term
"transformation." Throughout the whole of arithmetic, reductions
of one type or another will be encountered. They fit into the mathematical scheme of things somewhat as does a catalyst in the processes of chemistry. At times reductions are called upon to speed
up the process or operation, at others to set up or make possible a
next step, and at still others merely to simplify the data we have.

In the first chapter we met several instances of reduction.
Translating a number expression in the Roman system to its equivalent in the Hindu-Arabic was one example of a change in form
without a change in value; changing from one scale of notation to
another [37 (ten) = 122 (five) for instance], in either direction, in-

volved changing form without changing value; and expressing 4 thousands alternatively as 40 hundreds or as 400 tens, as we did on page 26, is yet another case of a change in form without any change in value. Now we have encountered the reduction concept under new circumstances, as a reorganizing step in the addition process. Generally, this type of reduction is referred to as "carrying."

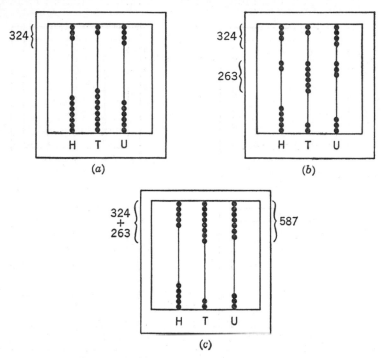

Figure 6. Abacus sequence in 324 + 263.

In a moment we shall discuss the more general case of the addition algorism, but before we do, let us consider two examples of addition on the (ten-bead) abacus.

The first involves no carrying or reduction. Assume that we wish to add 324 and 263. Figure 6(a) shows the abacus with the first addend, 324, recorded; (b) shows the beads representing each digit of the second addend, 263, on their way to combine with those of the first addend; (c) shows the abacus with the two addends combined, recording 587, their sum.

Now let us consider 456 + 279, which involves reduction. Figure 7(a) shows the abacus with the 456 addend recorded. We now add in the 279. Since there are only 4 beads at the bottom of the units strand, it is necessary to add in the units digit (9) of the second addend (279) piecemeal, as 4 and 5. Adding in the 4 on the units strand puts all ten beads in that column at the top of the abacus. These, it will be recalled, may be exchanged for one ten-bead, thus returning the ten unit-beads to the bottom ready for further duty. From these reusable unit beads the remaining five of the units digit (9) of the second addend may be recorded; (b) of Figure 7 shows the

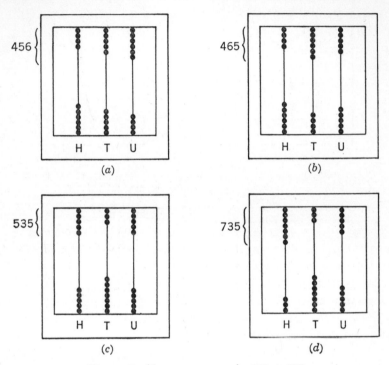

Figure 7. Abacus sequence in 456 + 279.

state of the abacus at the end of this step (456 + 9 = 465). A similar situation arises as we attempt to add in the 7 tens of this second addend: the 4 beads at the bottom of the tens strand make it necessary to also add in the 7 piecemeal, as 4 and 3. Adding in the 4 in this tens column places all ten of these beads at the top; these ten are then substituted for with one bead in the hundreds column, whereupon the remaining 3 tens can be duly added in; Figure 7(c) shows the state of the abacus after that step (465 + 70 = 535) is completed. Coming now to the hundred's digit (2) of the second addend, we find that there are enough beads available on the hundreds strand to take care of its recording. After these two are added in, the state of the abacus is that of Figure 7(d), which at the same time records the complete sum of 456 and 279.

It is important to note that the sequence in which the various digits of the second addend were handled is commutative; that is, we could have just as easily added in the hundreds digit (2) first, then perhaps the units digit (9) next, and the tens digit (7) last, reorganizing the beads, of course, whenever necessary. The end result would have been the same for that or any other sequence.

An outgrowth of the abacus method of addition was the "scratch" method of addition, current in Europe in the sixteenth century. See if you can follow the steps of this method as the second abacus problem above is repeated. (Scratching out of digits shows they have been added.)

(a)	(b)	(c)	(d)	(e)
		7	7	73
	1	1̸	1̸1	1̸1̸
6	62	6̸2	6̸25	6̸25
4̸56	4̸5̸6	4̸5̸6	4̸5̸6̸	4̸5̸6̸
2̸79	2̸79	2̸79	2̸79̸	2̸79̸

Answer: 735

Notice in this scratch method no mental effort beyond a knowledge of the primary combinations is required. On the surface, at least, this method is far more susceptible to a meaningful approach than is ours today, for not only does it show more clearly the reductions that take place, but it also assumes a more natural sequence by giving first consideration to the digits of greater importance, namely, those farthest to the left.

However, our modern algorism is a far speedier one. This advantage in speed is gained by doing mentally many of the steps which the scratch method recorded and reconsidered. Witness the computation

$$\begin{array}{r} 456 \\ +279 \\ \hline 735 \end{array}$$

which requires the writing of only nine symbols. Then witness the final phase of the scratch method, which shows that thirteen symbols have been written, to say nothing of the many scratch strokes. By reversing the procedure of the scratch method and working the orders from right to left, our modern algorism takes advantage of the fact that whenever a reorganization or carrying is necessary, it always involves only the present and next higher—and as yet uncomputed—order. Thus once an order or column in the modern addition algorism is left behind, we can be sure that its resultant will not be affected by any subsequent action among the higher orders. Hence, when the correct digit in the sum is recorded for a given order, it remains once and for all.

It is of further interest to note that most people today, despite all their training in the modern algorism of addition, when asked to add mentally 456 and 279, are likely to proceed as follows: $400 + 200 = 600$; $50 + 70 = 120$; $600 + 120 = 720$; $6 + 9 = 15$; $720 + 15 = 735$—a sequence of steps which is identical with those of the now obsolete scratch method.

4. *Checks for Addition.* In order to guarantee accuracy in computation, certain checks have been developed. Basically they fall into one of three categories: (a) commutative checks, (b) associative checks, and (c) excess checks.

(a) *Commutative checks.* These take advantage of the commutative law for addition and call for some reversal of the sequence in which the digits were added originally. For instance, if a column of figures has originally been added from top to bottom, adding a second time from bottom to top will most often involve a different series of combinations, though not a different ultimate sum. Thus, should the computer make an error with one of his combinations, there is less likelihood that that same combination will occur when the adding sequence is reversed.

(b) *Associative checks.* There are many variations of these. Basically they all involve the fact that any regrouping of the addends will not affect the sum. One such check calls for adding all the addends except the first (or last), then to the sum of these adding the excluded first (or last) addend. The final sum should be the same as the original. This technique is illustrated below as check (a). Check (b) to its right involves adding each column separately and then adding the subtotals, and is an alternative associative check. Check (c) is an interesting variation of this last one. It calls for placing the columnar subtotals on the side. The bottom-most figure, and the right-hand digit of each of those above it in sequence (as underlined) will form the correct answer. This differs from check (b) in that the subtotals 12, 21, 20, and 17 include the "carried" values of the previous subtotal.

	(a)	(b)		(c)
3,654	8,792	3,654	3,654	1⎸2↑
8,792	365	8,792	8,792	2⎸1
365	4,201	365	365	2⎸0
4,201	13,358	4,201	4,201	1 7
17,012	3,654	12	17,012	
	17,012	20		
		18		
		15		
		17,012		

(c) *Excess checks.* One of this ancient class of checks recognizes that the remainder (that which is left over) for any number when divided by 9 can be had by simply adding the digits of the number. In the decimal scale this remainder is known as the *excess of nines* and the rule is this: *The excess of nines in a given number expressed in the decimal scale is equal to the excess of nines in the sum of its digits.* To illustrate the rule, note that the number

41 when divided by 9 = 4 nines and 5 left over
34 when divided by 9 = 3 nines and 7 left over
62 when divided by 9 = 6 nines and 8 left over

In each of these cases we could have determined the amounts "left over" (or the excesses) simply by adding the digits of the original number. In cases were such sums exceed nine, the rule must be reapplied. Thus to find the excess of nines in 438, we add $4 + 3 + 8 = 15$, then add $1 + 5 = 6$. Hence 6 is the excess of nines in 438.

A short cut for this rule may be had by casting out nines whenever the sum of the digits reaches or passes nine. Thus, to find the excess of nines in 54,687, we notice that $5 + 4 = 9$; because we are excluding nines, we disregard these two digits, and go to $6 + 8 = 14$. Here $14 =$ one 9 and 5, so we disregard the 9 and carry the 5 (which is the sum of $1 + 4$) on to add with the 7. This results in $5 + 7 = 12$, which contains another 9 and an excess of 3 (or $1 + 2 = 3$). Hence the excess over 9's in 54,687 is 3.

The rationale behind the application of this rule to addition as a check is this: since the items of the component groups (addends) are to form ultimately the items in the resultant group (sum), the number of nines and whatever excess that exists among the addends collectively should equal the number of nines and excess in the sum. For example:

$$
\begin{aligned}
368 &=\;|\;\; 40 \text{ nines} +\;\; 8 \\
592 &=\;|\;\; 65 \text{ nines} +\;\; 7 \\
306 &=\;|\;\; 34 \text{ nines} +\;\; 0 \\
\hline
1{,}266 &\;|\; \underline{139 \text{ nines}} + \underline{15} = \underline{139 \text{ nines}} + \underline{(1 \text{ nine} + 6)} = \underline{140 \text{ nines} + 6} \\
&\longrightarrow \underline{140 \text{ nines} + 6}
\end{aligned}
$$

Since the rule for excess of nines speaks only of the excess and makes no mention of the quantity of full nines in the number, we operate our check entirely on the excess level. Thus in our example to check by using the excess of nines we see

$$
\begin{aligned}
368 &\rightarrow 3 + 6 + 8 = 17 \rightarrow 1 + 7 =\;\; 8 \\
592 &\rightarrow 5 + 9 + 2 = 16 \rightarrow 1 + 6 =\;\; 7 \\
306 &\rightarrow 3 + 0 + 6 =\;\; 9 \longrightarrow 0 =\;\; 0 \\
\hline
1{,}266 & \qquad\qquad\qquad\qquad\qquad\qquad 15 \rightarrow 1 + 5 = \boxed{6} \\
&\longrightarrow 1 + 2 + 6 + 6 = 15 \rightarrow 1 + 5 = \boxed{6}
\end{aligned}
$$

This leads to the general rule for checking addition by the excess of nines: *The excess of nines in a sum is equal to the excess of nines in the sum of the excesses of its addends.*

Because this rule takes no cognizance of the number of full nines involved, errors in the sum involving differences of nine or some multiple of nine will go undetected. Furthermore, from the way in which the excesses are computed it should be obvious that errors of transposition of digits also will go undetected. So the check is not foolproof. Instead it tells that the checked answer is probably correct, the degree of probability being rather high.

PROBLEMS SET 8

1. Which of the pairs of addends below involve like terms and which involve unlike terms?

(a) 3 men + 6 men
(b) 4 houses + 5 garages
(c) 3 figs + 7 figs
(d) 4 ships + 2 boats
(e) 4 boys + 3 girls
(f) 7 inches + 3 feet
(g) 6 + 9
(h) $\frac{1}{2} + \frac{1}{4}$

2. For those additions of Question 1 which involve "unlike" terms, find some common characteristic by which they might be grouped.

3. Give two practical illustrations (similar to the water and sulfuric acid one in Section 2) of the commutative law with respect to addition in which the law is valid and two illustrations in which it fails to hold. Do the same for the associative law with respect to addition.

4. Interpret the commutative law with respect to addition in terms of the hot dog, mustard, soft drink combination given in Section 2.

5. Add by the "scratch" method: 6,429 + 2,857. Count the pencil movements necessary to add 463 + 9,872 by the "scratch" method and by your usual method of adding. Time yourself in adding 6,387 + 9,596 by these two methods.

6. Outline the steps necessary to add the following on an abacus.
    (a) 322 + 143 + 203
    (b) 427 + 354
    (c) 678 + 593

7. How many days are there (a) between March 18 and September 23; (b) between August 12 and February 15?

8. If the road distance between Washington and Baltimore is 38 miles, between Baltimore and Philadelphia 99 miles, between Philadelphia and New York 88 miles, and if New York to Boston is 222 miles, how far is it (a) from Boston to Baltimore; (b) from Philadelphia to Washington?

9. How does the commutative law enter the solution to Question 8?

10. If the addition of $A + B + C + D$ equals the sum E,
    (a) How much would the sum increase if addend C is increased by G?
    (b) How much would the sum increase if addend B were doubled?
    (c) What would be the sum if A were increased by 8 and C were increased by 9?
    (d) What would be the sum if B were decreased by 12 and D were increased by 15?
    (e) What would be the sum if each addend were doubled?

11. Find the excess of nines in the following numbers by adding the digits. Check your work by dividing by nine.
    71; 35; 88; 173; 949; 8,462,571; 3,000,002

12. Add the following and check each by the three checks: commutative, associative, excess of nines.

(a)	(b)	(c)	(d)
4,386	8,637	4,379	48,627
7,297	5,922	10,621	35
8,163	3,872	4,372	9,687
5,728	6,795	30	2

13. Add 632 + 879 + 643. Now make your answer *incorrect* by (a) switching the digits around; (b) adding 27 to the answer. "Check" your problem with these two incorrect answers by casting out nines. How do you account for what happens?

Unit 9: Addition in Other Scales

1. *Introduction.* In Chapter 1 the point was developed that the effectiveness of our decimal system of notation was not due to the particular choice of ten for the base, but rather to the underlying principles of place value and addition. We shall develop here and in subsequent units the point that our fundamental arithmetic algorisms, like our system of notation, are not confined to the decimal scale alone.

The purpose for such a venture is twofold. First, by changing the frame of reference from the familiar decimal system to the less familiar ones of other scales, the invariable aspects of the operations (the principles) tend to stand out in bolder relief, while the modifying aspects (the accidentals) vary with every change. Second, successful computation in other bases is the most effective way of proving that the specific patterns assumed by the various algorisms truly emanate from the nature of the notational system and not from the choice of base. Principles, the things of greatest concern to us, arc intangible and can be appreciated only through the process of abstraction. Unless we are provided opportunities to see these principles in operation under varying sets of circumstances, they are likely to remain fuzzy in our minds.

Nothing serves so well to clarify a concept as contrasting illustrations in which the concept remains constant while the other factors change. To illustrate, suppose a Frenchman is trying to teach you a few words of French. He holds up an apple before your eyes and says, "Rouge." You are uncertain as to whether the word "rouge" applies to its red color, its oval shape, or to its fruitlike quality. You communicate this uncertainty with a bewildered look, whereupon the Frenchman notices your red necktie, puts his finger on it, and again says, "Rouge." Immediately you eliminate the inconsistencies (long shape of the tie vs. oval shape of the apple, the cloth vs. the fruit quality, etc.) and concentrate on the consistencies: the quality of redness which has remained invariant. Hence, you conclude "rouge" must mean "red."

2. *Addition in Other Scales.* As in the development of addition for the base of ten, this process in other scales depends upon the three basic principles of addition: likeness (A-1), commutation (A-2), association (A-3), and a host of memory facts. Once more the principles remain unchanged while the memory facts (accidentals) differ in appearance from scale to scale. The number con-

TABLE VII. PRIMARY ADDITION FACTS
(Base Five)

	0	1	2	3	4
0	0	1	2	3	4
1	1	2	3	4	10
2	2	3	4	10	11
3	3	4	10	11	12
4	4	10	11	12	13

TABLE VIII. PRIMARY ADDITION FACTS
(Base Twelve)

	0	1	2	3	4	5	6	7	8	9	T	E
0	0	1	2	3	4	5	6	7	8	9	T	E
1	1	2	3	4	5	6	7	8	9	T	E	10
2	2	3	4	5	6	7	8	9	T	E	10	11
3	3	4	5	6	7	8	9	T	E	10	11	12
4	4	5	6	7	8	9	T	E	10	11	12	13
5	5	6	7	8	9	T	E	10	11	12	13	14
6	6	7	8	9	T	E	10	11	12	13	14	15
7	7	8	9	T	E	10	11	12	13	14	15	16
8	8	9	T	E	10	11	12	13	14	15	16	17
9	9	T	E	10	11	12	13	14	15	16	17	18
T	T	E	10	11	12	13	14	15	16	17	18	19
E	E	10	11	12	13	14	15	16	17	18	19	1T

cept "three" plus the number concept "four" still equals the number concept "seven" whatever the base, but the number expressions for this fact will vary quite widely. Referring back to Table V, we note that seven, the sum of three and four, in base five is 12; in base four it is 13; in base two, 111.

Tables VII and VIII on page 61 provide us with the primary addition combinations in the two bases, five and twelve. If one were to put either of these two scales into frequent use it would be well worth while to memorize its primary combinations. Since our objective is not to attain any high degree of competence in these scales, but rather to observe the consistency of the principles in the algorisms, heavy reliance on the tables in forming the combinations is recommended. The frequency with which we will need to refer to these tables in this and other operations should impress us with the tremendous amount of memory work there is involved in the use of these modern computational algorisms. Habitual practice over the years tends to dim our appreciation of this fact.

Although memorizing the primary combinations is needless for our purposes here, we should not make the mistake of forming these combinations mentally by converting to the decimal scale for computation and then translating the results back to its equivalent in the desired base. Doing this would not only destroy, for those interested, the parallel between our experiences in these unfamiliar bases and those of the school child in his struggles with our decimal scale, but would also defeat our attempt to show the absolute independence of the algorisms from the decimal scale. It will be much to the advantage of the reader if he does his computations in these other bases slowly, even painfully slowly, relying solely upon his principles and table of addition facts. Only in this way can maximum benefit be derived from such exercises as these.

Illustrations:

    1. Add in the scale of five: 231 + 112.

$$231 \text{ (five)} = 2 \text{ twenty-fives} + 3 \text{ fives} + 1 \text{ unit}$$
$$\underline{112 \text{ (five)} = 1 \text{ twenty-five } + 1 \text{ five } + 2 \text{ units}}$$
$$3 \text{ twenty-fives} + 4 \text{ fives} + 3 \text{ units}$$
$$= 343 \text{ (five)}$$

    2. Add in the scale of five: 242 + 123.

$$242 \text{ (five)} = 2 \text{ twenty-fives} + \ 4 \text{ fives } + \ 2 \text{ units}$$
$$\underline{123 \text{ (five)} = 1 \text{ twenty-five } + \ 2 \text{ fives } + \ 3 \text{ units}}$$
$$3 \text{ twenty-fives} + 11 \text{ fives*} + 10 \text{ units*}$$

* See Table VII for addition facts base five.

But
$$10 \text{ units} = 1 \text{ five} + 0 \text{ units}$$
$$11 \text{ fives} = 1 \text{ twenty-five} + 1 \text{ five}$$

So   3 twenty-fives + 11 fives + 10 units* equals
   3 twenty-fives + (1 twenty-five + 1 five) + (1 five + 0 units)

Collecting according to the principle of likeness, we have
   4 twenty-fives + 2 fives + 0 units

which can be written, scale five, as 420. Hence

$$242 \text{ (five)}$$
$$\underline{123 \text{ (five)}}$$
$$420 \text{ (five)}$$

and the technique of "carrying" is established.

3. Add 613 (twelve) + 8T1 (twelve). Adding columnwise in accordance with the principle of likeness and noting that in the addition table given earlier for base twelve $3 + 1 = 4$, $1 + T = E$, and $6 + 8 = 12$, we solve the problem as below.

$$613 \text{ (twelve)} = \quad 6 \text{ gross} + 1 \text{ dozen } + 3 \text{ units}$$
$$\underline{8T1 \text{ (twelve)} = \quad 8 \text{ gross} + T \text{ dozens} + 1 \text{ unit}}$$
$$12 \text{ gross} + E \text{ dozens} + 4 \text{ units}$$
$$= 12E4 \text{ (twelve)}$$

4. Describe the computational steps in the addition below, scale twelve.

6TE (twelve)   The problem.
56 7 (twelve)

$\overset{1}{}$
6TE, (twelve)   Working right to left, E | 7 — 16.
$\underline{56 7 \text{ (twelve)}}$ Write 6 and carry 1.
        6

$\overset{1\ 1}{}$
6TE (twelve)   In the second order, $1 + T = E$; $E + 6 = 15$.
$\underline{56 7 \text{ (twelve)}}$ Write 5 and carry 1.
      5 6

$\overset{1}{}$
6TE (twelve)   In the third order, $1 + 6 = 7$; $7 + 5 = 10$.
$\underline{56 7 \text{ (twelve)}}$ Write 0 under the 5 in the bottom addend and write
1,05 6   1 to the left of the zero.
        Answer is *1,056* (*twelve*).

3. *Checks for Additions in Other Scales.* As we said in the development of addition in the decimal scale in the previous unit, the types of checks mentioned there have counterparts in other scales. Since it has been established that choice of base has no effect upon the principles underlying the operation of addition, it follows that we should be able to apply the commutative and associative checks

* Read "*three* twenty-fives plus *one-one* fives plus *one-zero* units."

with equal assurance in these other scales of notation. Witness the addition below in the base of five (box).

$$
\begin{array}{r}
341 \\
212 \\
304 \\
213 \\
\hline
2{,}130 \text{ (five)}
\end{array}
$$

A commutative check,
scrambled order of addends

An associative check

$$
\begin{array}{r}
304 \\
212 \\
341 \\
213 \\
\hline
2{,}130 \text{ (five)}
\end{array}
$$

$\left.\begin{array}{r} 341 \\ 212 \\ 304 \end{array}\right\}$ First three addends

$$
\begin{array}{l}
\underline{1{,}412} \\
\underline{213} \text{ Fourth addend} \\
2{,}130 \text{ (five)}
\end{array}
$$

The excess check requires some additional clarification before finding application to other bases.

It will be recalled that the excess of nines for a number, expressed decimally, could be found simply by adding the digits in that number. If the sum of these digits exceeded nine, then the digits of this resulting number were added, and so on repeatedly until the sum became nine or less. This final value coincided with the remainder which would have resulted had the original number been divided by nine.

It can be shown that this apparent phenomenon stems directly from the relationship which nine bears to the number ten, the base of the decimal scale. By extension, a similar situation arises when this relationship between the number of the base and one less than the base is duplicated in other scales. For instance, eleven in base five is 21. Eleven, when divided by four has a remainder of three. In base five the excess of 4's in eleven—21 (five)—is $2 + 1 = 3$. Similarly the excess of sevens for numbers expressed in base eight can be found by adding the digits of such number expressions. For example, thirty-nine in the scale of eight is 47. Adding the digits 4 and 7 *in base eight* we get 13. Adding the 1 and 3 we get 4. Hence 4 must be the excess of sevens (base less one) in 47 (eight). To verify: thirty-nine [47 (eight)] divided by seven is five, and the remainder is *four*.

Generalizing, we can now redefine the statement about excesses to read: *the excess of "base less one" for a given number expressed in any base is equal to the excess of the "base less one" in the sum of its digits.*

On the basis of that statement we can now proceed to the third type of check for addition, the excess check. Consider a previous addition problem in base five. By casting out *fours* in each of the addends and the sum

$$341 \rightarrow 3+4+1=13 \rightarrow 1+3=4 \rightarrow 0$$
$$212 \rightarrow 2+1+2=10 \rightarrow 1+0=1 \rightarrow 1$$
$$304 \rightarrow 3+0+4=12 \rightarrow 1+2=3 \rightarrow 3$$
$$213 \rightarrow 2+1+3=11 \rightarrow 1+1=2 \rightarrow 2$$
$$\rightarrow 0+1+3+2=11 \rightarrow 1+1 = \textcircled{2}$$
$$2{,}130 \rightarrow 2+1+3+0=11 \rightarrow 1+1 = \textcircled{2}$$

we get a check on the accuracy of our answer, since the excess in the sum of the excesses of the addends (2) equaled the excess in the sum (2).

4. *Algebraic Interpretation.* As might be inferred from the foregoing, the principle of likeness with regard to the algorism applies specifically to denomination or order. Similarly in algebra, "like" terms are those which are identical with respect to the variable or literal part. Thus $3x$ and $4x$ are like terms, while $3x$ and $3y$ are not. Nor would $3x$ and $6xy$, or $7x$ and $7x^2$ be pairs of "like" terms. *Like terms differ at most by the coefficient.*

By applying the principle of likeness (A-1) to the addition of two integers N_1 and N_2 where

$$N_1 = a_n x^n + a_{n-1} x^{n-1} + \ldots + a_1 x^1 + a_0 x^0$$
$$N_2 = b_n x^n + b_{n-1} x^{n-1} + \ldots + b_1 x^1 + b_0 x^0$$

we get, adding like terms to like terms,

$$N_1 + N_2 = (a_n + b_n)x^n + (a_{n-1} + b_{n-1})x^{n-1} + \ldots + (a_1 + b_1)x + (a_0 + b_0)$$

"Carrying" is in order whenever $(a_k + b_k)$ exceeds the base value. In such a case $(a_k + b_k) =$ base $(x) +$ some other value less than the base, which we shall call c_k. Thus,

$$(a_k + b_k) = x + c_k$$
$$(a_k + b_k)x^k = (x + c_k)x^k = x^{k+1} + c_k x^k$$

By the associative law the x^{k+1} combines with the $(k + 1)$ term,

$$(a_{k+1} + b_{k+1})x^{k+1} + x^{k+1} = (a_{k+1} + b_{k+1} + 1)x^{k+1}$$

and carrying has been effected. Obviously, since this development has not been predicated upon any special value for x (the base), the addition algorism will apply equally well for any base whatever.

As for the excess of nines in the decimal scale, this is but an application of the well-known remainder theorem of algebra, which is stated: If a polynomial $p(x)$ is divided by $(x - k)$ until a constant remainder is obtained, this constant remainder will be $p(k)$.

Illustration: $p(x) = 2x^3 + 3x^2 + 4x + 6$.

Assume $k = 3$. Divide $p(x)$ by $(x - 3)$ and note the remainder of 99.

$$
\begin{array}{r}
2x^2 + 9x\ + 31 \\
x - 3 \overline{)\, 2x^3 + 3x^2 + 4x + 6} \\
\underline{2x^3 - 6x^2} \\
9x^2 + 4x \\
\underline{9x^2 - 27x} \\
31x + 6 \\
\underline{31x - 93} \\
99
\end{array}
$$

The expression $p(3)$ means that a three is to be substituted in the original $p(x)$ for x wherever it appears. Thus $p(3)$ where $p(x) = 2x^3 + 3x^2 + 4x + 6$ is

$$
\begin{aligned}
p(3) &= 2(3)^3 + 3(3)^2 + 4(3) + 6 \\
&= 54 + 27 + 12 + 6 = 99
\end{aligned}
$$

Consider now a number in base ten, say 4,683. Its polynomial expression would be

$$
p(x) = 4x^3 + 6x^2 + 8x + 3 \quad \text{where } x = \text{ten}
$$

If $x = $ ten, nine would be $(x - 1)$. By the remainder theorem, to divide $p(x) = 4x^3 + 6x^2 + 8x + 3$ by $(x - 1)$, the remainder would be

$$
p(1) = 4(1) + 6(1) + 8(1) + 3 \quad \text{or} \quad 4 + 6 + 8 + 3
$$

or merely the sum of the digit coefficients.

In general, any polynomial

$$
p(x) = a_n x^n + a_{n-1} x^{n-1} + \ldots + a_2 x^2 + a_1 x^1 + a_0
$$

when divided by $x - 1$ would show a remainder equal to $p(1)$. Thus for any polynomial $p(x)$,

$$
p(1) = a_n + a_{n-1} + a_{n-2} + \ldots + a_3 + a_2 + a_1 + a_0
$$

Since this is in no way unique for $x = $ ten only, it follows that the excess of nines in the decimal scale will have its counterpart in any base.

Before leaving this topic, let us look at another well-known situation, the decimal scales' "excess of elevens." This time in our divisor $(x - k)$ let $k = -1$. When the base is ten, $x = 10$ and the divisor $(x - k) = [10 - (-1)] = 11$. If

$$p(x) = a_0x^0 + a_1x^1 + a_2x^2 + a_3x^3 + \ldots$$

then $\quad p(-1) = a_0(-1)^0 + a_1(-1)^1 + a_2(-1)^2 + a_3(-1)^3 + \ldots$

$$= a_0 - a_1 + a_2 - a_3 + a_4 - a_5 + \ldots$$

with the result that the coefficients of the odd powers of the base are all negative and the coefficients of the even powers of the base are all positive.

For example, find the excess of elevens in 4,357.

Answer: $7 - 5 + 3 - 4 = 1$. This means eleven divides 4,357 a certain number of times with a final remainder of 1. Upon application of the associative law, an alternative method for finding the excess of elevens is produced: add the digits in the *odd places* (first, third, fifth, etc.), starting from the right and subtract from this the sum of the digits in the *even places* (second, fourth, etc.). In the example, $(7 + 3)$ would be the sum of the odd-placed digits and $(5 + 4)$ the sum of the even-placed digits. Subtract the sum of the even-placed digits from the odd-placed digits $(7 + 3) - (5 + 4)$ and the remainder is the same as before. In the event that the sum of the even-placed digits exceeds that of the odd-placed digits, add some multiple of eleven to the odd-placed sum so that the difference between the two is positive and less than eleven.

Illustrations:

(a) Find the excess of elevens in 423,692.

$$S_0 = 2 + 6 + 2 = 10, \qquad S_E = 9 + 3 + 4 = 16$$
$$S_0 - S_E = 10 - 16 = (10 + 11) - 16 = 21 - 16 = 5$$

Excess of elevens in 423,692 is 5. Check this by dividing 423,692 by 11.

(b) Find the excess of elevens in 829,190.

$$S_0 = 0 + 1 + 2 = 3, \qquad S_E = 9 + 9 + 8 = 26$$
$$S_0 - S_E = 3 - 26 = (3 + 33) - 26 = 10$$

Excess of elevens in 829,190 is 10. Check this by division.

As in the case for $(x - 1)$, the case for $(x + 1)$ also has application in bases other than ten. Thus the same pattern of treatment of the digits as outlined above $(S_0 - S_E)$ should yield the excess of the "base plus one" in any base. For example, in base five the excess over sixes can be found by adding the digits in the odd places, subtracting the sum of the digits in even places. To illustrate, the excess over sixes in forty-four is two. Computing in base five we have

$$\text{forty-four} = 134 \text{ (five)}$$
$$S_0 = 4 + 1 = 10, \qquad S_E = 3$$
$$S_0 - S_E = 10 - 3 = 2 \text{ (five)}$$

PROBLEMS SET 9

1. Make a table of primary addition combinations for the scale of seven; four; two.

2. Add the following in scale of five and check by casting out fours.
    (a) 321 + 122   (d) 433 + 212 + 3,001 + 23
    (b) 4,321 + 324   (e) 312 + 123 + 213 + 321
    (c) 432 + 320 + 4,312   (f) 302,314 + 203,132 + 124,432

3. Add the following in the scale of twelve and check by casting out elevens.
    (a) 3T6 + 103 + 4E7   (d) 3T7 + 42T + 976 + 83E
    (b) 302 + T0E + 6,327 + 4   (e) 124 + 37T + 89E + TEE
    (c) 4,638 + T,765 + 9,328   (f) 5T6,973 + E48,207 + TE5,76E

4. Translate the following number concepts to their proper expressions in the scales of seven, four, two, and ten. Add them and then translate the sums back to the number concept.
    (a) Six + seven + fifteen + thirty-two
    (b) Thirteen + eight + twelve + twenty-four
    (c) Seventeen + four + sixteen + twenty-one

5. Apply a commutative check to Questions 2(c) and 3(b). Apply an associative check to Questions 3(a) and 3(c).

6. In what scales were the following added?

(a)	(b)	(c)	(d) 1,877	(e) 351	(f)
3,421	3,421	3,421	4,797	576	424
2,234	2,234	2,234	3,646	392	312
11,210	10,055	5,655	9,210	1,099	736

7. (a) A salesman makes a road trip and spends 5 days in New York, 4 days in Wilmington, 4 days in Philadelphia, 6 days in Baltimore, and a week and 4 days in Washington. How many weeks and days was he on the road?

(b) Find the total number of days he was on the road, doing your computation in the base of seven. Compare this answer with that of (a).

8. (a) A boy scout troop collected empty soft-drink bottles. One patrol of 8 boys brought in 6, 7, 10, 5, 11, 8, 7, and 9 bottles. How many cartons of twelve did they collect?

(b) Find the total number of soft-drink bottles collected by this patrol by adding in the scale of twelve. Compare this answer with that of (a).

9. Find the excess over elevens for the following decimal scale numbers.
    (a)   302   (b)   4,646   (c)   4,664   (d) 43,627
    (e) 32,371   (f)   147,383   (g) 807,190
Check by dividing each by eleven.

10. Add the following and check by casting out elevens (decimal scale).
   (a) 4,632 + 7,963 + 43,827 + 3
   (b) 8,376 + 47,381 + 36,429 + 62,392

11. Check the additions of Questions 2 and 3 by casting out sixes and thirteens, respectively.

Unit 10: Multiplication

1. *Introduction.* The second synthesizing process is that of multiplication. This synthesis differs from that of addition in that the groups put together must not only be composed of like things, but must also be of the same size. Thus, multiplication may be thought of as a special case of addition, one in which all the addends are of equal size. For example, 6 + 6 + 6 + 6 = 24 can be readily translated to 4 × 6 = 24, while 6 + 4 + 5 + 9 cannot.

Names for the basic items in a multiplication in terms of the already known process of addition are as follows: the *multiplicand* is the typical addend; the *multiplier* is the number of times the typical addend appears, and the *product* is the result of the operation, corresponding to the sum. Thus our 6 + 6 + 6 + 6 = 24 translated to multiplication would be

$$
\begin{array}{r}
6 \leftarrow \text{multiplicand} \\
\underline{\times 4} \leftarrow \text{multiplier} \\
24 \leftarrow \text{product}
\end{array}
$$

It should be noted that in the corresponding addition problem the principle of likeness guarantees agreement between the addends and the sum (if the addends are "people," the sum will have to be "people" also). From this it follows that in multiplication there will be agreement between the multiplicand (typical addend) and the product (sum)—or as it is sometimes said, "the multiplicand is homogeneous with the product." The multiplier, since it accounts only for the number of constituent groups involved in the total, is necessarily a nonconcrete or abstract number.

To appreciate the operation of multiplication at a more advanced level of generalization, we must understand the important term *factor*. *Factor* comes from the Latin *facere*, meaning "to make." Thus the factors of a number are in effect the "makers" of that number when the "manufacturing" process is multiplication. The multiplier and multiplicand are the makers, hence factors, of the product. But the multiplicand and multiplier are themselves numbers and consequently may be thought of as being made up of factors. For instance, in the case of 8×15, the 8 may be factored as (4×2) or (8×1) and 15 as (3×5) or (15×1). Substituting equals for equals, we obtain $8 \times 15 = (4 \times 2) \times (3 \times 5)$, both sides of which equal the same product, 120. This leads us to a statement of our first principle, the *associative law with respect to multiplication*.

Principle M-1: *The product of a multiplication is unaffected by the combinations by which the factors are grouped.*

This principle, applied to our preceding problem, means that the product 120 will be arrived at either (a) by multiplying the factors 4 and 2 and then 3 and 5, and finally multiplying the products of these pairs together (in effect 8×15) or (b) by multiplying the factors singly in sequence $(4 \times 2 \times 3 \times 5)$. By extension it follows that there are other possible groupings; for instance,

$$4 \times 2 \times 3 \times 5 = 4 \times (2 \times 3 \times 5) = 4 \times 30 = 120$$
$$= (4 \times 2 \times 3) \times 5 = 24 \times 5 = 120$$

Thus we see that the various groupings of the factors are of no consequence to the ultimate product.

The second important principle which underlies the modern algorism of multiplication is the *commutative law with respect to multiplication*.

Principle M-2: *The product of a multiplication is unaffected by the sequence or order in which the factors are multiplied.*

This principle means that 120 will be the result for $4 \times 2 \times 3 \times 5$ or $2 \times 5 \times 3 \times 4$ or any other order assumed by the factors. Stated generally we have for factors a and b, $a \times b = b \times a$.

Among other things this principle offers an economy of operation which most of us utilize every day. For instance, suppose we wish to know how many people to provide refreshments for at a bridge party involving 17 tables. The 4 people per table constitute the multiplicand and the 17 groups the multiplier. Formally speaking, the multiplication* should go 17×4 or

$$
\begin{array}{r}
4 \ \text{people} \\
\underline{17} \\
28 \\
\underline{4} \\
68 \ \text{people}
\end{array}
$$

* Usually this is read "17 times 4" which implies that the multiplier precedes the operational symbol ($\times$) and the multiplicand follows.

But because of the commutative law, we know the multiplier and multiplicand may be interchanged without affecting the product. So, for most people, the simpler computation of

$$\begin{array}{r} 17 \\ \underline{\times 4} \\ 68 \end{array}$$

would be chosen.

By making the number with the most digits the multiplicand and the one with the fewer digits the multiplier, an undeniable economy of time and motion is achieved, but often at the expense of meaning. Indiscriminate designation of factors as multiplier and multiplicand for convenience only, with no awareness of the commutative law being at the root, frequently adds a touch of unnecessary confusion to a meaningful understanding of this computation.

The third principle which forms the basis for multiplication is the *distributive law*.

> **Principle M-3:** *To arrive at the product of a given number and the sum of several numbers either:* (a) *add the several numbers and multiply their sum by the given number,* or (b) *multiply each of the several numbers by the given number and add the resulting products.*

As an example, $4 \times (6 + 3 + 2)$ can be solved either by (a) adding $6 + 3 + 2$ to 11, then multiplying the 11 by 4 to get the product 44, or (b) multiplying each of the several numbers 6, 3, and 2 by 4, for 24, 12, and 8, respectively, then adding these products: $24 + 12 + 8 = 44$. Fundamentally the modern algorism of multiplication is substantially a reflection of this distributive law.

2. *The Multiplication Algorism.* The modern algorism of multiplication, like that of addition, is based upon a few basic principles and a certain set of memory facts. The principles are those of our notational system (addition and place value), the principles M-1, M-2, and M-3 discussed above, and the addition principles A-1, A-2, and A-3 discussed in Unit 8. The memory facts required are those for addition, along with a new set, the primary multiplication combinations. A primary multiplication combination is the product of any two single-digit numbers, such as $6 \times 5 = 30$ or $8 \times 6 = 48$. All told, there are again in the decimal system one hundred of these, including the zero facts, which run through 9×9.

Perhaps some of us in our school days learned these "tables" through to 12 × 12. As far as the algorism is concerned, there is no need to learn beyond 9 × 9, although some deem it advantageous to memorize the combinations through to 12's because of the many practical situations arising in daily life which involve dozens, feet, and other measurements based on twelve. Since we are concerned here only with the multiplication algorism, our primary combinations will end at 9 × 9, that is, actually involve only the products of pairs of single-digit factors. For effective use, the memorization and near-automatic response to these combinations is practically a prerequisite to the modern algorism of multiplication.

The primary multiplication combinations for our decimal scale are given in Table IX. Each of the products can be arrived at

TABLE IX. PRIMARY MULTIPLICATION COMBINATIONS
(Decimal Scale)

	0	1	2	3	4	5	6	7	8	9
0	0	0	0	0	0	0	0	0	0	0
1	0	1	2	3	4	5	6	7	8	9
2	0	2	4	6	8	10	12	14	16	18
3	0	3	6	9	12	15	18	21	24	27
4	0	4	8	12	16	20	24	28	32	36
5	0	5	10	15	20	25	30	35	40	45
6	0	6	12	18	24	30	36	42	48	54
7	0	7	14	21	28	35	42	49	56	63
8	0	8	16	24	32	40	48	56	64	72
9	0	9	18	27	36	45	54	63	72	81

either by counting (for instance the column of 5's is the same as counting by 5's) or by exploiting the known relationship between multiplication and addition. There are psychological advantages to having a learner "discover" the result of, say, 6 × 7 by the application of some principle or through some bit of previous knowledge before embarking on the less interesting task of memorizing the fact.

So to gain a better appreciation of the logic behind the precepts of the modern algorism, we shall approach it through a series of progressive steps.

(a) *Multiplication with a single-digit multiplier.* Consider $4 \times 3,816$. The multiplicand 3,816 may be thought of as the sum of 3 thousands + 8 hundreds + 1 ten + 6 units (principles of place value and addition); hence the problem can be reformulated to $4 \times$ (3 thousands + 8 hundreds + 1 ten + 6 units). According to the distributive law (M-3) this may be multiplied to 12 thousands + 32 hundreds + 4 tens + 24 units. By reduction this sum may be expressed alternatively as

$$\lvert 1 \text{ ten-thousand} + 2 \text{ thousands}\rvert + \lvert 3 \text{ thousands} + 2 \text{ hundreds}\rvert + \lvert 4 \text{ tens}\rvert + \lvert 2 \text{ tens} + 4 \text{ units}\rvert$$

Then collecting terms according to the principle of likeness (A-1) we get

$$\lvert 1 \text{ ten-thousand}\rvert + \lvert 5 \text{ thousands}\rvert + \lvert 2 \text{ hundreds}\rvert + \lvert 6 \text{ tens}\rvert + \lvert 4 \text{ units}\rvert$$

Finally, reversing our earlier use of the principle of place value, this sum may be written more concisely as 15,264. From this it follows that the product of $4 \times 3,816$ is 15,264.

Repeating this problem in summary form:

$$\begin{array}{r} 3,816 \\ \times 1 \\ \hline \end{array}$$

1.	By principle of place value and addition:	$3th + 8h + 1t + 6u$	
		$\times 4$	
2.	By M-3	$12th + 32h + 4t + 24u$	(level a)
3.	Reorganizing, (A-3)	$1t\text{-}th + 2th + 3th + 2h + 4t + 2t + 4u$	(level b)
4.	Collecting, (A-1)	$1t\text{-}th\ +\ 5th\ +\ 2h\ +\ 6t\ +\ 4u$	(level c)
5.	By principle of place value,	15,264	(level d)

The reorganizing and collecting steps (3, 4) in effect constitute what we know in the algorism as *carrying*, except that in the algorism we reorganize and collect as we go along. As in the algorism of addition, this can be done most expeditiously by operating from right to left, through progressively higher orders. Our modern algorism is but an abbreviated version of the outlined development above with many of the steps done mentally.

To show that the bulk of the algorism rests heavily upon mental effort we now repeat the problem $4 \times 3{,}816$, underscoring the few physical or nonmental actions of the computation. Also note how the algorism skips around among the steps (designated by levels) of the foregoing rationalization.

1. $4 \times 6 = 24$ (level a):
    <u>write 4</u> (level d) and carry 2 (level b)

2. $4 \times 1 = \ 4$ (level a) plus carried $2 = 6$ (level c):
    <u>write 6</u> (level d)

3. $4 \times 8 = 32$ (level a):
    <u>write 2</u> (level d) and carry 3 (level b)

4. $4 \times 3 = 12$ (level a) plus carried $3 = 15$ (level c):
    <u>write 15</u> (level d)

Notice that carrying in multiplication is decidedly more difficult than carrying in addition, because in multiplication there is an intervening activity (the finding of the next product) which comes in between the point at which one mentally decides to "carry" a certain value and the point at which he actually employs the carried value. For instance, in 6×37 we multiply $6 \times 7 = 42$, write the 2 and carry the 4. But before using the 4 we must first multiply $6 \times 3 = 18$; *then* the 4 is added. In the process of addition this problem is not so complex, for the carried amount from any given column can be pressed immediately into service at the outset of addition in the next column; hence there is less difficulty in keeping the carried quantity in mind in addition.

(b) *Multiplying by the base or power of the base.* In the decimal scale multiplying an integer by ten has the effect of upgrading each of the component parts of the number expression to the next higher order. Thus $(10 \times 674) = 10 \times (6 \text{ hundreds} + 7 \text{ tens} + 4 \text{ units}) = 60 \text{ hundreds} + 70 \text{ tens} + 40 \text{ units} = $ (by reduction) 6 thousands $+ 7$ hundreds $+ 4$ tens. In order to write this resulting number in our place-value system a zero is needed in the units place. Thus $10 \times 674 = 6{,}740$. Multiplication by one hundred (or 10^2) is in effect multiplying by ten and again by ten, which amounts to twice upgrading the orders of the component parts of the number. Therefore two zeros will be necessary in the two inferior orders. By extension, a similar situation will be seen to prevail for other and higher powers of ten. Thus this rule evolves: *To multiply an integer*

*by some power of ten, write the integer and annex to its right the number
of zeros found in the multiplier.*

From this, the step to a multiplication of such numbers as
60 × 324 and 300 × 714 is a simple one.

	The Problem	
300 × 714	The Problem	60 × 324
(3 × 100) × 714	Any number may be expressed as a product of factors	(6 × 10) × 324
3 × 100 × 714	M-1	6 × 10 × 324
3 × 714 × 100	M-2	6 × 324 × 10
(3 × 714) × 100	M-1	(6 × 324) × 10
2,142 × 100	Multiplication by single-digit multiplier	1,944 × 10
214,200	Multiplication by powers of ten—the answer	19,440

We can circumvent these several steps by applying this general
rule:

*Multiply the multiplicand by the nonzero digit in the multi-
plier and annex to the right of this product the number of zeros
found in the multiplier.*

(c) *The general case—long multiplication.* The algorism which
governs the finding of the product of two multidigit factors such as
539 × 7,625 is actually a composite of much of the foregoing. First
we look upon the multiplier as a sum of its component parts
(539 = 500 + 30 + 9) thus reducing the problem to a specific instance of the distributive law [(500 + 30 + 9) × (7,625)]. Carrying out the (b) alternative of the distributive law, we compute
(500 × 7,625), (30 × 7,625), and (9 × 7,625). Then, adding together each of the resulting products, in reverse order, we get

	Millions	Hundred-thousands	Ten-thousands	Thousands	Hundreds	Tens	Units
(9 × 7625) = 68625				7	6	2	5
(30 × 7625) = 228750					5	3	9
(500 × 7625) = 3812500							
Their sum			6	8	6	2	5
(product): 4109875		2	2	8	7	5	
	3	8	1	2	5		
	4	1	0	9	8	7	5

Note the parallel between these sums and our algorism in which we multiply 7,625 successively by 9, 3, and 5, indenting each resulting partial product after the first. Obviously our "indenting" is but an acknowledgment that the second digit in the multiplier is actually not a 3 but 30, and any resulting product will necessarily have a zero in the units place; and that the 5 in the multiplier is really 500, and consequently any resulting product will have two zeros in the lowest two orders. But since speed is a major objective in our modern algorisms, it is a waste of time to write in these zero symbols when appropriate indentation will serve the purpose. Once the rationale behind the algorism is understood, one major source of difficulty in multiplication, errors in indentation, particularly when there are zeros in the multiplier, should be minimized.

3. *Checks for Multiplication.* Generally speaking the checks most frequently employed to verify multiplications are of two kinds: commutative checks and excess checks.*

The commutative check makes use of the fact that if multiplier and multiplicand are interchanged, the product remains unchanged. Thus if we had originally multiplied 34 × 869, a check by the commutative method would require finding the product of 869 × 34.

$$
\begin{array}{rr}
869 & 34 \\
34 & 869 \\
\hline
3476 & 306 \\
2607 & 204 \\
\hline
29546 & 272 \\
& \hline
& 29546 \\
\end{array}
$$

Basically the same primary multiplication combinations are involved in both computations, but in the second case a new set of partial products contribute to what should be the same sum as produced by the original. A discrepancy between the two products indicates that either the original or the check is incorrect. Agreement between the two means that the original is correct if some highly unlikely compensating error was not committed in the check to produce this second equal, though incorrect, answer.

The excess check can best be explained by a little algebra. Assume that there are d nines in the multiplicand with an excess

---

* A third type is a division check. This calls for dividing the product by one of the factors, which should produce a quotient equal to the other factor. The rationale of such a check will be better understood after the process of division has been handled in the next chapter.

of q, and r nines in the multiplier with an excess of p. Then the multiplicand can be expressed as $(9d + q)$ and the multiplier as $(9r + p)$. Since

$$\text{multiplier} \times \text{multiplicand} = \text{product}$$
$$(9r + p) \times (9d + q) = 81dr + 9dp + 9rq + pq$$

A term-by-term analysis of the product shows quite clearly that the first three terms will be evenly divisible by 9, and that should there be any excess in the whole product it would have to be found in the last term pq. Since pq constitutes the product of the excesses of multiplicand and multiplier, we arrive at the general rule:

The excess of nines in the product of two factors equals the excess in the product of the excesses in the two factors.

To illustrate, multiply (a) 34×869 and (b) $539 \times 7{,}625$ and check by excess of nines.

(a)
```
   869   ← excess of nines = 5
    34   ← excess of nines = 7
  3476      product of excesses 35
  2607      excess in product of excesses = ⑧
 29546   ← excess in product = ⑧
```

(b)
```
   7625   ← excess of nines = 2
    539   ← excess of nines = 8
  68625       product of excesses = 16
  22875       excesses in product of excesses = ⑦
  38125
4109875   ← excess in product = ⑦
```

PROBLEMS SET 10

1. Solve the following problems and identify the multiplier, multiplicand, and product in each. Check to see if multiplicand and product are like terms.

(a) Jones earns $1.25 per hour. What is his daily wage for an 8-hour day?

(b) How many lines of print in a book of 212 pages, if there are 30 lines per page?

(c) How many eggs in 15 dozen eggs?

(d) How many miles will an auto travel in 12 hours at the average rate of 35 miles per hour?

(e) If pencils cost 6 for 25¢, how much will 42 pencils cost?

(f) How many words in a book if there are 270 pages, 30 lines to a page, and an average of 11 words per line?

(g) How many minutes are there in three days?

2. To find the area of a rectangle which is 6 by 5 ft we multiply the length (6 ft) by the width (5 ft) and get an area of 30 sq ft. This appears to violate the statement that the multiplier is *always* abstract. Explain.

3. Using the associative law, suggest a way for multiplying the following mentally.

(a) 50×16 (c) 26×50 (e) $8 \times 7 \times 25$
(b) 25×36 (d) $8 \times 25 \times 6$ (f) 16×125

4. By virtue of the commutative law, how many different ways can the product of the three factors A, B, and C be found?

5. The distributive law, stated symbolically, is $[a \times (b + c)] = (a \times b) + (a \times c)$. Verify this law when

(a) $a = 4$, $b = 6$, $c = 2$
(b) $a = 7$, $b = 8$, $c = 9$
(c) $a = 5$, $b = 6$, $c = 8$

6. Explain the multiplication of $7 \times 8{,}369$ in a manner similar to (a) on page 73. Write out in detail reasons for each step.

7. Multiply $8{,}369 \times 7$, using 7 as the multiplicand.

8. Write a rule for multiplying some number by 6,000; by 2,000,000.

9. Develop a set of directions for multiplying $863 \times 1{,}437$ in which one multiplies first by the 8, then by the 6, and finally by the 3. Multiply $863 \times 5{,}267$ by multiplying first by the 6, then the 8, then the 3.

10. Check the following multiplications by (a) commutative check, (b) excess of nines check.

$$832 \times 6{,}743 \qquad 674 \times 4{,}732 \qquad 302 \times 6{,}021$$

11. Check the problems in Question 10 by casting out 11's. *just one*

12. In the multiplication of $A \times B = C$,
   (a) What happens to the product if B is doubled?
   (b) What happens to the product if A is halved?
   (c) What happens to the product if B is doubled and A is halved?
   (d) How much larger will the product be if B is increased by one?
   (e) What can you say about A and B if C equals zero?
   (f) What is A if $C = B$?

Unit 11: Multiplication in Other Scales

1. *Introduction.* Following the proposition established earlier
that computation in other scales aids in one's appreciation of the
logic behind our modern algorisms, we now direct our attention to
multiplication in scales other than ten. The principles of the multiplication operation—which we are most interested in observing—
of course remain invariant whatever the base. Thus we shall see
that multiplication in other scales depends upon the three principles
established earlier, the associative (M-1), the commutative (M-2),
and the distributive (M-3) laws. The basic memory facts of multiplication, like those of addition in other scales, will also differ
somewhat from scale to scale. For instance, the number facts for
three times six, which equals the number concept eighteen in any
scale, take on the following number expressions in the scales of
eight, ten, and twelve:

$$\text{Scale eight:} \qquad 3 \times 6 = 22$$
$$\text{Scale ten:} \qquad 3 \times 6 = 18$$
$$\text{Scale twelve:} \qquad 3 \times 6 = 16$$

A primary multiplication combination is the product of two
single-digit values. In scales four and five "three times six" is not
one of the primary combinations, but the product of a single-digit
multiplier and a multidigit multiplicand, solvable by the algorism.
In the scale of five "three sixes" would be $3 \times 11 = 33$, and in the
scale of four it would be $3 \times 12 = 102$.

As a matter of convenience in presentation we shall again restrict
our illustrations to the scales of five and twelve. Of course, the
reader is encouraged to develop tables for scales other than these
and to test his learning in problems involving them. As is true in
the decimal scale, development of the multiplication algorism for
these scales requires initially an understanding of the basic principles
of the operation as well as a knowledge of the primary combinations.
Table X provides the primary combinations for base five and twelve.
These latter, of course, need not be committed to memory, but
frequent reference to the proper primary combination table during
computations is suggested.

The development of a table of primary combinations for a given
scale of notation in itself offers a good review of earlier work as well
as an exercise in some of the basic laws of multiplication. The
following is a suggested approach in the scale of five, varied to
include as many different ideas as possible.

TABLE X. PRIMARY MULTIPLICATION COMBINATIONS, SCALES FIVE AND TWELVE

×	0	1	2	3	4
0	0	0	0	0	0
1	0	1	2	3	4
2	0	2	4	11	13
3	0	3	11	14	22
4	0	4	13	22	31

×	0	1	2	3	4	5	6	7	8	9	T	E
0	0	0	0	0	0	0	0	0	0	0	0	0
1	0	1	2	3	4	5	6	7	8	9	T	E
2	0	2	4	6	8	T	10	12	14	16	18	1T
3	0	3	6	9	10	13	16	19	20	23	26	29
4	0	4	8	10	14	18	20	24	28	30	34	38
5	0	5	T	13	18	21	26	2E	34	39	42	47
6	0	6	10	16	20	26	30	36	40	46	50	56
7	0	7	12	19	24	2E	36	41	48	53	5T	65
8	0	8	14	20	28	34	40	48	54	60	68	74
9	0	9	16	23	30	39	46	53	60	69	76	83
T	0	T	18	26	34	42	50	5T	68	76	84	92
E	0	E	1T	29	38	47	56	65	74	83	92	T1

Assume we are developing the base five portion of Table X and that the numbers across the top row are multiplicands and that those along the left-hand side are the multipliers. All entries for the first row proper will be zeros, since zero times anything is zero. The entries in the second row will be exactly the same as the multiplicands across the top because the multiplier here is one.* The commutative law, which states that the multiplier and multiplicand

* One (1) is also known as the "identity element" in multiplication (and division) since it is the only multiplier (divisor) which produces a product (quotient) equal to the multiplicand (dividend). Similarly, zero (0) is known as the identity element in addition (and subtraction) for it is the only value which when added to (subtracted from) another number yields that same number. For example:

$$1 \times 6 = 6 \qquad 7 \div 1 = 7 \qquad 3 + 0 = 3 \qquad 4 - 0 = 4$$
$$1 \times 18 = 18 \qquad 19 \div 1 = 19 \qquad 15 + 0 = 15 \qquad 18 - 0 = 18$$
$$1 \times N = N \qquad N \div 1 = N \qquad N + 0 = N \qquad N - 0 = N$$

A knowledge of this concept is frequently helpful in explaining many of the "unwritten" things in arithmetic, such as denominators of one, factors of one, a value raised to the first power, zero addends, so-called "transpositions" in equations, etc.

may be interchanged without a change in the product, is evidenced in the table by the fact that the nth row, counting from the top, contains the same sequence of entries as the nth column, counting from the left. This means that when constructing the table, completion of any given row automatically furnishes the values for completing the corresponding column.

The next computation after the first two rows and columns have been completed is 2×2. This combination might be evaluated by resorting to its addition parallel in base five, namely, $2 + 2 = 4$. Similarly, for 2×3 and 2×4, our knowledge of the addition combinations in the scale of five $(3 + 3 = 11)$ and $(4 + 4 = 13)$ (see page 61) provides these required products. Once more by the commutative law, completion of the 2-row in effect means completion of the 2-column.

To vary our tactics a bit, let us compute the value of the next entry, 3×3, by an application of the distributive law. We do know (from addition in this scale) that $3 = 2 + 1$, and by the distributive law (M-3) we know that 3×3 may be calculated alternatively as $3 \times (2 + 1) = (3 \times 2) + (3 \times 1)$. Earlier in the table we had calculated that $3 \times 2 = 11$ and $3 \times 1 = 3$; thus $3 \times 3 = (3 \times 2) + (3 \times 1) = 11 + 3 = 14$ (scale five).

In similar fashion the remaining entries of the table can be "discovered," depending entirely upon our knowledge of the principles and previous developments in that scale. It is significant that this whole undertaking can be accomplished without once leaving the scale of five or drawing upon some prior knowledge in the decimal scale. Of course this is not to say that the scale five multiplication table could not have been developed by falling back upon the decimal scale for computation, and then translating the answers into the scale of five. However, to do so deprives us of additional evidence that the algorisms are applicable in all bases; and furthermore, calling on our prior knowledge of the decimal scale destroys, for those interested, the parallel between our experiences in these foreign bases and those of the school child who has no prior number experience to facilitate his learning of the basic elements of computation.

2. *Multiplication Algorisms in Other Scales.* Once the primary combinations are known, the algorism develops along the same lines as those found in the previous unit.

(a) *Multiplication with a single-digit multiplier.* Consider the problems 3 × 243 (five) and 7 × 6T2 (twelve).

3 × 243 (five)

$B^3 = 1000$	$B^2 = 100$	$B^1 = 10$	$B^0 = 1$	
"One hundred twenty-five"	"Twenty-five"	"Five"	"One"	When B = five ←
	2	4	3	
			3	
	1 1 ←	2 2 ←	①4	
1 ←	①3	②3	4	
1	3	3	4	

Condensed, we get: 3 × 3 = 14; write 4 and carry 1; 3 × 4 = 22, plus carried 1 = 23; write 3, carry 2; 3 × 2 = 11 plus carried 2 = 13; write 13. Answer is 1,334. Note that all work was done *entirely* in the scale of five.

7 × 6T2 (twelve)

$B^3 = 1000$	$B^2 = 100$	$B^1 = 10$	$B^0 = 1$	
"One thousand seven hundred twenty-eight" (great gross)	"One hundred forty-four" (gross)	"Twelve" (dozen)	"One" (units)	When B = twelve ←
	6	T	2	
			7	
	3 6 ←	5 T ←	①2	
3 ←	③E	⑤E	2	
3	E	E	2	

Abbreviated we get: 7 × 2 = 12; write 2 and carry 1; 7 × T = 5T plus carried 1 = 5E; write E and carry 5; 7 × 6 = 36 plus carried 5 = 3E; write 3E. Answer 3,EE2. Again all work has been done entirely in the scale of twelve.

(b) *Multiplying by the base or a power of the base.* As illustrated in the previous unit, multiplication by a value equal to some power of the base (the base value is considered to be the base raised to the first power) has the effect of upgrading each component part of the multiplicand a number of orders equal to the power of the multiplier. Thus the base times any three-digit number results in a four-

digit product whose first three digits (reading from left to right) are
the digits of the multiplicand with the fourth digit zero; the "base
squared" times a three-digit number results in a five-digit product
whose first three are the digits of the multiplicand and the last two
are zeros. Thus:

(1) Five times seventy-three in scale five is
$$10 \times 243 = 2{,}430 \text{ (scale five)}$$
(2) Twelve times one hundred fifty, scale twelve, is
$$10 \times 106 = 1{,}060 \text{ (scale twelve)}$$

Also,

(3) Twenty-five times seventy-three, scale twelve, is
$$100 \times 243 = 24{,}300 \text{ (scale five)}$$
(4) One hundred forty-four times one hundred fifty, scale twelve, is
$$100 \times 106 = 10{,}600 \text{ (scale twelve)}$$

By extension,

(5) Fifteen $\times$ seventy-three, scale five, would be
$$30 \times 243 = 3 \times 10 \times 243 = (3 \times 243) \times 10$$
$$= (1{,}334) \times 10 = 13{,}340 \text{ (scale five)}.$$
(6) Thirty-six $\times$ one hundred fifty, scale twelve, would be
$$30 \times 106 = 3 \times 10 \times 106 = (3 \times 106) \times 10$$
$$= (316) \times 10 = 3160 \text{ (scale twelve)}$$

(c) *Long multiplication.* The algorism for this type of computation is again pretty much a composite of the foregoing. For instance,
thirty-eight $\times$ seventy-three, base five, would be expressed numerically as 123×243, which is to say $(100 + 20 + 3) \times 243 =$
$(100 \times 243) + (20 \times 243) + (3 \times 234)$ (scale five). Evaluating
these in reverse order, we have

$$
\begin{array}{ll}
\begin{array}{rl}
3 \times 243 = & 1334 \\
20 \times 243 = & 10410 \\
100 \times 243 = & \underline{24300} \\
& 42044
\end{array}
\quad \text{or} \quad
&
\begin{array}{r}
243 \\
\underline{123} \\
1334 \\
1041 \\
\underline{243} \\
42044
\end{array}
\end{array}
$$

3. *Checks for Multiplication in Other Scales.* The commutative
check needs no further elaboration other than the direction to interchange the multiplier and multiplicand and proceed with the operation as though it were a new problem. The product of both computations should be identical.

The technique for the excess check is similar to that of checking
a decimal scale multiplication by the excess of nines. Aside from
the fact that adding the digits of a number in some scale other than

ten produces the excess over that number which is one less than the base, the procedures and reasons for the validity of the check are the same as those encountered in the previous unit. Thus the statement is still true, whatever the base: *The excess over the "base less one"* (e.g., nine in decimal scale, four in base five, eleven in base twelve, etc.) *in the product of two factors equals the excess in the product of the excesses of the two factors.* By way of illustration:

Base five:

$$243 \rightarrow \text{excess of fours (base less one)} = 1$$
$$\underline{123} \rightarrow \text{excess of fours (base less one)} = \underline{2}$$

1234	product of excesses = 2
1041	excess in product of excesses = 2
243	

$$\overline{42044} \rightarrow \text{excess of fours in product} = 2 \leftarrow$$

Base twelve:

$$4TE3 \rightarrow \text{excess of elevens (base less one)} = 6$$
$$\underline{27} \rightarrow \text{excess of elevens (base less one)} = \underline{9}$$

| 2T469 | product of excesses = 46 |
| 99T6 | excess in product of excesses = T |

$$\overline{108309} \rightarrow \text{excess of elevens in product} = T \leftarrow$$

4. *Algebraic Approach to Multiplication.* Multiplication in any scale of notation whatever can be generalized as the multiplication of two polynomials in x, where x = base, and the coefficients when multiplied together conform to the primary combinations for that scale. Thus to multiply $N_1 \times N_2$, where

$$N_1 = a_n x^n + a_{n-1} x^{n-1} + \ldots + a_2 x^2 + a_1 x^1 + a_0 x^0$$
$$N_2 = b_n x^n + b_{n-1} x^{n-1} + \ldots + b_2 x^2 + b_1 x^1 + b_0 x^0$$

We apply the distributive law and get

$$N_1 \times N_2 = a_n x^n (b_n x^n + b_{n-1} x^{n-1} + \ldots + b_0 x^0) + a_{n-1} x^{n-1}(N_2) + \ldots + b_0 x^0 (N_2)$$

After expansion we collect "like" terms.

Consider a particular case in which

$$N_1 = a_2 x^2 + a_1 x + a_0 \quad \text{and} \quad N_2 = b_3 x^3 + b_2 x^2 + b_1 x + b_0$$

Then

$$N_1 \times N_2 = a_2 x^2 (b_3 x^3 + b_2 x^2 + b_1 x + b_0) + a_1 x (b_3 x^3 + b_2 x^2 + b_1 x + b_0)$$
$$+ a_0 (b_3 x^3 + b_2 x^2 + b_1 x + b_0)$$
$$= a_2 b_3 x^5 + a_2 b_2 x^4 + a_2 b_1 x^3 + a_2 b_0 x^2 + a_1 b_3 x^4 + a_1 b_2 x^3 + a_1 b_1 x^2 + a_1 b_0 x$$
$$+ a_0 b_3 x^3 + a_0 b_2 x^2 + a_0 b_1 x + a_0 b_0$$

Collecting "like" terms, we get

$$a_2b_3x^5 + (a_2b_2 + a_1b_3)x^4 + (a_2b_1 + a_1b_2 + a_0b_3)x^3 + (a_2b_0 + a_1b_1 + a_0b_2)x^2$$
$$+ (a_1b_0 + a_0b_1)x + a_0b_0$$

Considerable writing could have been saved had the problem been given the form which is usual for the arithmetic algorism.

$$b_3x^3 + b_2x^2 + b_1x + b_0$$
$$a_2x^2 + a_1x + a_0$$

$a_2b_3x^5 + a_2b_2x^4$	$+a_2b_1x^3$	$+a_2b_0x^2$		
$a_1b_3x^4$	$+a_1b_2x^3$	$+a_1b_1x^2$	$+a_1b_0x$	
	$a_0b_3x^3$	$+a_0b_2x^2$	$+a_0b_1x$	$+a_0b_0$

$$a_2b_3x^5 + (a_1b_3 + a_2b_2)x^4 + (a_2b_1 + a_1b_2 + a_0b_3)x^3 + (a_2b_0 + a_1b_1 + a_0b_2)x^2 + (a_1b_0 + a_0b_1)x + a_0b_0$$

Notice that in algebra we are not concerned with "carrying" from one order to the next, and so it is actually easier to work from left to right. There is no harm in working from right to left, but when this is done, difficulties arise with the spacing of the symbols.

Of course if this problem represents some specific base (that is, the variable x is fixed at some value), then carrying is in order whenever the sum of the (a_kb_k) terms in any given set of parentheses equals or exceeds the base value.

PROBLEMS SET 11

1. Construct a table of primary multiplication combinations for the base of two; four; seven.

2. Multiply the following in base four.*

(a) 132
21

(b) 133
120

(c) 321
123

(d) 30210
213

3. Multiply the following in base seven.*

(a) 326
32

(b) 405
206

(c) 325
163

(d) 3426
216

4. Multiply the following in base two.*

(a) 111
11

(b) 1011
101

(c) 11010
1011

(d) 10001
110

5. Check the problems of Question 2 by casting out "threes" and the problems of Question 3 by casting out "sixes."

6. In what scale were the following multiplied?

(a) $8 \times 6 = 40$ base 12 (d) $7 \times 12 = 85$
(b) $8 \times 6 = 28$ base 20 (e) $6 \times 15 = 103$
(c) $8 \times 6 = 14$ base 44 (f) $5 \times 13 = 113$

* Addition tables for these bases were developed in Question 1 on p. 68.

7. In the problems of Questions 3 and 4, convert the factors and products to their equivalents in base ten, then multiply in base ten, to see if they check.

† 8. Check the problems of Question 3 by casting out "eights" (base plus one) and the problems of Question 4 by casting out "threes."

9. Solve these problems, using base twelve.

(a) How many eggs all told are there in four boxes of two dozen each?

(b) A manufacturer of bottle caps packs in each box a gross and four spare caps. How many bottle caps will be needed for each ten boxes?

† 10. Multiply algebraically $N_1 \times N_2$, where $N_1 = a_3x^3 + a_2x^2 + a_0$ and $N_2 = b_4x^4 + b_2x^2 + b_1x$. Assuming that $x =$ ten, verify your answer by assigning values to a's and b's and multiplying them out. Assuming $x =$ five, do the same.

Unit 12: Other Synthesizing Algorisms

1. *Geometric Approach to Synthesis.* In the last unit of Chapter 1 a distinction was drawn between number used in a discrete sense and number to represent a continuum. It was also pointed out that the paper and pencil algorisms usually taught in the schools are better understood when the numbers are looked at from the discrete point of view, while mental arithmetic is often facilitated by the use of the continuum or geometric concept. Basic to the latter is the number line beginning with zero on the left and extending indefinitely to the right.

(a) *Addition and the number line.* Using the number line, addition is explained as being the final stopping point after a series of steps, the size of which are determined by the size of each addend. Thus the sum $3 + 5 + 4 = 12$ depicted on this line would be (follow the solid lines):

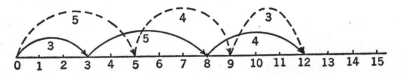

In this illustration the commutative law with respect to addition can be readily verified by the dotted lines which trace the addition of $5 + 4 + 3$ to the same final point 12. And just as readily the associative law with respect to addition can be verified as follows.

† For those who understand the algebraic parallels.

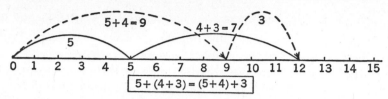

When the sequence of steps carries us from one decade to the next or from one hundred to the next, we have what is known as "bridging" the decade, or "bridging" the hundred. In effect this bridging corresponds to the carrying process in the paper and pencil algorism. Thus to add 9 to 16, we add 4 of the 9 to the 16, which bridges the twenties, and then add the remaining 5 to get the total 25.

We shall present here the mental thought pattern for an addition problem. Note how it differs from the paper and pencil algorism, which calls for adding all the units first and then all the tens. The problem is $26 + 32 + 27$. Thinking in terms of the number line, we picture the point represented as 26, twenty-six units to the right of the initial zero. The next addend of 32 means a total jump from 26 of 3 decades and 2 units. Thus 26 and 3 decades brings us to 56, and 2 units further will be 58. Resting on 58 we contemplate our next addend, 27, which means a jump of 2 decades and 7 units. The first leg of this jump takes us into the seventies, and the second leg involves bridging to the next decade, the eighties. Thus $78 + 7 = 78 + (2 + 5) = (78 + 2) + 5 = 80 + 5 = 85$. Influenced somewhat by the more frequently used paper and pencil algorism, some may prefer to "add in" the units first and then the decades. Thanks to the commutative law this variation is irrelevant to the final sum. It should be noted, however, that in the continuum or number-line approach the packaging idea for number is not completely overlooked. Its influence can be seen in that the jumps are usually either unit jumps, decade jumps, hundred jumps, and so on—all powers of ten.

(b) *Multiplication and the number line.* It will be recalled that multiplication was introduced earlier in this chapter as being a specialized case of addition, one in which all the addends are of equal size. On the number line this means jumps of equal size; for instance, 4×6 means ultimately the sum of four sixes. Thus

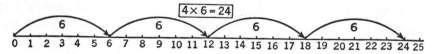

To review this situation in terms of multiplier, multiplicand, and product relationships, the multiplicand is the size of the typical jump, the multiplier is the number of such jumps to be taken, and the product is that number upon which the last jump terminates.

Characteristically the paper and pencil algorisms proceed from right to left, so as to systematize the carrying process, while generally speaking, the mental approach to these computations is in the opposite direction. For instance, to multiply 3×264 along the number line, we recognize that 3 jumps of 264 units each are the same collectively as 3 jumps of 200, plus 3 jumps of 60, plus 3 jumps of 4. Notice the distributive law here: $3(200 + 60 + 4) = (3 \times 200) + (3 \times 60) + (3 \times 4)$. Thus we figure 3 jumps of 200 is 600; 3 jumps of 60 is 180; 600 and 180 is 780; and 3 jumps of 4 is 12 units; 780 and 12 is 792. Therefore $3 \times 264 = 792$.

2. *Historical Perspective.* Our modern algorisms are but the present-day phase of an evolutionary process. They have profited by past experience and been influenced not a little by both the availability of certain materials, such as cheap paper and pencil, and the amount of general education, which makes possible the memory training for these algorisms. The fact that many a school child in the fourth or fifth grade today is able to perform computations that only the best scholars of four or five centuries ago could perform is a real monument to this evolutionary process.

The story is told of a fifteenth-century German merchant who asked a university professor where he should send his son for special commercial training. He was advised that if only addition and subtraction were wanted, German universities might suffice, but that in Italy only could instruction in the advanced art of multiplication and division be obtained.*

By considering some of the earlier forms of the basic algorisms we stand to gain considerable insight into our present-day form. And it may be pointed out that antiquated approaches often have a popular and motivating appeal—a point of interest for teachers.

Earlier addition techniques, such as those employed with the abacus, the counter board, and the scratch method, have already been dealt with in preceding units. In the realm of multiplication there are several other interesting ones.

Multiplying on the abacus is almost immediately obvious when it is looked upon as repeated addition. To multiply 6×83 for in-

* Tobias Dantzig, *Number, the Language of Science*, Macmillan, 1930, p. 26.

stance, the computer merely "adds in" on his abacus 83 six times. For more complicated computations the experienced abacist had a short-cut procedure of doubling, similar to what is described later as the Russian method of multiplication.

(a) *Lattice method.* An ancient though persistent forerunner to our modern algorism of multiplication is the lattice method. It required of the computer less mental effort than our present-day approach does but considerably more physical effort with his writing materials. It fell into disuse mainly because its diagrammatic requirements were too cumbersome for printers to handle.

This diagram was a rectangle subdivided into as many columns as there are places in the multiplicand and as many rows as places in the multiplier. The result was an array of squares, each of which was cut by a diagonal. Following are two diagrams which are necessary to this method to multiply (left) a three-digit number by a two-digit number, and (right) a three-digit number by a three-digit number.

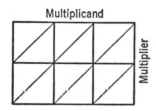

Multiplicand / Multiplier

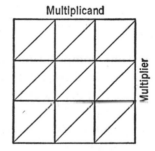

Multiplicand / Multiplier

To multiply 24 × 683, the 2-by-3 lattice is used. The three digits of the multiplicand are arranged in order from left to right at the top of this rectangle, while the digits of the multiplier are arranged in sequence from top to bottom on its righthand edge. (See Figure 8.)

Each square of the lattice receives the product of its particular column digit and row digit, with the unit value written below the diagonal and the tens digit (when present) above the diagonal. Starting at the top right combination of 2 × 3 = 6, the 6 is

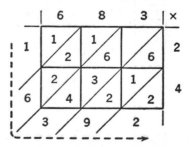

Figure 8. 24 × 683 by the lattice method.

written in its coordinate square below the diagonal. Then going to the left in this top row to the second sequence, 2 × 8 = 16. The six is written below the diagonal and the 1 above the diagonal, and so on until all squares (or all combinations) have been filled. The ultimate product is found by starting at the lowest right-hand square and adding *diagonally*, writing the units digit of the sum below and carrying the tens digit when necessary into the next diagonal. Thus we see that $24 \times 683 = 16,392$.

Two further illustrations of the lattice method are given here, which should be verified by the reader.

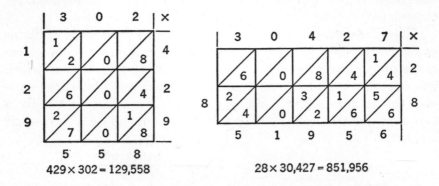

429 × 302 = 129,558   28 × 30,427 = 851,956

Notice that computation by the lattice method not only does away with the need for mental carrying, but is automatically self-aligning with respect to partial products. It requires of the computer only a knowledge of the primary multiplication combinations and an ability to add single-digit values.

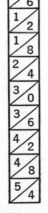

One of the earliest computing "machines" was a mechanical adaptation of the lattice system of multiplication. It was invented by the great Scotch mathematician, John Napier (1550–1617), and was popularly called "Napier's Bones." His device consisted of flat wooden sticks which contained successive multiples of values from 1 to 9. (See Figure 9 for an illustration of the 6-stick or bone.) In order to multiply, say, 385×467, the 4, 6, and 7 sticks are laid side by side in that order, with a special index stick laid to the right of them. (See Figure 10.) To perform the multi-

Figure 9.   plication, the partial products are gotten directly from the sticks by adding down the diagonals of each row corresponding to each of the multiplying digits. The pertinent partial products for the multiplier 385 have been boxed and their results tabulated at the side of Figure 10. Then arranging these partial products thus

$$
\begin{array}{ll}
2335 & (5 \times 467) \\
3736 & (80 \times 467) \\
\underline{1401} & (300 \times 467) \\
179795 &
\end{array}
$$

the product 179,795 is found by addition.

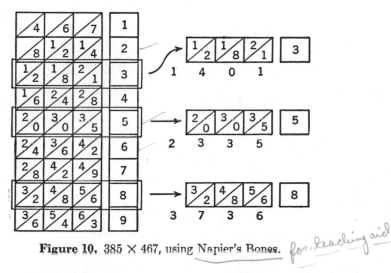

Figure 10. 385 × 467, using Napier's Bones. *for teaching aid*

(b) *Finger counting*. When formal training is at a minimum, the fewer the memory facts required of an algorism, the better. Consider next this rather ingenious finger method of multiplication, a form of which is reportedly used even today in parts of France. For such users each of the primary combinations as we know them falls into one of these separate classifications, and is handled in a different way. First, all the combinations up to 5 × 5, the easiest, are memorized. Second, those combinations involving one factor below 5 and one above 5 are handled by the distributive law. Thus, 7 × 3 = (4 × 3) + (3 × 3) = 12 + 9 = 21. Finally, those combinations involving both factors above five are found by the following finger method:

For each hand the closed fist is considered to be 5, one finger extended is 6, two fingers extended is 7, three fingers extended is 8, four fingers extended is 9, all fingers extended is 10. If one hand represents one factor and the other hand the second factor, their product can be determined piecemeal by adding the extended fingers for the tens digit and multiplying the closed fingers (which will involve only combinations below 5 × 5) to find the units digit of the product. For instance, in 8 × 6 (Figure 11) the left hand would show 3 fingers extended (for 8), while the right hand shows one finger extended (for 6). The product of 8 × 6 has a 4 in the tens place (a total of 4 fingers are extended), and an 8 in the units place (the product of 2 closed fingers on the left hand times 4 closed fingers on the right hand).

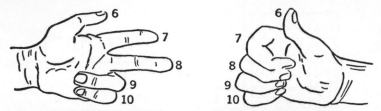

Figure 11. Finger arrangement for 8 (left hand) times 6 (right hand).

In effect this is a method of multiplying by complements. Consider expressing 8 as (10 − 2) and 6 as (10 − 4). Then

$$8 \times 6 = (10 - 2) \times (10 - 4) = 100 - 20 - 40 + 8$$
$$= (10 \text{ tens} - 2 \text{ tens} - 4 \text{ tens}) + 8$$
$$= 4 \text{ tens} + 8 = 48$$

For those who might profit from such an explanation, the following is offered as a demonstration of the general case. Let L_f and R_f be the number of fingers folded on the left and right hand, respectively, and L_e and R_e be the extended fingers. Then, to multiply $N_1 \times N_2$ we would have

$$N_1 \times N_2 = (10 - L_f)(10 - R_f)$$
$$= 100 - 10L_f - 10R_f + (L_f \times R_f)$$
$$= 10[10 - (L_f + R_f)] + (L_f \times R_f).$$

But $\qquad [10 - (L_f + R_f)] = (L_e + R_e).$

So $\qquad N_1 \times N_2 = 10(L_e + R_e) + (L_f \times R_f)$

(c) *Doubling.* Another rather ancient way of multiplying is known as duplation or doubling. Fundamentally it rests upon the fact that any number can be expressed as the sum of powers of 2. For example, $13 = 8 + 4 + 1 = 2^3 + 2^2 + 2^0$; $24 = 16 + 8 = 2^4 + 2^3$; $47 = 32 + 8 + 4 + 2 + 1 = 2^5 + 2^3 + 2^2 + 2^1 + 2^0$. This fact was put to practical use in the following way:

Multiply 47 × 51.

Since

$$47 = 32 + 8 + 4 + 2 + 1$$
$$= 2^5 + 2^3 + 2^2 + 2^1 + 2^0$$

then $47 \times 51 = (32 + 8 + 4 + 2 + 1) \times 51$
$$= 1{,}632 + 408 + 204 + 102 + 51 = 2{,}397$$

$$
\begin{array}{rcl}
51 \times 1 = & & 51 \\
51 \times 2 = & & 102 \\
51 \times 4 = 2 \times 102 = & & 204 \\
51 \times 8 = 2 \times 204 = & & 408 \\
51 \times 16 = 2 \times 408 = & & \cancel{816} \\
51 \times 32 = 2 \times 816 = & & \underline{1632} \\
& & 2397
\end{array}
$$

From a practical point of view, it is more economical to keep doubling the 51 as far as necessary (in this case five times, since the highest power of two in 47 is five). Then discarding the products of unneeded powers of two (in this case the fourth, for there was no 2^4 in the multiplier 47) we need only to add the remaining values to get the ultimate product.

$$19 \times 42 = 798$$

42	1
84	2
~~168~~	~~4~~
~~336~~	~~8~~
672	16
798	**19**

Another illustration, 19×42, using a more abbreviated version of this doubling method, is at the right. Thus $19 \times 42 = 798$.

A variation of this doubling technique is known as the Russian Method of Multiplication. Consider again 19×42. Arrange the factors side by side, then successively halve the left one and double the right one. Should the halving process involve a remainder, ignore it. Repeat the halving and doubling until 1 is reached on the left-hand column. Now cross out each pair in which there is an even number in the left-hand column, and then add the remaining figures in the right-hand column. This sum is the required product of 19×42. The explanation of why this works is a bit involved for our presentation here. However,

RUSSIAN METHOD	
19	42
9	84
~~4~~	~~168~~
~~2~~	~~336~~
1	672
	798

the more interested reader might discover the basis for its rationale himself by converting 19 (ten) to the binary or base two scale and noting the relationship between zeros in certain orders and crossed out values in the Russian system.

(d) *The lightning method.* From these antiquated, cumbersome methods we go now in the opposite direction, and introduce a speedy adaptation of our present-day algorism. This method telescopes the basic algorism, replacing a great deal of its physical (writing) requirements with mental computation. In fact, the physical application involves nothing more than directly writing the answer to the problem. At first glance it seems to involve a high order of intellectual gymnastics. Actually, though, with a little practice, it is not beyond the control of the average individual.

Consider first the problem of multiplying a two-digit number by a two-digit number: 24×36.

$$
\begin{array}{r}
36 \\
\times 24 \\
\hline
864
\end{array}
$$

Multiply $4 \times 6 = 24$. Write *4*, carry 2. "Cross multiply" $4 \times 3 = 12$ and $2 \times 6 = 12$, add 12 and 12 and carried $2 = 26$. Write *6*, carry 2. Multiply $2 \times 3 = 6$ plus carried $2 = 8$. Write *8*.

Once we've sharpened our ability to a point where such computations come easily, we are ready for larger game: three-digit numbers by three-digit numbers by the lightning method. Let us try 426×837.

$$
\begin{array}{r}
837 \\
\times 426 \\
\hline
356562
\end{array}
$$

Multiply $6 \times 7 = 42$. Write *2*, carry 4. "Cross multiply" $6 \times 3 = 18$ and $2 \times 7 = 14$; add $18 + 14$ and carried $4 = 36$. Write *6*, carry 3. Then (and this is the worst) "cross multiply" (6×8), (2×3), and (4×7), and add with the carried 3. Thus $48 + 6 + 28 +$ carried $3 = 85$. Write *5*, carry 8. "Cross multiply" 2×8 and 4×3 for 16 and $12 = 28$ and carried $8 = 36$. Write *6* and carry 3. Finally, $4 \times 8 = 32$ plus carried $3 = 35$. Write *35*.

To summarize these various "cross products" in this three-by-three type, consider the generalized problem:

$$
\begin{array}{r}
XYZ \\
\times ABC
\end{array}
$$

The steps are in order from right to left, with carrying when necessary assumed.

(1) CZ (C times Z)
(2) $CY + BZ$
(3) $CX + BY + AZ$
(4) $BX + AY$
(5) AX

PROBLEMS SET 12

1. Using the number line, demonstrate with the sum $8 + 3 + 4 + 2 = 17$ the commutative and associative principles of addition.

2. Using the number line, demonstrate with the product $3 \times 2 \times 4 = 24$ the commutative and associative principles of multiplication.

3. Using the number line and the following problems, demonstrate the distributive law of multiplication.

    (a) $4 \times 5 = 4(2 + 3)$ (c) $2 \times 13 = 2(10 + 3)$
    (b) $2 \times 12 = 2(2 + 10)$

4. Shoes are seen on sale at $6.54 per pair. Write down each step in the process of computing mentally the cost of three pairs.

5. Multiply $832 \times 6{,}743$ and $674 \times 4{,}732$ by the lattice method. Check your answer against those of Question 10, page 78.

6. Using the illustration of Napier's Bones on page 91, compute the product of 265×467; 467×923.

7. Using the finger method described on page 92, find the product of the following.

    $6 \times 9, \quad 8 \times 7, \quad 9 \times 9, \quad 7 \times 9, \quad 6 \times 6, \quad 6 \times 7$

8. Multiply the following by "doubling."

    $17 \times 63, \quad\quad 36 \times 42, \quad\quad 40 \times 602$

9. Multiply the following by using the Russian method.

    $17 \times 63, \quad\quad 28 \times 41, \quad\quad 36 \times 42$

10. Using the lightning method, multiply

    $15 \times 42, \quad\quad 28 \times 63, \quad\quad 421 \times 452$

Chapter 3

ANALYSIS

Unit 13: Subtraction

1. *Introduction.* In the previous chapter we have discussed the two synthesizing operations of addition and multiplication. In this chapter we concern ourselves with subtraction and division, which reverse the processes of synthesis. These we classify as *analysis*.

Before we begin to work in the area of analysis, we must make an important distinction. It will be recalled that we have subdivided the whole realm of arithmetic into three basic activity categories: synthesis, analysis, and comparison. While the operations of addition and multiplication serve only synthesis, the operations of subtraction and division serve both analysis and comparison. Since the goals of analysis and comparison differ fundamentally, the rationales or meanings of these two operations will also differ; it will be well therefore to treat these two categories separately. In this chapter we shall limit ourselves to "taking numbers apart"—analysis; in a later chapter we shall take up the cases of subtraction and division as they express relationships between numbers—comparison.

2. *Subtraction.* The operation of subtraction is the inverse of the process of addition. Whereas addition, in its simplest form, involves the *putting together* of two groups, whose sizes may or may not be alike, to form one group, subtraction *breaks* the whole group into two subgroups, whose sizes may or may not be alike. Basically, addition involves the type of problem in which we are given one addend and then another, and then are required to find the number property of the resultant group. Subtraction, on the other hand, involves the type of problem in which we know the number property

of one of the addends and of the resultant group, and are required to find the other addend. In this light, subtraction takes on the following *analytic* definition: *Subtraction is that operation by which we find the number property of the missing addend where the other addend and the sum of the two addends are known.*

The known sum of the two addends is called the *minuend,* the known addend is called the *subtrahend;* the missing addend, in effect the solution of the problem, is called the *remainder.*

Frequently this solution to the subtraction problem is referred to as the *difference.* For purposes of clarity it seems advisable to reserve the use of this term *difference* for our discussions of subtraction in its comparison role.

3. *Principles.* There is not today any one universally accepted algorism for the operation of subtraction. In fact there are four variations operative in the United States, some more popular than others.* Considerable research has been expended in an effort to determine the best method, but the results so far have been inconclusive. Thus it will be necessary to consider all four variations.

In the realm of algebra, where signed numbers are assumed, subtraction becomes nothing more than algebraic addition of a positive value to a negative value. And because it is addition, the principles of addition apply completely. In elementary arithmetic we deal only with positive real values; consequently subtraction becomes a separate operation, carrying with it a particular set of principles.

The first principle stems directly from the nature of subtraction: finding the missing addend. Since Principle A-1 of addition requires that there be "likeness" existing among the addends and the sum, it follows conversely that subtraction, too, should have a *principle of likeness:*

Principle S-1: *Only like numbers can be subtracted.*

In Unit 8 we established the fact that in a two-term addition problem, if one addend is increased and the other addend is left unchanged, a corresponding increase will occur in the sum. Thus, if $8 + 4 = 12$, then $(8 + 3) + 4 = (12 + 3)$. It was stated in the first section of this unit that the subtrahend and remainder of a subtraction problem can be thought of as the addends of an addition

---

* A fifth, the complementary method, which is no longer widespread in the United States, is discussed in the next unit.

problem, while the minuend corresponds to the sum. In the problem just mentioned above, if the subtrahend is identified with the addend receiving the increase, and the minuend is identified with the increased sum, then the third term of the subtraction, the remainder, must correspond to the unchanged addend. In substance we have verified the *principle of compensation with respect to subtraction:*

> **Principle S-2:** *An equal increase in the minuend and the subtrahend produces no change in the remainder.*

This principle, which is of basic importance for justifying a type of subtraction algorism, is reflected in many everyday situations: the age difference between two persons remains the same throughout their lives; a flat, across-the-board pay raise to all employees keeps the gaps between various individuals' salaries constant; or a clock set five minutes fast remains in advance of the hour at any hour, and so on.

4. *Modern Subtraction Algorism.* As in the operations of synthesis, a considerable group of memory facts and a few basic principles are necessary to the algorisms of subtraction. Actually there are two sets of memory facts necessary to service the four variations of the subtractive algorism.

The first set is drawn from the primary combinations of addition and emphasizes the concept of subtraction as a case of finding the missing addend. For example, the subtraction of 6 from 8 is solved by locating that particular addition combination which involves 6 as one of the addends and 8 as the sum. Thus $6 + ? = 8$. By reviewing the addition combinations we come up with the fact that $6 + 2 = 8$. Hence, 2 is the missing addend and the remainder of our subtraction problem. Such an approach to subtraction is known as *additive subtraction.*

The second set of subtraction memory facts emphasizes the removal or "take-away" concept of subtraction: the minuend is the initial whole group, the subtrahend is the removed subgroup, and the remainder is the remaining subgroup. For instance if we have a group of 8 apples, and 6 are removed, the number of the remaining group is 2. Thus 8, take away 6, is 2, or $8 - 6 = 2$.

Most of today's school children in the United States are taught by the "take-away" method, for it ties in well with what is thought to be the most fruitful way to teach the primary combinations. No longer are "tables" memorized; instead the child is led to build up his number concepts and combinations, first with real and tangible objects, and finally as abstractions. By this method the child learns, for instance, "the whole story of five" before he goes on to explore "six." While exploring "five" he notes that 3 blocks and 2 blocks, when combined, equals 5 blocks, and that when 4 blocks and 1 block are combined, he has 5 blocks, and vice versa (commutative law). Eventually he generalizes about these concrete situations and arrives at the abstraction $3 + 2 = 5, 2 + 3 = 5, 4 + 1 = 5,$ and $1 + 4 = 5.$ The obvious time to get across the "taking apart" idea of subtraction is when he is in the process of manipulating these objects and putting them together. So while he is learning that $3 + 2 = 5,$ he can easily see the *inverse,* that 5 with 3 removed is 2, or $5 - 3 = 2.$ As a result of these experiences, the child in the modern school actually learns his addition and subtraction operations simultaneously. This, of course, heavily favors the teaching of subtraction by the "take-away" method.

Thus we have two distinct ways of rationalizing subtraction. Given the problem $12 - 7 = ?,$ the person using the additive approach determines the answer by "7 and 5 equal 12," while those using the "take away" method conjure up the memory fact: 12 take away 7 equals 5, or 7 from 12 is 5.

Extending the operation now beyond situations involving the so-called primary combinations (cases where subtrahend and remainder are single digit values) application of the principle of likeness (S-1) is necessary. For instance, to perform the subtraction $65 - 23,$ we shall find it advantageous to express the minuend and subtrahend as a sum of their respective orders. Thus 65 is 6 tens and 5 units, while 23 is 2 tens and 3 units.

$$
\begin{array}{l}
65 \rightarrow 6 \text{ tens} + 5 \text{ units} \\
\underline{23 \rightarrow 2 \text{ tens} + 3 \text{ units}} \\
42 \leftarrow 4 \text{ tens} + 2 \text{ units}
\end{array}
$$

Principle S-1, which requires that we subtract only likes from likes, directs us in this problem to subtract units from units and tens from tens, and so on. Either the additive or take-away method will produce the resulting 4 tens and 2 units, which, collectively as 42, is the solution to the problem. By extension, this same approach holds true for values running to any number of places. For example,

$$
\begin{array}{l}
6843 \rightarrow 6 \text{ thousands} + 8 \text{ hundreds} + 4 \text{ tens} + 3 \text{ units} \\
\underline{2701 \rightarrow 2 \text{ thousands} + 7 \text{ hundreds} + 0 \text{ tens} + 1 \text{ unit}} \\
4142 \leftarrow 4 \text{ thousands} + 1 \text{ hundred } + 4 \text{ tens} + 2 \text{ units}
\end{array}
$$

5. *Decomposition and Equal Additions.* As long as we are restricted to the realm of *positive* integers, as we are in elementary arithmetic, a problem in which the minuend is smaller in size than the subtrahend is impossible of solution. In the process of employing this piecemeal approach to subtraction, we break down the minuend and subtrahend into their various orders, and then carry out the operation on the order level; occasionally in one or more of these orders we meet a situation in which the number value in a given order in the minuend is less than the number value in that order in the subtrahend. Again there are two alternatives for overcoming this obstacle, both of which are currently in use.

The first and more widespread in this country is known as the *decomposition method.* It draws its authority from the fact that a number can be decomposed, or broken down into its component parts, in a variety of ways. Take, for example, the subtraction problem of $86 - 39 = ?$ If 86 is decomposed by orders to 8 tens and 6 units, and similarly, 39 to 3 tens and 9 units, an impasse results in the unit order when one attempts to subtract 9 units from 6 units. (From the additive point of view, there is a parallel dilemma in the attempt to find "what" added to 9 equals 6: $9 + ? = 6$.) However, had the 86 been decomposed as 7 tens and 16 units, instead of 8 tens and 6 units, no impasse would have resulted, for $16 - 9 = 7$ is one of the primary subtraction combinations.

$$86 \rightarrow 8 \text{ tens} + 6 \text{ units} \rightarrow 7 \text{ tens} + 16 \text{ units}$$
$$39 \rightarrow 3 \text{ tens} + 9 \text{ units} \rightarrow 3 \text{ tens} + \underline{9 \text{ units}}$$
$$\overline{47} \longleftarrow 4 \text{ tens} + 7 \text{ units}$$

Thus a way around the obstacle of insufficiency in the orders in the minuend has been found.

The following abbreviated version of this problem illustrates this technique of decomposition.

$$
\begin{array}{r}
^{7}\\[-4pt]
\cancel{8}^{1}6\\
-\ 3\ 9\\
\hline
4\ 7
\end{array}
$$

Frequently this technique is referred to as "borrowing," which is a misnomer, for borrowing usually includes at least the intention of repayment, which certainly is not the case here. Actually, what we have is another reduction, an exchange in which the minuend's supply of tens is lowered by one ten (from 8 tens to 7 tens) while its supply of units is increased by ten ones (from 6 units to 16 units). (Note that this exchange is an opposite reduction to the one we meet in addition called "carrying.") There has been no total change in value whatever in the minuend, merely a change in form, a reclassification of one of its parts from one denomination to another. Consequently the ultimate remainder, or missing addend, is unaffected.

When these obstacles to subtraction occur in orders beyond the first, a similar reduction technique is employed. For example, here is one with the order impasse occurring in the hundreds order.

$$3247 \rightarrow 3\text{th} + 2\text{h} + 4\text{t} + 7\text{u} \rightarrow 2\text{th} + 12\text{h} + 4\text{t} + 7\text{u} \Big\downarrow \Big\} \quad \text{or} \quad \overset{2}{\cancel{3}}{}^{1}247$$
$$1532 \rightarrow 1\text{th} + 5\text{h} + 3\text{t} + 2\text{u} \rightarrow \underline{1\text{th} + \ 5\text{h} + 3\text{t} + 2\text{u}} \Big\downarrow \qquad \quad \underline{1\ 532}$$
$$1715 \leftarrow \underline{\hphantom{xxxxxxxxxxxxx}} 1\text{th} + \ 7\text{h} + 1\text{t} + 5\text{u} \qquad \qquad 1\ 715$$

The occasional presence of several zeros in the minuend sometimes leads to confusion when the decomposition method is employed. This is because the concept of reduction is not clearly understood. Consider the problem

$$40003$$
$$-21738$$

It can be seen immediately that an impasse occurs in the units order, so a reduction is necessary before the subtraction can proceed. There being in this particular instance no tens (the next higher order to that of the impasse) to reduce to units—or for that matter no hundreds or thousands either—we are forced to convert one of the 4 ten-thousands to an equivalent 10,000 units. Should we use 10 of these units to resolve our units-impasse, there would remain 9990 units, or by reduction, 9 thousands + 9 hundreds + 9 tens. As a consequence, the original minuend has changed form so as to better accommodate the subtrahend, but it has not in any way changed value. In summary form, then:

$$40003 \rightarrow 4\text{t-th} + 0\text{th} + 0\text{h} + 0\text{t} + 3\text{u} \rightarrow 3\text{t-th} + 9\text{th} + 9\text{h} + 9\text{t} + 13\text{u} \Big\downarrow\Big\} \quad 40003$$
$$21738 \rightarrow 2\text{t-th} + 1\text{th} + 7\text{h} + 3\text{t} + 8\text{u} \rightarrow \underline{2\text{t-th} + 1\text{th} + 7\text{h} + 3\text{t} + \ 8\text{u}} \Big\downarrow \ \text{or} \ 21738$$
$$18265 \leftarrow \underline{\hphantom{xxxxxxxxxxxx}} 1\text{t-th} + 8\text{th} + 2\text{h} + 6\text{t} + \ 5\text{u} \qquad \quad 18265$$

What we have accomplished in one step (1 ten-thousand = 9 thousands + 9 hundreds + 9 tens + 10 units) can also be thought of as the result of a series of reductions. Thus, in order to resolve this units-impasse, we (1) again take one of the minuend's 4 ten-thousands and reduce it to 10 thousands; (2) take one of the 10 thousands, leaving 9 thousands, and reduce it to 10 hundreds; (3) take one of the 10 hundreds, leaving 9 hundreds, and reduce it to 10 tens; (4) finally, take one of the 10 tens, leaving 9 tens, and reduce it to 10 units. Again, the net result is a change in form without a change in value:

$$4t\text{-}th + 0th + 0h + 0t + 3u = 3t\text{-}th + 9th + 9h + 9t + 13u$$

The second alternative for overcoming this obstacle to subtraction in a given order is known as the *equal additions method;* it draws its substance from the principle of compensation (S-2). Whereas the decomposition method involved only a rearrangement in one term with no actual increase in value to any of the terms, the equal additions method actually *increases* both the minuend and the subtrahend. The amount of increase depends upon the order in which the impasse occurs, though so long as the increases to the minuend and subtrahend are equal, the remainder, by the principle of compensation, remains unaffected.

Consider one of the problems used to illustrate the decomposition method: $86 - 39 = ?$ The difficulty, of course, again occurs at the same point in the units order. Only this time the difficulty will be resolved by *increasing* both the minuend and subtrahend by ten each.

$$
\begin{array}{l}
86 \rightarrow 8 \text{ tens} + 6 \text{ units} \rightarrow 8 \text{ tens} + 16 \text{ units}\\
39 \rightarrow 3 \text{ tens} + 9 \text{ units} \rightarrow \underline{4 \text{ tens} + 9 \text{ units}}\\
\overline{47} \longleftarrow 4 \text{ tens} + 7 \text{ units}
\end{array}
$$

The increase in the minuend is in the form of ten ones, which actually increases this number from eighty-six to ninety-six (8 tens + 16 units), while in the subtrahend the increase takes the form of one ten, increasing it from thirty-nine to forty-nine (4 tens + 9 units). Since the increases to minuend and subtrahend have been equal, by the principle of compensation the remainder is unaffected at 47. Abbreviated, this technique appears thus:

$$
\begin{array}{r}
8^16\\
-{}^4\!\!\not3\,9\\
\hline
4\,7
\end{array}
$$

In the second decomposition method illustration, $3{,}247 - 1{,}532 = ?$ the impasse, which occurs in the hundreds order, is resolved by increasing both the minuend and subtrahend by one thousand: ten hundreds to the minuend and one thousand to the subtrahend:

$$
\left.
\begin{array}{l}
3{,}247 \rightarrow 3th + 2h + 4t + 7u \rightarrow 3th + 12h + 4t + 7u\\
1{,}532 \rightarrow 1th + 5h + 3t + 2u \rightarrow \underline{2th + 5h + 3t + 2u}\\
\overline{1{,}715} \longleftarrow 1th + 7h + 1t + 5u
\end{array}
\right\} \text{ or }
\begin{array}{r}
3{,}^1247\\
-{}^2\!\!\not1{,}532\\
\hline
1{,}715
\end{array}
$$

The presence of zeros in the minuend causes little trouble when the equal additions method is employed. Impasses are resolved here by actual increases, not rearrangement, so there is no need to skip around among the orders. Our previous problem involving zeros in the minuend would thus be handled with the following succession of steps.

$$13 - 8 = 5$$
$$10 - 4 = 6$$
$$40003 \qquad 10 - 8 = 2$$
$$21738 \qquad 10 - 2 = 8$$
$$\overline{18265} \qquad 4 - 3 = 1$$

Consequently we see that there are two distinct ways of rationalizing the subtractive process (the additive and take-away) and two distinct ways of overcoming frequent order impasses (decomposition and equal additions); hence there will be four distinct combinations of these two variations possible. They are illustrated below on the same problem with accompanying verbalizations:

Take-away—decomposition:

8206
3837   7 from 16 = 9
4369   3 from 9 = 6
        8 from 11 = 3
        3 from 7 = 4

Additive—decomposition:

8206
3837   7 and 9 = 16
4369   3 and 6 = 9
        8 and 3 = 11
        3 and 4 = 7

Take-away—equal additions:

8206
3837   7 from 16 = 9
4369   4 from 10 = 6
        9 from 12 = 3
        4 from 8 = 4

Additive—equal additions:

8206
3837   7 and 9 = 16
4369   4 and 6 = 10
        9 and 3 = 12
        4 and 4 = 8

PROBLEMS SET 13

1. Make up five word problems which illustrate subtraction in its analytic sense. Identify the whole group, the known addend, and the missing addend (remainder) in each.

2. Give four illustrations, other than those in the text, to illustrate the principle of compensation (S-2).

3. Give two real-life situations which can be used to demonstrate the concept of "decomposition."

4. Work each of the problems below by the (a) take-away decomposition method, (b) additive decomposition method, (c) take-away equal additions method, (d) additive equal additions method.

$$6357 \qquad 8324 \qquad 4003$$
$$\underline{3146} \qquad \underline{6817} \qquad \underline{2629}$$

5. Work the following subtraction problems, resolving order impasses in the way which is less familiar to you. Write out each step.

$$4362 \quad 3003 \quad 5682 \quad 9000 \quad 34062$$
$$\underline{2745} \quad \underline{2609} \quad \underline{4007} \quad \underline{27} \quad \underline{999}$$

6. Readings of an electric meter were:

January 1	47,386 kilowatt hours
February 1	51,627
March 1	54,822
April 1	57,901
May 1	60,004

(a) What were the monthly electric bills if the unit charge is 1 cent per kilowatt hour?

(b) How many kilowatt hours were used (a) between January 1 and May 1? (b) between March 1 and May 1?

7. If March 15 is the 74th day and August 12 is the 224th day of a non-leap year, how many days are there between (a) March 15 and August 12; (b) March 17 and August 12; (c) March 8 and August 30? (d) How many days would there be between these dates in a leap year? (e) What principle is illustrated in (d)?

8. Outline the steps necessary to subtract 5 weeks, 3 days, 16 hours, 32 minutes from 9 weeks, 2 days, 4 hours, 17 minutes by (a) decomposition method; (b) equal additions method.

9. In a certain college enrolling 675 students, 17 students were under eighteen years of age, 203 were eighteen, 181 were nineteen, 179 were twenty, and the rest were twenty-one or over.

(a) How many students were twenty-one or over?

(b) Show two ways of finding: (1) how many students were under twenty-one; (2) how many students were twenty or over.

10. In a subtraction, $M - K = R$.

(a) What happens to R if M and K are both increased by L?

(b) What happens to R if both M and K are doubled?

(c) What happens to R if only M is doubled?

(d) Can we predict what $K + R$ will equal?

(e) Can we predict the remainder for $M - R$?

(f) If K is decreased by G, then subtracted from M, what would the remainder be?

(g) If M is increased by 35 and K is increased by 18, what change will there be in R?

Unit 14:   Subtraction in Other Bases, Checks for Subtraction

1. *Subtraction in Scale of Five.* Once again we shall demonstrate, by applying the various forms of the modern subtraction algorism to problems in scales other than ten, the fact that the algorisms work for any given base.

If we use the additive method—and this will be sufficient for demonstration—there is no need to formulate a special table of the basic combinations, for the table of primary addition combinations will suffice. At the right is repeated the table of primary addition combinations for the scale of five.

A primary subtraction combination is one involving a single-digit subtrahend and a single-digit remainder. Suppose we wish to determine the remainder for the subtraction "three from seven." In base five, this number concept

+	0	1	2	3	4
0	0	1	2	3	4
1	1	2	3	4	10
2	2	3	4	10	11
3	3	4	10	11	12
4	4	10	11	12	13

would find expression as $12 - 3$. The answer will be found by choosing that row headed by the subtrahend (3) and searching among its elements for the minuend (12). The column (4) which bears this minuend value is the remainder.

The whole procedure makes rather obvious the fact that we are utilizing the addition tables in such a way as to find the missing addend when the sum and the other addend are known. Furthermore, since the commutative law applies to these addends, it should be equally obvious that the column heads might equally well have been considered the subtrahends and the row values the remainders. To provide a similar demonstration for the "take-away" method a special table must be made. This is left as an exercise for the student; remember, a primary subtraction combination involves single-digit subtrahends and remainders, and indicates nothing about the minuend.

Below are a few more subtraction problems involving terms of several digits each, all in the base of five. Notice how occasional deficiencies in certain orders of the minuend can be overcome by either decomposition or equal additions. Hence the four types of subtraction algorism work as well in the scale of five—or for that matter, in any scale—as they do in the scale of ten.

Take-away—decomposition:		*Additive—decomposition:*	
(Scale five)		(Scale five)	
312	3 from 12 = *4*	302	3 and *4* = 12
−143	4 from 10 = *1*	−133	3 and *1* = 4
114	1 from 2 = *1*	114	1 and *1* = 2

Take-away—equal additions:		*Additive—equal additions:*	
(Scale five)		(Scale five)	
423	4 from 13 = *4*	431	2 and *4* = 11
−134	3 from 11 = *3*	−242	10 and *3* = 13
234	1 from 3 = *2*	134	3 and *1* = 4

2. *Checks for Subtraction.* Accuracy of computation in the operation of subtraction may be determined in two ways: (1) by the additive method and (2) by the excess method.

The additive method for checking merely utilizes the fact that the solution to a subtraction problem is in effect a missing addend. The natural way to check on this newly fashioned addend is to slip it into its proper place and see if it really fits. Thus, by summing the missing addend (the remainder) with the known addend (the subtrahend), the result should be the minuend. To illustrate in the decimal scale:

The subtraction	*The additive check*
63,025	43,781
−43,781	19,244
19,244	63,025

This method is so simple and the form which the written algorism takes is so conducive to a check of this sort, any other is rarely used. However, if either form of the additive method of thinking is used to perform the subtraction, a check of this sort is merely a repetition, so some other type of check is recommended.

The excess check is also applicable to subtraction in terms of its addition relationship. Since it is true that

$$\text{subtrahend} + \text{remainder} = \text{minuend}$$

then "the excess of the sum of the excesses of the addends (subtrahend and remainder) should equal the excess of the sum (minuend)." We illustrate in the decimal scale with the excess of nines.

$$
\begin{array}{l}
68324 \rightarrow \text{excess of 9's} = ⑤ \leftarrow \\
\underline{-37416} \rightarrow \text{excess of 9's} = 3 \\
30908 \rightarrow \text{excess of 9's} = 2
\end{array} \quad \rightarrow 3 + 2 = ⑤
$$

This excess fact is made use of in many mystifying "mathematical recreations." For instance, if we take any multidigit number (say 4,386); scramble the digits in any way (say, 8,634); then subtract the smaller from the larger of these two numbers, we invariably get a value (in this case 4,248) which is divisible by 9!

This phenomenon is easily explained in terms of the excess of nines. In the minuend there will be a given number of nines and a certain excess. Since the subtrahend in this case contains the same digits as the minuend, only scrambled, the number of full nines it contains will of course be different, but the excess will be the same. Hence the excess in the remainder *must* be zero if it is to add with the excess of the subtrahend and equal the excess in the minuend. Consequently, if the excess in the remainder is zero, it must be divisible by 9.

$$\text{Excess}$$
$$8634 \to 3$$
$$4386 \to 3$$
$$\overline{4248 \to 0}$$

The trick may be varied and the mystery enhanced if the subject is directed to choose any number, scramble the digits, subtract the smaller from larger value, discard any digit except 0 or 9 in the remainder, then give back the remaining digits in any order. The "mathe-magician" reproduces the discarded digit by mentally adding the given remaining digits and determining what value would be necessary to make the excess for this sequence zero. Can you see why the subject is not permitted to discard a 9 or a zero?

3. *Checks in Other Bases.* The additive and excess checks have similar applicability to subtraction problems performed in the other scales. To illustrate:

Check the subtraction 4,320 − 3,121 in scale five (1) by the additive check, (2) by an excess check.

The subtraction (scale five):

$$4320$$
$$-3121$$
$$\overline{1144}$$

(1) The additive check (scale five):

$$1144$$
$$+3121$$
$$\overline{4320}$$

(2) The excess check will involve the excess over fours (base less 1) or casting out fours.

$$4320 \rightarrow (4 + 3 + 2 + 0) = 14$$
$$\underline{-3121} \rightarrow (3 + 1 + 2 + 1) = 12$$
$$1144 \rightarrow (1 + 1 + 4 + 4) = 20$$

Excess over 4's

$$\rightarrow (1 + 4) = 10 \rightarrow (1 + 0) = 1 \text{ (minuend)}$$
$$\rightarrow (1 + 2) = \longrightarrow 3 \text{ (subtrahend)}$$
$$\rightarrow (2 + 0) = \longrightarrow 2 \text{ (remainder)}$$

Adding the excess over fours of the remainder and subtrahend $(3 + 2)$ we get five (10), whose excess over 4's is $(1 + 0)$ or 1. This corresponds to the excess over 4's in the minuend, so the problem checks.

4. *Geometric Interpretation of Subtraction.* At the base of the geometric interpretation of subtraction is the fact that subtraction is the inverse process of addition. Thus we should expect that subtraction would reverse whatever addition does on the number line.

Addition of two numbers was conceived (Unit 12) as two steps to the right of zero, with the size of each step determined by the size of each addend. The final resting point, of course, is the sum. Thus

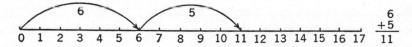

Subtraction starts at the minuend and steps to the left (toward zero) one step the size of the subtrahend. The resting point is the remainder. Thus

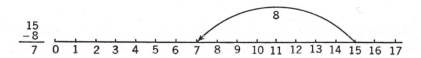

5. *The Complementary Method of Subtraction.* An algorism in frequent use in your great-grandparents' day was known as the complementary method of subtraction. Though still rather widely used in Europe today, in the United States it is little more than an interesting relic. However, it might be stated parenthetically that students who pursue their mathematics as far as logarithms will find this concept of subtraction an extremely useful tool for expressing logarithms of numbers less than one.

The complement of a number is gotten by subtracting that number from its next higher power of ten. For instance the complement of 4 is 6, since $10 - 4 = 6$; of 32 is 68, since $100 - 32 = 68$;

of 580 is 420, since 1,000 − 580 = 420. If instead of subtracting a number from the minuend, we add the complement of that number to the minuend, we get a result which is too large by precisely that power of ten next higher to that of the subtrahend. For instance, if when given the subtraction 496 − 235 (whose solution is 261) we add the complement of 235 (which is 1,000 − 235 = 765) to the minuend 496, we get 1,261 (see below) which is exactly 1,000 in excess of the correct answer. By ignoring the 1 in the first place to the left of the remainder, we can in effect subtract by adding the complement of the subtrahend to the minuend.

The problem		*The solution*
496	496	(minuend)
−235	+765	(complement of subtrahend)
261	1̄261	

The complementary method can be speeded up by evaluating the complement of the subtrahend order by order instead of all at once. This is accomplished by subtracting in the subtrahend the units digit from 10 and all the others from 9. For instance, to arrive at the complement of 8,427, which is 1,573, subtract 8 from 9 = *1*, 4 from 9 = *5*, 2 from 9 = *7*, 7 from 10 = *3*. As a check: 8,427 + 1,573 = 10,000. To note a parallel, subtract 8,427 from 10,000 by the take away decomposition method.

To illustrate the abbreviated version of this complementary algorism, two examples are given.

$$(1) \quad 423$$
$$147$$
$$\overline{1̄276}$$

(a) 3 and *3* (complement of 7) = 6
(b) 2 and *5* (complement of 4) = 7
(c) 4 and *8* (complement of 1) = 12
(d) cross off leading 1. Answer, 256.

$$(2) \quad 4,379$$
$$2,736$$
$$\overline{1̄1,643}$$

(a) Add 9 and *4* (complement of 6) = 13. Write 3 and carry 1.
(b) 7 and *6* (complement of 3) = 13 and carried 1 = 14. Write 4 and carry 1.
(c) 3 and *2* (complement of 7) = 5 and carried 1 = 6. Write 6.
(d) 4 and *7* (complement of 2) = 11. Write 11.
(e) Cross off leading 1. Answer, 1,643.

PROBLEMS SET 14

1. Perform the following subtractions in the scale of twelve and check them by two different methods. (Use base twelve addition table, page 61.)

    (a) 4386   (b) 40030   (c) 800004 (d) 30706
       2799   17049   9999   27078

2. Subtract the following in the scale of five.

    (a) 3432 (b) 3024 (c) 30002 (d) 4321 (e) 10001
       1312   2131   4203   1234   102

3. Check the subtractions of Question 2 by casting out fours.

4. Subtract the following in the scale of twelve; check by casting out elevens.

    (a) 4T36 (b) 67E8 (c) 300T (d) 407T
       2142   EEE   10E   200E

5. In what scale were the following subtractions performed?

    (a) 1300 (b) 1216 (c) 6075 (d) 7048 (e) 3427 (f) 5553
       222   252   3512   2411   2360   3241
     1023   634   2463   4637   1047   2312

6. (a) From a pile of 880 oranges, 331 were culled out as defective or too small. How many gross, dozens, and units remained?

    (b) Solve (a) after changing 880 and 331 to their scale twelve equivalents. Compare your solution with that of (a).

7. (a) Solve the following, using the decimal scale.

    (1) 6 ft 3 in. − 2 ft 1 in.   (4) 9 ft 0 in. − 3 ft 7 in.
    (2) 7 ft 4 in. − 5 ft 7 in.   (5) 10 ft 3 in. − 3 ft 10 in.
    (3) 5 ft 2 in. − 4 ft 6 in.   (6) 11 ft 6 in. − 4 ft 7 in.

    (b) Convert the dimensions in the subtraction problems in (a) to scale twelve by making the units order inches and the base order feet. (For example, 6 ft 3 in. = 63, 2 ft 1 in. = 21, etc.) Then subtract, using the scale of twelve addition table on page 61, and note that your answers can be interpreted directly.

8. (a) In scale two, how many more must be added to 110,111 to make a total of 1,011,010?

    (b) In scale seven 324 and 526 are combined and then diminished by 1,036. How many are left?

    (c) In scale five, how many apples were removed from a pile of 342 if there were 124 left?

9. Perform the following subtractions, using the complementary method. Itemize the steps in your procedure.

    632 346 4836 5608 60003
    484 297 2008 4212 2947

Unit 15: Division

1. *Introduction.* The second analyzing process is that of division. In the same sense that multiplication is thought of as "repeated addition," division may be thought of as "repeated subtraction." Multiplication may be interpreted as that special case of addition in which all the addends are alike; division is subtraction in which all of the subtrahends are alike.

For example, if we wish to determine how many groups of four could be removed from a total group of 36, we could find out by subtracting fours successively until the 36 was exhausted; or we could, since each of the removed groups is of the same size, predict the solution by dividing 36 by 4. Appreciation of this repeated subtraction characteristic of division will be of considerable aid in understanding the rationale which lies behind today's division algorism.

In addition to this relationship to subtraction, division also bears an important relationship to another of the basic processes: multiplication. Just as subtraction is the inverse process of addition, division is the inverse process of multiplication. Whereas subtraction in its analytic form was defined as a process by which we seek the missing addend, division in its analytic form may be defined as a process by which we determine the missing factor in multiplication.

For instance, if we are told that "something" *multiplied* by 7 equals 84, we can determine the value of that "something" (the missing factor) by *dividing* 84 by 7. By definition, that number which corresponds to the "product" in a multiplication (the whole, which in analysis is broken apart into factors) is called the *dividend;* the known factor is called the *divisor;* the unknown factor, the one which is sought and hence is the solution to the problem, is called the *quotient.* Accordingly, if we arrange the previous problem as

$$\frac{12}{7)84}$$ then 84 is the dividend, 7 is the divisor, and 12 is the quotient.

2. *Partitioning and Measurement.* It will be recalled that the multiplicative term "factor" is actually a more general term for either the multiplier or the multiplicand. With respect to specific concrete problems it makes a difference as to which is which. The multiplicand is the typical addend, hence, in practical instances, a concrete number. The product was also a concrete number, a "like" term to (homogeneous with) the multiplicand. On the other hand, the multiplier tells how many times the multiplicand is to be re-

peated and is an abstract number. Now since division produces *one* of the missing factors, in some cases it will be what was originally the multiplicand, while at other times it will be what was originally the multiplier. This leads to two distinct types of division problems: (1) partitioning, and (2) measurement.* Following are some comparisons by which one may distinguish partitioning from measurement. Though listed separately, these features are not necessarily unrelated to each other.

PARTITIONING	MEASUREMENT
(1) Seeks the *multiplicand.*	(1) Seeks the *multiplier.*
(2) *Quotient* concrete, homogeneous with dividend.	(2) *Divisor* concrete, homogeneous with dividend.
(3) *Divisor* abstract.	(3) *Quotient* abstract.
(4) Seeks "how many in each group" when number of groups is fixed.	(4) Seeks "how many groups" when number in each group is fixed.

Analysis we said involves actions in which we take numbers or groups apart. When the separating is based upon a share-and-share-alike principle (how many apples will each of 4 boys get from a basket of 36?) partitive division is implied; when the separating is based upon each group getting precisely so many (how many quartets in 36 singers?) then we have measurement division. This latter concept of division, that of measurement, plays an important role in the third category of "things we do with number"—comparison— about which we shall say more in the next chapter.

3. *Closure.* Up to this point in our discussions we have been interested only in the set of natural numbers or the counting numbers. When the operations of addition, multiplication, and subtraction were performed, using these numbers, the result of each operation was invariably a natural number also. Thus the set of natural numbers is said to be *closed* under addition, multiplication, and subtraction. In mathematical parlance, *closure* is defined as that property of a set which is shown when an operation with numbers of that set invariably yields a number in that set.

However, when we divide one natural number by another, we sometimes find the answer among the set of natural numbers (e.g., $36 \div 4 = 9$),† but at other times we do not (e.g., $26 \div 3$).

* In some books measurement division is referred to as "quotitioning."

† Read as "36 divided by 4 equals 9"; the dividend is stated before the operation symbol and the divisor after it.

Consequently we state that the set of natural numbers is *not* closed for division.* In Chapter 5 we shall introduce a new type of number, different from the natural numbers, called *fraction*. Together these two types of numbers form a set which *is* closed for division, as well as addition, subtraction, and multiplication.

Without the use of fractions it will be necessary to look at the result of the division of, say, 26 ÷ 3 as 8 with 2 left over undivided. In other words, in 26 there are 8 threes which can be extracted, after which there will be 2 of the dividend left over. This "left-over" amount we call the *remainder*. In terms of division as the process for finding the missing factor of a multiplication, the problem 26 ÷ 3 would have to be interpreted somewhat left-handedly as "8 is the missing factor of a number which is 2 less than the given one."

Depending upon whether this missing factor is the multiplier or the multiplicand, that is, whether the division is measurement or partitioning, this undivided remainder is open to a dual interpretation. In cases of measurement division, where the divisor represents the size of a fixed or unit group, the remainder represents a part of that group. For example, 26 feet ÷ 3 feet = 8 (groups of 3 feet, which might be called yards) with 2 feet left over as undivided, insufficient to form the ninth group of 3 feet. In Chapter 5 we shall find that one of the interpretations of fractions is particularly suited to the expression of partial groups; in this case the partial group would be expressed as $\frac{2}{3}$ of a group of 3 feet, or $\frac{2}{3}$ yard. Hence, we see that

$$26 \text{ feet} \div 3 \text{ feet} = 8\tfrac{2}{3} \text{ (groups of 3 feet—yards)}$$

In terms of partitioning, the divisor is no longer thought of as representing a unit group, but is now the number of individual equal shares. Consequently, the undivided remainder takes on a role different from that of measurement. To illustrate, suppose 26 cookies are to be divided equally among 3 boys. Distribution of the cookies shows that each boy receives 8 whole cookies, and that there are two left to be shared. To express each boy's share of those two remaining cookies, once more fractions are utilized (although this time under a different interpretation). Each boy receives $\frac{1}{3}$ of

---

* An interesting sidelight is the fact that in many practical cases the set of integers *is* closed for division. For instance, How many trips are necessary with a three-ton truck to carry eleven tons? The answer is 4 trips; hence, at least here, 11 ÷ 3 = 4. Also, What is the cost of a single article on sale 2 for 25 cents? The answer is 13 cents. Thus 25 ÷ 2 = 13.

2 cookies, or $\frac{2}{3}$ cookie. Hence

$$26 \text{ cookies} \div 3 \text{ (boys)} = 8\frac{2}{3} \text{ cookies per boy}$$

In general, note that in measurement division the fraction part of the quotient represents a part of the divisor, the unit group; in partitioning, the fraction represents a part of whatever the unit in which the divisor is expressed.

For the time being, however, we shall avoid division problems which result in remainders, since we are at this point primarily concerned with the principles which direct the division process.

4. *Principles of Division.* For the modern algorism of division, the most important principle is that of *distribution* with respect to addition.

> **Principle D-1:** *To arrive at the quotient of the sum of several numbers divided by a given number, either:* (a) *add the several numbers and divide their sum by the given number, or* (b) *divide each of the several numbers by the given number and add the resulting quotients.*

Thus, to divide the sum of $6 + 9 + 15$ by 3, following alternative (a) we would add $6 + 9 + 15 = 30$, and divide 30 by 3 for a quotient of 10. Following (b) we would divide each of 6, 9, and 15 by 3 and get, respectively, 2, 3, and 5, and upon adding these several quotients, again arrive at 10. An appreciation of these alternatives with respect to the modern division algorism will make what frequently seems like a mumbo-jumbo ritual become a reasonable procedure.

Of much less consequence to the algorism is the second principle of division, that of *compensation.*

> **Principle D-2:** *If the dividend and divisor are both multiplied (or divided) by the same number, not zero, the quotient remains unchanged.*

To illustrate, consider $24 \div 4 = 6$	Dividend		Divisor		Quotient
The problem......................	24	÷	4	=	6
Multiply divisor and dividend by 3....	72	÷	12	=	6
Multiply divisor and dividend by 5....	120	÷	20	=	6
Divide divisor and dividend by 2......	12	÷	2	=	6

A knowledge of this principle becomes most important when we work with fractions, when division is extended into the realm of decimals, and when the process of division is called upon in matters of comparison.

5. *The Division Algorism.* ~~read carefully~~ We offer here two rationalizations to account for the steps we take in the modern algorism called long division. The first keeps the idea of repeated subtraction paramount, while the second reflects strongly the distributive principle (D-1). In each instance we shall start with a relatively simple case to establish the rationale and then carry it on into a more complicated situation.

(a) *Repeated subtraction rationalization.* Consider the problem of 693 ÷ 3. We are interested in how many groups of 3 there are in 693; we shall ascertain that number by repeated subtraction. A long way would be to remove 3's successively from the original 693, and then count how many times we are able to do this. For instance,

$$693 - 3 = 690, \quad 690 - 3 = 687, \quad 687 - 3 = 684, \quad 684 - 3 = 681, \; \ldots ,$$
$$\underbrace{}_{1} \quad \underbrace{}_{2} \quad \underbrace{}_{3} \quad \underbrace{}_{4}$$

$$9 - 3 = 6, \quad 6 - 3 = 3, \quad 3 - 3 = 0$$
$$\underbrace{}_{229} \quad \underbrace{}_{230} \quad \underbrace{}_{231}$$

With a little ingenuity this could be shortened by removing various quantities of 3's at one time. For instance, we may guess that there are at least 215 threes in 693; 215 threes would be 645 (215 × 3 = 645), so we record the 215 fact above the dividend and remove its effect by subtracting 645 from 693. This leaves 48 yet to be worked upon [see (a) below]. Guessing again at how many 3's there are in 48, we may hit upon 12. Again we record the 12 above the dividend and remove that number of 3's from the remainder: 48 − 36 = 12. Thus there remain 12 out of the original 693 [see (b) below]. Our final guess that there are four 3's in 12 is recorded in a similar manner [see (c) below], and the zero which is the result of 12 − 12 shows we have taken all of the 3's from 693 that were possible. How many did we take out all together? First there were 215, then 12, and finally 4, so all told we removed 4 + 12 + 215 = 231 threes. This completely exhausted the dividend 693, and completes the division.

(a)	215	(b)	12	(c)	4 ⎫
	3)693		215		12 ⎬ 231
	645		3)693		215 ⎭
	48		645		3)693
			48		645
			36		48
			12		36
					12
					12
					0

As a further improvement, this approach might be systematized even more by looking at the 693 and estimating how many 3's there are likely to be in it, estimating first by powers of 10. For example, are there likely to be as many as one 3 in 693? (yes); 10? (yes, that would only be 30); 100? (yes, that would be only 300); 1,000? (no, that would be 3,000). So the largest block of threes that could be removed all at once would be in the hundreds. But how many hundreds? Five hundred 3's would be too many, and so would three hundred. However, two hundred 3's would only amount to 600, so

$$\begin{array}{r} 200 \\ 3)\overline{693} \\ 600 \\ \hline 93 \end{array}$$

Now, how many 3's in 93? One hundred? (no); ten? (yes)—but how many tens? Twenty 3's would be 60; thirty 3's would be 90; forty 3's would be 120—too much. So the next largest block of 3's that can be removed would be thirty. [See (a) below.] Finally, at the risk of belaboring the obvious, how many 3's in the value remaining? Ten? (no); one? (yes, exactly). The result is as shown in (b) below, and we see that in 693 there are 200 + 30 + 1 threes, or 231 all together.

(a)	30	(b)	1	(c)	1	(d)	231
	200		30		3		3)693
	3)693		200		2		6
	600		3)693		3)693		9
	93		600		6		9
	90		93		93		3
	3		90		9		3
			3		3		
			3		3		
			0				

Now, since this sequence of estimations and removals proceeded from order to order, many of the zeros in (b) above could have been left unwritten, as in (c) above. This, it may be recalled, parallels the writing of partial products in multiplication. Once at (c) above, however, there is but a small and obvious step to the abbreviated form of the division algorism which we are most used to seeing, (d) above.

Consider now the problem 19,826 ÷ 23: Following this same type of rationalization, are there as many as one thousand 23's in 19,826? The answer is no. As many as one hundred? Yes. About how many? Well, nine hundred 20's would be only 18,000, so we try that

$$\begin{array}{r} 900 \\ 23\overline{)19826} \\ 20700 \end{array}$$

Since 20,700 is greater than 19,826, it follows that nine hundred are too many. Let's try the next lower hundred, eight hundred. That does all right. Instead of writing in the zeros, we shall indicate their location with a small dash.

$$\begin{array}{r} 8-- \\ 23\overline{)19826} \\ 184-- \\ \overline{1426} \end{array}$$

Next, how many 23's in 1,426? From the previous step it is obvious that there are not so many as a hundred of them; sixty 20's is 1,200, and seventy 20's is 1,400. The latter is too close to 1,426, so we try sixty. [See (a) below.] Finally, how many 23's in 46? The answer is two. [See (b) below.] The final form usually seen for this problem is not much different. [See (c) below.]

$$\begin{array}{lll}
\text{(a)} \quad
\begin{array}{r} 6- \\ 8-- \\ 23\overline{)19826} \\ 184-- \\ \overline{1426} \\ 138- \\ \overline{46} \end{array}
&
\text{(b)} \quad
\begin{array}{r} 2 \\ 6- \\ 8-- \\ 23\overline{)19826} \\ 184-- \\ \overline{1426} \\ 138- \\ \overline{46} \\ 46 \end{array}
&
\text{(c)} \quad
\begin{array}{r} 862 \\ 23\overline{)19826} \\ 184 \\ \overline{142} \\ 138 \\ \overline{46} \\ 46 \end{array}
\end{array}$$

(b) *Distributive rationalization.* To treat the original 693 ÷ 3 division problem according to the distributive rationalization, we need to look upon the quantity 693 as the sum of its component parts: $693 = 6$ hundreds $+ 9$ tens $+ 3$ units.

Actually the division problem itself is stated in terms of alternative (a) of principle of distribution (D-1), and its solution is found by utilizing alternative (b). Alternative (b), it will be recalled, allows for the piecemeal division of a quantity: dividing each of the several numbers by the divisor and adding the resulting quotients is equal to the quotient of the sum (which is the dividend) divided by the divisor. In this case

$$3\overline{)693} = 3\overline{)600 + 90 + 3} = \overset{200}{[3\overline{)600}]} + \overset{30}{[3\overline{)90}]} + \overset{1}{[3\overline{)3}]}$$
$$= 200 + 30 + 1 = 231$$

This can be abbreviated somewhat to

$$\frac{200 + 30 + 1}{3\overline{)600 + 90 + 3}}$$

and then further condensed to

	H	T	U
	2	3	1
3)	6	9	3

which finally leads to the familiar

$$\frac{231}{3\overline{)693}}$$

An alternative presentation of the same thing, only using the specific denominations instead of zero spacers to show homogeneity between dividend and quotient, leads us to the same solution:

$$693 \div 3 = (6 \text{ hundreds} + 9 \text{ tens} + 3 \text{ units}) \div 3$$
$$= 3\underline{)6 \text{ hundreds}} + 3\underline{)9 \text{ tens}} + 3\underline{)3 \text{ units}}$$
$$ \ 2 \text{ hundreds} + \ \ 3 \text{ tens} + \ \ \ 1 \text{ unit}$$
$$= 231$$

Consider now our second problem, $19{,}826 \div 23$, in light of this approach.

First we look upon the dividend as

1 ten-thousand $+ 9$ thousands $+ 8$ hundreds $+ 2$ tens $+ 6$ units

After noting that 23 won't divide any of the denominations as they now stand, we call upon the associative law (A-3) with respect to addition and a reduction to regroup the dividend as

19 thousands $+ 8$ hundreds $+ 2$ tens $+ 6$ units

But again 23 will not divide any of the denominations. So we further regroup to

198 hundreds + 2 tens + 6 units

Here at least we have division possibilities among the hundreds. So, as shown in (a) below, 198 hundreds ÷ 23 produces 8 hundreds in each of 23 groups (partitioning) and 14 hundreds left over, undistributed. As in (b) below, these 14 hundreds are then reduced to 140 tens, which, when added to the already present 2 tens, produces a total of 142 tens. Then distributing the 142 tens among the 23 (142 tens ÷ 23) we get 6 tens for each of the 23 and 4 tens left over. In (c) these remaining 4 tens are reduced to 40 units and added to the already present 6 units to form 46 units. Then 46 units ÷ 23 = 2 units per each of the 23 and none left over.

```
         H  T U                 H  T U                 H  T U
(a)                   (b)                   (c)
           8 |                     8 6 |                   8 6 2
  2 3 ) 1 9 8 2 6       2 3 ) 1 9 8 2 6       2 3 ) 1 9 8 2 6
        1 8 4             1 8 4                   1 8 4
          1 4             1 4 2                   1 4 2
                          1 3 8                   1 3 8
                              4                       4 6
                                                     4 6
```

To summarize this partitive distribution, we have succeeded in showing that there are 23 groups of (8 hundreds + 6 tens + 2 units) or 862 in 19,826, and our division is complete.

PROBLEMS SET 15

1. Give two nonmathematical illustrations which demonstrate the concept of "closure."

2. Given two sets of numbers, the set of odd natural numbers (odd) and the set of even natural numbers (even). Determine whether or not the set involved is closed for the operations indicated below.

    (a) odd + odd   (e) odd × odd
    (b) odd + odd + odd   (f) even × even
    (c) even + even   (g) odd × odd × odd
    (d) even + even + even   (h) even × even × even

3. What is the "identity element" for the process of division?

4. Using "the process for finding the missing factor of multiplication" as the definition of division, show why division by zero is impossible.

5. In the following problems (1) identify the dividend and divisor in terms of multiplicand, multiplier, and product, stating which is the missing

factor, (2) identify the problem as one of partitioning or measurement, (3) solve for the quotient, making clear whether it is abstract or in agreement with the dividend:

(a) What would be an equal share of 30 cookies for each of 5 boys?

(b) How many yards in 30 ft?

(c) How many dozens of eggs are there in 108 eggs?

(d) What would Smith be expected to pay if he and his neighbor erect a $74 fence along their mutual property line?

(e) What is my daily wage if I work 8 days and receive $96 pay?

(f) How many quarters in $6.00?

6. Make up eight word problems, different from those of Question 5, four of a measurement nature and four of a partitioning nature.

7. Make up two word problems which demonstrate the principle of distribution with respect to division; the principle of compensation with respect to division.

8. Find how many 13's there are in 156 by using the repeated subtraction process.

9. Using the distributive rationalization, show how you would determine (a) how many 13's there are in 156, (b) how many 12's there are in 1,032.

10. (a) How many trips must an elevator (capacity 20 persons) make to carry down 53 persons?

(b) How many dozen-egg cartons are necessary to carry home 52 eggs?

11. (a) To find the average (arithmetic mean) of a group of test scores we add the scores and divide that sum by the number of scores. Is this partitioning or measurement?

(b) To find the number of scores when the total of the scores and the average score is known, we divide the total by the average score. Is such a division partitioning or measurement?

12. (a) Into how many parts must we divide 68,208 so that there are 42 in each part?

(b) What number multiplied by 84 yields a product of 26,544?

(c) What number must be divided by 21 to yield a quotient of 429?

(d) What number is contained 52 times in 16,536?

(e) What number divided by 26 yields a quotient of 374 and a remainder of 16?

(f) What number contains 656 fifty-threes?

Unit 16:   More About Division

1. *Trial Divisors*. Not only does the process of division of integers differ basically from the other three elementary operations in the matter of closure, but also in the actual carrying out of the algorism. Once the algorisms for addition, subtraction, and multiplication are mastered, the computation is direct and the solution is inevitable. But in division the algorism is not entirely straightforward; for the first time among the algorisms the element of trial and error is encountered. This complicates the whole matter, both mathematically and psychologically. The psychological implications are not for us to discuss here, for they properly belong to a course in method; but it is pertinent to comment here upon certain of its mathematical aspects.

Whether one favors the repeated subtraction or the distributive way of rationalizing the algorism, the mechanics of the computation as it is used today will be pretty much the same. To arrive at the first digit of the quotient we compare the divisor with the first, or first and second, or first, second, and third digits of the dividend (or as many as might be needed) in an attempt to decide how many times the divisor is contained in this number. If the divisor is more than a single-digit number, this problem exceeds the primary combinations, which one usually memorizes, and so at best we can only make a guess. Sometimes this guess will be accurate, but sometimes not. To minimize error we resort to the technique known as "trial divisors."

Consider the division problem used in the previous unit: $23\overline{)19,826}$. Since we have no ready knowledge of combinations of 23 (how many 23's in 198?) we draw from principle of compensation (D-2) that there will be *roughly* about as many 23's in 198 as there are 2's in 19. This brings our deliberations into the realm of the primary combinations ($2 \times 9 = 18$) by which we decide that 9 is likely to be the first digit of our quotient. With that we multiply 23 by 9 and get 207, which is larger than 198.

$$\begin{array}{r} 9 \\ 23\overline{)19826} \\ \underline{207} \end{array}$$

The reason for calling this approach "trial and error" is obvious at this point. We then erase the 9, reduce our guess by one, and try again.

$$\frac{8}{23)\overline{19826}}$$
$$\underline{184}$$

This time we meet with success. Next we subtract the 184, bring down the 2, and make ready to go through the whole guessing process again, except that this time we are asking, "How many 23's in 142?"

$$\frac{8}{23)\overline{19826}}$$
$$\underline{184}$$
$$\overline{142}$$

The technique just described is probably well known to most of us, yet one can readily see why it bodes evil for teachers, especially in the early grades. Without encroaching upon the province of method, the citing of a few statistics might be helpful in minimizing the frequency of error in this matter of trial divisors.

Upton* in 1935 published the following results in a detailed study of the problem of trial divisors. In cases of two-digit divisors, where the second digit (units) is zero (such as 30, 50, 80), the first or tens digit when used as a trial divisor will of course produce the correct quotient 100% of the time. When the second digit is one (such as 21, 41, 81), using the first digit as trial divisor, will produce the correct quotient digit 91.11% of the time; when the second digit is two (as 42, 72, 92), the first digit trial divisor will be correct 82.57% of the time.

Table XI, Column A gives these per cents for each instance in which the trial divisor is the first (tens) digit and the second (units) digit is 1, 2, 3, . . . , 9.

However, when the divisor is, say, 49, increasing the first digit by one (from 4 to 5) and using it as the trial divisor will produce the correct quotient digit 91.70% of the time. What happens when this "increase-by-one" method is used for numbers whose second digit is 8, 7, 6, and 5 is given in Column B of Table XI.

These statistics seem to indicate that error in this guessing at the correct quotient digit by use of trial divisors is minimized by: (a) using the first digit as the trial divisor when the second digit is 0, 1, 2, 3, 4, or 5; (b) using the first digit increased by one when the

* Upton, Clifford B., "Making Long Division Automatic," *Tenth Yearbook National Council of Teachers of Mathematics*, National Council of Teachers of Mathematics, 1201 Sixteenth St., N.W., Washington, D.C., 1935.

TABLE XI. TRIAL DIVISORS

When units digit in divisor is	A — Tens digit as trial divisor will be correct	B — Tens digit increased by one as trial divisor will be correct
0	100.00%	
1	91.11%	
2	82.57%	
3	74.49%	
4	67.10%	
5	62.44%	62.44%
6	54.45%	68.12%
7	49.15%	76.22%
8	44.47%	84.42%
9	39.37%	91.70%

second digit is 6, 7, 8, or 9. This conclusion is based entirely upon probabilities and does not recognize any of the psychological difficulties which might be created in the teaching of such a method.

2. *Quotient Adjustment.* Before leaving the topic of trial and error in the division algorism, let us consider a somewhat more mature way to salvage as much as possible of the effort which has been expended when the quotient digit *is* found to be in error. The rationale here depends heavily upon the concept of division as repeated subtraction.

First compare the division problem 28,208 ÷ 328 = 86 and the multiplication of 86 × 328 = 28,208.

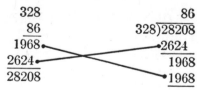

$$
\begin{array}{r}
328 \\
86 \\
\hline
1968 \\
2624 \\
\hline
28208
\end{array}
\qquad
\begin{array}{r}
86 \\
328\overline{)28208} \\
2624 \\
\hline
1968 \\
1968
\end{array}
$$

Reviewed in this light it can be clearly seen in the multiplication how the partial products 1,968 and 2,624 *contribute to* the product 28,208, while the division problem they *take from* the 28,208.

Suppose now that in the division we had underestimated the first quotient figure and said 7 instead of 8. After multiplying 7 × 328 and subtracting this product from 2,820, we see that the remainder 524 is larger than the 328 [as in (a) following]. Thus 328 would have divided 2,820 at least one more time (or 28,208 ten times more) and 8 is the correct quotient digit. Instead of starting all over again [as in (b) following], why not subtract one more 328 from the 524 (that is all 8 × 328 subtracted from 2,820 would have accomplished), and make the incorrect 7 into an 8 [as in (c) following], and go on our way?

	(a)		(b)		(c)	
	7		8		8	
	328)28208		328)28208		7	
	2296		2624		328)28208	
	524		196		2296	
					524	
					328	
					196	

When the quotient digit is in error by being too high [as in (a) below], the error becomes obvious a bit earlier—after the multiplication of divisor by the quotient digit. In this case a reverse procedure is necessary: by subtracting the 2,820 from the 2,952 we get 132, which is the amount by which the 2,952 was too large. Since there was one too many 328's in 2,952, by subtracting the 132 from 328 [as in (c) below], and reducing the 9 to 8 in the quotient, the result is the same as if we had chosen the correct 8 in the first place.

(a)
$$9$$
$$328\overline{)28208}$$
$$2952$$
$$132$$

(b)
$$8$$
$$328\overline{)28208}$$
$$2624$$
$$196$$

(c)
$$8$$
$$9$$
$$328\overline{)28208}$$
$$2952$$
$$132 \\ 328 \Big\} 328 - 132$$
$$196 \leftarrow$$

3. *Short Methods of Division.* In Europe where the additive equal additions method of subtraction is more widely used, a shortened form of the division algorism as we know it is frequently seen. This shorter algorism is known as the *Austrian method of division.* Its brevity is traced to the fact that, compared with our process of long division, more steps are done mentally and fewer physically (less writing). By this method it is necessary for the computer to combine mentally the multiplicative and subtractive phases of the division algorism (in much the same way as we mentally combine multiplication and addition when "carrying" in our multiplication algorism). Subtracting by the additive equal additions method is particularly well suited to this.

To illustrate, the division 17,997 ÷ 52 is performed by the usual long division method in the box below, with certain key points in its progress lettered for reference. This same division problem is then performed by the Austrian method.

$$
\begin{array}{r}
346 \\
52)\overline{17997} \\
156 \downarrow \\
\text{(a)} \longrightarrow 23\,9 \\
20\,8 \downarrow \\
\text{(b)} \longrightarrow 31\,7 \\
31\,2 \\
\text{(c)} \longrightarrow 5
\end{array}
$$

The Austrian Method. (1) In the usual way, determine the first quotient digit (3) and proceed to multiply the divisor (52) by it; as the product is formed, subtract it term by term from the proper digits in the dividend, using the additive equal additions method of subtraction. Thus $3 \times 2 = 6$; $6 + 3 = 9$ (instead of 6 from $9 = 3$); write *3*. Then $3 \times 5 = 15$; $15 + 2 = 17$; write *2*.

$$
\begin{array}{r}
3 \\
52)\overline{17997} \\
\text{(a)} \longrightarrow 23
\end{array}
$$

(2) Bring down the 9.

$$
\begin{array}{r}
3 \\
52)\overline{17997} \\
239
\end{array}
$$

(3) Divide 239 by 52. The quotient digit is 4. Proceed with $4 \times 2 = 8$; $8 + 1 = 9$; write *1*. Then $4 \times 5 = 20$; $20 + 3 = 23$; write *3*.

$$
\begin{array}{r}
34 \\
52)\overline{17997} \\
239 \\
\text{(b)} \longrightarrow 31
\end{array}
$$

(4) Bring down the 7.

$$
\begin{array}{r}
34 \\
52)\overline{17997} \\
239 \\
317
\end{array}
$$

(5) Divide 317 by 52. The quotient digit is 6. Proceed with $6 \times 2 = 12$; $12 + 5 = 17$; write *5*. Then $6 \times 5 = 30$, add the carried 1 (to compensate for making the 7 in the previous subtraction a 17) for 31; $31 - 31 = 0$.

$$346$$
$$52\overline{)17997}$$
$$239$$
$$317$$

(c) ───→*5*

The division is completed.

For those to whom the additive equal additions process of subtraction is not native, carrying sometimes provides a mental obstacle. Therefore a second illustration of the Austrian method of division is given below, which involves a certain amount of carrying.

The problem: 3,067 ÷ 48.
The steps:
(1) 6 × 8 = 48 (carry the 4; subtract the 8); 8 + *8* = 16; write *8* and carry one more to compensate for making the previous 6 a 16; 6 × 4 = 24, plus the carried 5 (4 + 1) yields 29; 29 + *1* = 30; write *1*.

$$6$$
$$48\overline{)3067}$$
$$\textit{18}$$

(2) Bring down the 7; 3 × 8 = 24 (carry the 2; subtract the 4); 4 + *3* = 7; write *3*; 3 × 4 = 12, plus carried 2 yields 14; 14 + *4* = 18; write *4*.
The result: 3,067 ÷ 48 = 63 + remainder 43.

$$63$$
$$48\overline{)3067}$$
$$187$$
$$\textit{43}$$

A little practice with a few problems in subtraction using the additive equal additions method of subtraction, particularly with those which involve order impasses, plus a conscious comparison of the Austrian method with our own, should readily resolve most difficulties which the reader will have in comprehending this European approach.

In this country, the term *short division* represents a different process, although it too is an abridgement of the long division algorism. Usually it is employed in cases of division which involve a single-digit divisor. Its procedure rests heavily upon reductions and closely resembles that of the distributive rationalization of division developed in the previous unit.

As an illustration, the division problem 43,652 ÷ 7 is performed by long division in the box below.

$$\begin{array}{r} 6236 \\ 7\overline{)43652} \\ 42 \\ \hline 16 \\ 14 \\ \hline 25 \\ 21 \\ \hline 42 \\ 42 \\ \hline \end{array}$$

The steps of the more abbreviated algorism, known as *short division*, are given below:

(1) 43 thousand ÷ 7 = 6 thousands, plus. (Write 6).
7 × 6 thousands = 42 thousands.
43 thousands − 42 thousands = 1 thousand.
Reduce the 1 thousand remainder to 10 hundreds, and add them to the dividend's 6 hundreds for a total of 16 hundreds.

$$\begin{array}{r} 6 \\ 7\overline{)43^1652} \end{array}$$

(2) 16 hundreds ÷ 7 = 2 hundreds, plus. (Write 2).
7 × 2 hundreds = 14 hundreds.
16 hundreds − 14 hundreds = 2 hundreds.
Reduce the 2 hundreds remainder to 20 tens, and add them to the dividend's 5 tens, for a total of 25 tens.

$$\begin{array}{r} 62 \\ 7\overline{)436^252} \end{array}$$

(3) 25 tens ÷ 7 = 3 tens, plus. (Write 3).
7 × 3 tens = 21 tens.
25 tens − 21 tens = 4 tens.
Reduce the 4 tens remainder to 40 units, and add them to the dividend's 2 units, for a total of 42 units.

$$\begin{array}{r} 623 \\ 7\overline{)4365^42} \end{array}$$

(4) 42 units ÷ 7 = 6 units exactly. (Write 6).
The division is completed.

$$\begin{array}{r} 6236 \\ 7\overline{)43652} \end{array}$$

In frequent practice where speed rather than meaning is paramount, we can as usual rely upon the form of the algorism to take care of the denominational lines, thereby leaving us free to concentrate upon the various computations. Consequently, further telescoping of the process is possible as shown below. For example, we repeat our previous problem:

$$\begin{array}{r} 6\,2\,3\,6 \\ 7\overline{)43^16^25^42} \end{array}$$

(1) 7's in 43 are 6; *write 6*; $6 \times 7 = 42$; $43 - 42 = 1$; carry 1.
(2) 7's in 16 are 2; *write 2*; $2 \times 7 = 14$; $16 - 14 = 2$; carry 2.
(3) 7's in 25 are 3; *write 3*; $3 \times 7 = 21$; $25 - 21 = 4$; carry 4.
(4) 7's in 42 are 6 exactly; *write 6*.

4. *Checks for Division.* Since division can be thought of as that operation which locates the missing factor in a multiplication, the most obvious way to check on the accuracy of this newly found factor is to try it out by multiplying it with the given factor. The product of such a multiplication should equal the dividend of the division. Thus

divisor × quotient = dividend

If the division happens to be one in which a final remainder results, then this relationship becomes

(divisor × quotient) + remainder = dividend

To illustrate:

$$\begin{array}{r} 173 \\ 37\overline{)6436} \\ 37 \\ \hline 273 \\ 259 \\ \hline 146 \\ 111 \\ \hline 35 \end{array}$$

$$\begin{array}{ll} 37 \times 173 = 6401 & \text{(divisor × quotient)} \\ {+35} & \text{(remainder)} \\ 6,436 & \text{(dividend)} \end{array}$$

Considerably briefer, though less certain, is the excess check. The relationship (divisor × quotient) + remainder = dividend stated above can be thought of basically as a sum of two addends where the first addend is the product of "divisor and quotient" and the second addend is the "remainder." The "dividend" of course would be the sum. It follows that the excess of nines in the sum of the excesses of these two addends, should equal the excess of nines in the sum. Since one of the addends is the product of two numbers, its excess would equal the excess in the product of their respective excesses. From these observations is distilled the following rule:

The excess of nines in the product of the excesses in divisor and quotient, increased by the excess in the remainder, equals the excess of nines in the dividend.

```
        173
   37)6436     Excess of nines in 37 × 173:  1 × 2 =  2
        37     Excess of nines in 35:                  8
       273     Sum of excesses:                       10
       259     Excess in sum of excesses:      (1 + 0 = 1) → 1←┐
       146     Excess in dividend: 6 + 4 + 3 + 6 = 19 → 1 + 9 = 10 │
       111                                        → 1 + 0 = 1←┘
        35
```

5. *Geometric Interpretation of Division.* At the base of the geometric interpretation of the process of division is the fact that it is the inverse process of multiplication.

Multiplication, it will be recalled (Unit 12) was depicted as a series of equal steps to the right. The size of each step was determined by the multiplicand, and the number of steps was determined by the multiplier; the final resting point was the product.

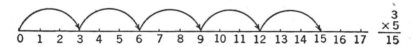

In division the reverse holds true as we step left toward zero, starting at a point determined by the dividend. The size of the step is again one of the factors, and the number of steps required to reach zero is the other factor. In measurement division the size of each step is known and the number of steps is unknown. Thus, in the illustration below, the size of each step is fixed at 3 and the number of steps of this size necessary to reach zero is sought.

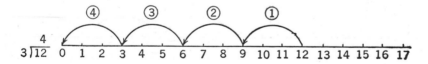

In partitive division, however, the number of equal steps to reach zero is known and the size of each step is sought. Thus in the illustration below, the number of steps is fixed at 3, while the size of each equal step is sought.

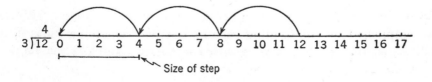

There is another schematic or number-line interpretation of partitioning which perhaps emphasizes more the sharing aspects of this phase of division.

To divide 12 by 3 partitively, for example, we recognize the fact that the divisor 3 represents the number of equal shares of the dividend 12; consequently each jump along the number line should contain an equal portion for each of the sharers. If each jump is made in units of three, then each of the sharers receives one unit out of each three covered on the scale. Thus we see that each sharer receives exactly 4 units, which is the quotient.

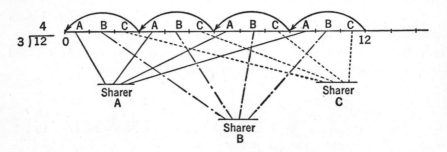

The matter of remainders fits neatly into these geometric schemes also. In measurement division, such as

$$\frac{4\frac{2}{3}}{3)14}$$

we get the usual 4 steps of 3 units each, plus a partial step of 2 units. Thus we see that there are $4\frac{2}{3}$ steps of 3 units each in 14 units.

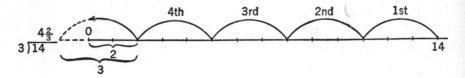

Interpreting the remainder in accordance with the second partitive scheme above, we get the usual shares of 4 units each, that is,

$$\frac{4\frac{2}{3}}{3)14}$$

with the remaining two units also being shared equally. This is accomplished by subdividing each of the two remaining units into thirds, so that each sharer gets two of these $\frac{1}{3}$ units. Thus we see that each of the 3 sharers in the dividend of 14 units receives a total of 4 whole units and 2 thirds of a unit, or, collectively, $4\frac{2}{3}$ units each.

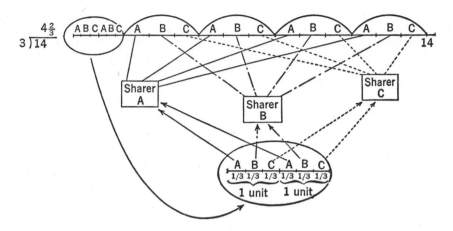

6. *Algebraic Approach to Subtraction and Division.* The primary difference between arithmetic and algebra is the introduction of negatively signed numbers. The extension of the number line indefinitely to the left of zero, as well as to right, and defining the distances from zero to the left as negative allows valuable generaliza-

tions in algebra. Thus the processes of subtraction become merely those of addition in a negative direction. As a result such things as 4 − 6 (four, take away 6) are quite possible. We merely start at 4, and, in accordance with the technique already established, move to the left 6 steps. This brings us to rest on −2, the result of 4 − 6.

In subtracting one polynomial from another, the law of likeness still prevails, but there is no need to bother with equal additions and decomposition. Any time the minuend digit in a given order is smaller than the one in the subtrahend, the remainder digit merely becomes negative. Thus

$$
\begin{array}{r}
6x^3 - 3x^2 + 5x + 7 \\
(-) \quad 2x^3 + 5x^2 + 2x + 9 \\
\hline
4x^3 - 8x^2 + 3x - 2
\end{array}
$$

Later, after fractions have been introduced and studied, it will be seen that still another condensation of the four arithmetic processes can be made: division becomes merely *multiplication* of the dividend by a unit fraction (numerator of one) whose denominator is the divisor. Thus

$$\frac{6}{2)\overline{12}}$$

can be thought of as $\frac{1}{2} \times 12 = 6$.

When long division is required in algebra, its form closely parallels that of the arithmetic algorism. It, too, is intent upon finding out, by repeated subtraction, how many times the divisor is contained in the dividend, and perhaps demonstrates a little more clearly the idea of taking apart the dividend order by order. For example,

$$
\begin{array}{r}
x^2 + x + 2 \\
x + 3)\overline{x^3 + 4x^2 + 5x + 7} \\
\underline{x^3 + 3x^2} \\
x^2 + 5x \\
\underline{x^2 + 3x} \\
2x + 7 \\
\underline{2x + 6} \\
1
\end{array}
$$

Notice that each quotient digit is determined entirely by answering the question, "What must I multiply the divisor by so that the highest powered term of the resulting product will equal the highest powered term remaining in the dividend?"

7. *Division in Other Scales.* We shall not make a special case for division in bases other than ten. From our work in these last two chapters, it should be clear to the reader that division in these other scales is equally consistent with what we know is true in the decimal scale. The algebraic long division above should be further evidence of this fact, since it is merely division of one polynomial in x by another. We have already learned that the scale is determined by the value which is assigned to x in the polynomial; so, when $x = $ ten, we have a division in the decimal scale; when $x = $ twelve, we have a valid division in scale twelve; and so on.

PROBLEMS SET 16

1. Using Table XI, determine the per cent of times the following divisors will be correct by (a) using the tens digit of the divisor as trial divisor, and (b) using the tens digit increased by one as trial divisor.

$$47)\overline{} \qquad 85)\overline{} \qquad 27)\overline{} \qquad 39)\overline{} \qquad 58)\overline{}$$

2. Solve the following division problems, using quotient adjustments as described in Section 2 of this unit whenever an incorrect quotient digit happens to be chosen.

(a) $19,136 \div 32$ (d) $368,439 \div 573$

(b) $1,949,461 \div 487$ (e) $682,277 \div 864$

(c) $196,372 \div 875$

3. Solve the following, using the Austrian method of division.

$$6,375 \div 12 \qquad 4,987 \div 24 \qquad 36,825 \div 68$$

4. Check the division problems of Question 3 by the

dividend = (quotient × divisor) + remainder relationship

5. Check the division problems of Question 2 by the excess of nines check.

6. Perform the following, using short division.

(a) $83,232 \div 6$ (c) $36,250 \div 10$

(b) $487,623 \div 9$ (d) $637,294,087,675 \div 7$

7. Demonstrate the following problems by use of the number line.

$$7 - 4 \qquad 15 - 8 \qquad 78 - 67$$
$$15 \div 5 \qquad 18 \div 3 \qquad 16 \div 4$$

8. Using the number line, show that

$$8 - 15 = -7 \qquad -5 - 3 = -8$$
$$3 - 8 = -5 \qquad -4 - 5 = -9$$

9. Divide
(a) $2x^3 - 3x^2 - 6x - 1$ by $x + 1$
(b) $x^3 - 8$ by $x - 2$
(c) $6a^{3x} + 3a^{2x} - 5a^x + 6$ by $2a^x + 3$

10. Given the division $32\overline{)576}$ with quotient 18, predict your answers to the following by applying your knowledge of the division process and the interrelationship of its parts. If in doubt, make a guess, then compute the answer and reconsider your guess.

(a) What would be the quotient if the 576 were doubled?

(b) What would be the quotient if the 32 were halved?

(c) What would be the quotient if the 576 is increased by 32?

(d) What would be the quotient if the 576 were reduced by 64?

(e) What would be the quotient if both the 576 and 32 were doubled?

(f) How many times could 18 be subtracted from 576?

(g) If the 32 were doubled and the quotient kept at 18, what would the dividend have to be?

(h) If the divisor (32) were halved and the quotient (18) were doubled, what would the dividend have to be?

11. The quotient of two numbers is 24. What would be the quotient (a) if the dividend is tripled? (b) if the divisor is halved? (c) if the dividend is halved? (d) if the divisor is doubled?

Unit 17: Factors, Multipliers and Divisors

1. *Introduction.* In Unit 10 the term *factor* was introduced and referred to as one of the "makers" of a number when the manufacturing process is multiplication. Thus in the product of $4 \times 6 = 24$, the 4 and 6 were identified as the "factors" of 24. Conversely, any whole number which contains a certain factor may be spoken of as a *multiple* of that factor; thus 24 is a multiple of both 6 and 4. Furthermore, for 24 there are several other sets of "makers" available among the integers, such as 3 and 8, and 2 and 12. As a consequence, 24 may also be thought of as a multiple of 2, 3, 8, or 12. While we are still in the area of analysis, it is pertinent to discuss the matter of "taking numbers apart" with respect to their factors, for the results of such manipulations have far-reaching effect in elementary arithmetic.

2. *Prime Factors.* In the case of the number 24 we have just recognized that there are several "sets" of makers for that number; on the other hand, numbers such as 23 or 17 each have but one set of integral* factors which will make that number. This fact leads us to an important distinction and a pair of definitions. A whole number which has for integral factors *only itself and one* is called a *prime number*. A whole number which has for integral factors *at least* one other set besides itself and one is called a *composite* number.

Since "one" is the "identity element" of multiplication, it follows that any whole number will possess at least the pair of factors "itself and one." Over and above this, all whole numbers then fall into one of two classes: primes and not-primes (composites).

The problem of determining whether a whole number is prime or not can be reduced to one of finding at least one integral factor of that number other than itself or one. If such a factor can be produced, the number is automatically a composite by definition; if none can, the number must be a prime number. Multiplication, it will be recalled, deals with putting numbers or factors together,

---

* All factors spoken of in this unit are assumed to be integers or whole numbers. If fractions are permitted, then 23 has unlimited pairs of factors: (46 and $\frac{1}{2}$), (69 and $\frac{1}{3}$) and so on.

while division takes numbers apart and produces the missing factor. Thus our prospecting for primes becomes a matter for division.

3. *Sieve of Eratosthenes.* The question of primeness of numbers has a rather ancient lineage. In bygone eras all sorts of mystical properties were attributed to number. In fact, a great deal of the mathematics studied by the ancient Greeks and Romans was little more than numerology. Certain mystical powers for good or evil as well as significant properties were associated with various numbers. For instance, the odd numbers were considered to be strong and masculine, since they were not so easily divisible, while the even numbers, always divisible at least by two, were considered weak and feminine. Consequently, marriage was symbolized by five, since it involved the combining of the first odd and first even number (3 + 2). The number *one* was considered to be neither odd nor even; instead it was looked upon somewhat mystically as the fountainhead of all numbers.

As might be suspected, the primes came in for a great deal of speculation and interest, particularly the three and seven, which occur with considerable frequency throughout mythology.

Eratosthenes (third century B.C.), a Greek mathematician, developed an ingenious device for isolating all the prime numbers below a certain number. To determine all the primes below, say, 30, he wrote out all the numbers up to 30. Then he began to reason, "Two is a prime, but every second number after two has a factor two in it (or in other words, every other number after two is a multiple of two)." So he proceeded to obliterate every second number after two by punching a hole in the parchment (circled by ○ in Figure 12). Then he went on, "Three is a prime and every third

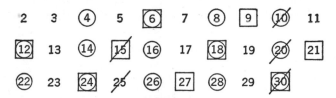

Figure 12. Isolating primes below 30 by Sieve of Eratoshenes.

number after 3 is a multiple of 3, hence a composite." He then punched out every third number after 3 (designated thus □ in Figure 12; some numbers, of course, had previously been punched out in the first step). Next, "Five is a prime and every fifth number after five is a composite," and they were duly punched out (/ in Figure 12). Continuing in this way, Eratosthenes eventually worked his way through to 30; when he was finished, his parchment, by now pierced like a sieve, contained only the prime numbers under 30.

There is a shorter and more subtle way than that of Eratosthenes for testing the primeness of a number. The reasoning goes this way: If a number is a composite, it will have at least one factor equal to or less than its square root, for if two factors are *both* greater than a number's square root, their product will be greater than that number. Hence, *to determine whether or not a number has integral divisors besides itself and one, we need test only those primes equal to or less than the square root of the number in question.* Obviously there is no need to try composite divisors, since such composite divisors ultimately have primes for their factors which will already have been tested. To demonstrate: Are the following numbers prime? (a) 97, (b) 143?

(a) Since we are interested only in integral divisors, we need to find only the whole number part of the square root of 97, which is 9 since $\sqrt{97} = 9+$. The primes below 9 are 2, 3, 5, 7. We divide 97 by each of these and find there is a remainder in each case; hence 97 is not integrally divisible by 2, 3, 5, or 7, and is therefore prime.

(b) $\sqrt{143} = 11+$. We test with the primes of 11 or less: 2, 3, 5, 7, and 11. Eleven divides 143 (13 times), so 143 is composite.

4. *Prime Factors of a Number.* A composite number, we have seen, can be decomposed or broken down into a pair of integral factors other than itself and one. Each of these factors in turn must be either prime or composite. If one or both are composite, further decomposition may take place until ultimately the original number is expressed as a product of primes. These collectively are called the "prime factors" of a given number and constitute a unique set. In other words, each whole number possesses exactly one set of prime factors which, as a totality, is different from the prime sets of all other numbers; conversely, any set of prime factors when multiplied out produces a unique whole number. In this light, the primes may be thought of as the irreducible building blocks of whole numbers.

To determine the exact prime factor make-up for a number, there are two standard techniques, one somewhat more systematic than the other.

First, the less systematic one literally breaks the number to "pieces" and continues to do so until all "pieces" are prime numbers.

For example, in finding the prime factors of 420 we might recognize that 420 can be factored as 42 × 10 (see Figure 13). Attacking 10, we break it into the factors 5 and 2, both of which are prime; 42 may be seen as 21 × 2, and then the 21 as 7 × 3. Thus the prime factors are found at the end of the various breakdowns (circled) and are in this case 7, 3, 2, 5, and 2. Expressing these in a more organized fashion, we have "the prime factors of 420 are 2^2, 3, 5, and 7" and of course $2^2 \times 3 \times 5 \times 7 = 420$.

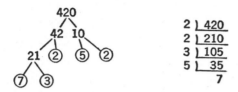

Figure 13. Prime factors of 420.

The second and more systematic way is a continuous division process. Starting with the lowest prime we continue to divide with it so long as integral quotients result. When this fails, we go on to the next prime, and so on until the ultimate quotient is itself a prime. See the computation to the right of Figure 13.

5. *Least Common Multiple.* An aid in computations involving fractions, to be considered two chapters hence, is the concept of least common multiple. The least common multiple of several given whole numbers is one number, the smallest possible, which is exactly (integrally) divisible by each of these given numbers. Its determination involves the building up of a number by admitting prime factors most grudgingly, the reason for which will be obvious in a moment.

First let us analyze the thing we are to construct. Most important, it is to be a *multiple,* and that means we are particularly concerned with its factors and divisors. If it is to be a *common* multiple, the implication is that it must be divisible by more than one number. Finally, the fact that it is to be a *least* common multiple implies that it is to be the smallest possible number which is divisible by these several other numbers.

For instance, suppose we are to find the least common multiple for the set of numbers 120, 225, and 252.

One guaranteed *common* multiple would be 120 × 225 × 252 = 6,804,000, since 120 would divide it 225 × 252 times, while 225 would divide it 120 × 252 times, and 252 would divide it 120 × 225 times. But how does one known whether or not 6,804,000 is the *least* common multiple possible?

To guarantee that the number we construct is the smallest common multiple, we build it up by prime factors, admitting only those which are absolutely necessary. To avoid overlap we first express each of the several numbers in its prime factor form. Thus

$$120 = 2^3 \times 3 \times 5, \quad 225 = 3^2 \times 5^2, \quad 252 = 2^2 \times 3^2 \times 7$$

We start with 120. If 120 is to divide this new multiple (which we shall call LCM) it must have among its factors the factors of 120. So our LCM *must* have among its factors three 2's, a 3, and a 5. If 225 is to divide LCM, LCM must have all the factors of 225 among its factors. So an extra 3 and an extra 5 are admitted, and our LCM is now: $2^3 \times 3^2 \times 5^2$. Finally, if 252 is to divide LCM, LCM must contain all the factors of 252 ($2^2, 3^2, 7$). To accommodate 252, LCM must admit one more factor, a 7. So our LCM is ultimately $2^3 \times 3^2 \times 5^2 \times 7$, or 12,600, which is considerably less than 6,804,000.

The skeptic can verify the validity of this solution by removing any one of the factors of the LCM as being superfluous and noting that in each case at least one of the several numbers will fail to divide the LCM evenly.

There is a somewhat more rapid though perhaps less meaningful way for determining the LCM of several numbers. It is a continued division type of process which is demonstrated in Figure 14.

	120	225	252
2)	60	225	126
2)	30	225	63
2)	15	225	63
3)	5	225	63
3)	5	75	21
5)	5	25	7
5)	1	5	7
7)	1	1	7
	1	1	1

Figure 14. Prime factors of LCM of several numbers.

The numbers are arranged in a row; then we divide across this row wherever possible using a prime divisor. When one of the several numbers is not evenly divisible by the divisor, it is brought down undivided to the next line. This process is continued line by line until only quotients of 1 result. The resulting set of successful prime divisors constitutes the minimum set of prime factors for the LCM.

In this case, wherever there is a successful division, that divisor is a necessary factor in the LCM for whichever number(s) (120, 225, or 252) it divides. Once the student has become familiar with this technique, several short cuts will suggest themselves to him and make it clearly a shorter approach than the first method discussed.

Geometrically, the concept of least common multiple can be illustrated rather easily on the number line. Starting from the zero point, picture the path of an object making jumps of 4 units each along the top of the line; along the bottom of the line picture the path of an object making jumps of 3 units each. At whatever point

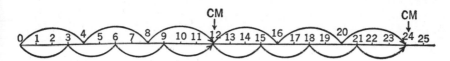

on the scale these two paths coincide, we have a common multiple. At the *first* point on the scale at which they coincide, we have the *least* common multiple. Hence, in this problem illustrated above, 12 and 24 are two of the common multiples for 4 and 3, with 12 (the first point at which the two paths were coincident) the *least* common multiple.

6. *Tests of Divisibility*. Before we leave the topic of divisors and divisibility, we might consider several tests of divisibility which sometimes prove helpful in computations.

Certain of these tests for divisibility (when the divisor is 2, 4, 5, 8, or 10) can be verified by a knowledge of our decimal system of notation and the distributive principle of division (D-1). An extension of this principle of distribution holds that the sum of two numbers will be evenly divisible by a third number if each of the two numbers is evenly divisible by the third. Thus any number ending in a digit divisible by two can be thought of (according to our system of notation) as the sum of [so many tens] plus [the units (even) digit]. Since two will divide the "ten" (making the value of the "so many" immaterial) as well as the even units digit, we get the rule: *If a number ends in a digit evenly divisible by two, then the number is assured to be divisible by two.* [Example: 376 = (37 × 10) + 6; 2 divides 10, so 2 will divide 37 × 10; 2 will divide 6; hence 2 will divide 376.]

By the same token, a test for divisibility by four can be had by thinking of numbers as the sum of so many "hundreds" plus a two-digit number. Four will clearly divide the hundred (making the "so many" multiplier immaterial), and if it will also divide the two-digit number evenly, then it will divide the whole number. Thus: *A number is divisible by 4 if the number made by the digits in the two lowest orders is divisible by 4.* [Example: 376 = (3 × 100) + 76; 4 will divide 100, so 4 will divide (3 × 100); 4 will divide 76 (19 times); hence 4 will divide 376.]

Similarly, tests for 8, 5, and 10 can be established: *A number will be divisible by eight if the number formed by the digits in the three lowest orders is divisible by eight.* The reason why is left as an exercise for the student.

A number will be divisible by five if its unit digit is divisible by five, which is to say, *A number is divisible by five if it ends in either zero or five.*

By the same line of reasoning, the only number which will be evenly divisible by ten must be devoid of units, so: *A number is divisible by ten if it ends in zero.*

The excess of nines offers a perfect test for determining divisibility by nine. Thus, *A number is divisible by nine if its excess of nines is zero.*

Extending the ideas basic to "excess of nines" which holds that any number can be thought of as so many nines (which of course will be divisible by 3) plus a remainder (excess), we are then guaranteed divisibility by three if this excess is divisible by three. So: *A number is divisible by three if its excess of nines is evenly divisible by three.*

The excess of elevens check discussed in Unit 9 provides a handy test for divisibility by 11.

Tests for divisibility by certain composite numbers made up of factors which are *relatively prime* to each other (that is, no common integral factor except 1 exists between the two factors) can be had by testing the divisibility of the number in question in terms of these prime factors. For instance, if a number (such as 42) is tested and found divisible by both 2 and 3, it follows that the number is also divisible by six. (In the same way numbers divisible by both 4 and 3 are guaranteed divisible by 12.)

The requirement that the factors of the questionable divisor be relatively prime to each other is an important one. Consider a test for determining divisibility by 18. If 3 and 6 are used as the cotesters, certain numbers would test true as being divisible by 18, while actually they are not. For instance, 48 would pass the test for divisibility by both 3 and 6, yet it is not divisible by 18. On the other hand, had the factors of 18 been chosen as 2 and 9, which are relatively prime to each other, the test would have shown that 48 is not divisible by 18 because it is not divisible by 9. Similarly, the factors of 3 and 8 would be a foolproof set of testing factors for "divisibility by 24," while 6 and 4 or 12 and 2 would not.

PROBLEMS SET 17

1. Using an approach similar to that of Eratosthenes, determine all the prime numbers below one hundred.

2. Determine whether the following numbers are prime or composite.

(a) 163   (b) 171   (c) 227   (d) 159   (e) 263   (f) 311   (g) 493

3. Find the prime factors of the following using two methods:

(a) 4,200   (b) 1,584   (c) 53,295   (d) 2,970   (e) 17,150

4. Find the least common multiple for the following sets of numbers using the prime factor method.

(a) 24, 36, 15   (d) 42, 54, 1, 28
(b) 98, 105, 56, 45   (e) 180, 189, 77, 60
(c) 15, 99, 40, 12   (f) 1,800, 200, 360

5. Find the LCM for each of the sets of numbers in Question 4 by the continued division method.

6. Show geometrically that a common multiple for 2, 3, and 4 is 24; that the *least* common multiple is 12.

7. Demonstrate, as was done in the text for the test of divisibility by two and four, the test for divisibility by eight. Use the number 73,864 for your demonstration.

8. Develop a rule for testing the divisibility of a number by twenty-five.

9. Write out for each of the following a set of three four-digit numbers which you know will be divisible by 2; by 3; by 4; by 5; by 6; by 8; by 9; by 10; by 12; by 18; by 20; by 25. Use your knowledge of tests of divisibility in formulating these sets.

10. Using the numerals 0, 2, 3, and 4, write all possible numbers which are simultaneously divisible by 2, 3, 4, 5, 9, and 10.

11. Given the numbers below in which certain digits are missing (as denoted by the asterisk, *), determine which are certainly divisible by 2; by 3; by 4; by 5; by 6; by 8; by 9; by 10; by 12.

(a) 6, 2*6, *40   (c) 7, ***, 560
(b) 2, *36, 712

Chapter 4

COMPARISON

Unit 18: Expressing Relationships

1. *Introduction.* Were it not for man's ability to make comparisons and value judgments, reality for him would be at best a bewildering experience. His daily life involves literally one comparison after another as he forms the multitudinous judgments upon which his actions are based. Sometimes the elements which are weighed in these judgments are highly qualitative, sometimes they are essentially quantitative, many times they are both. When the data are such that they can be expressed in quantitative terms, it is often possible for one to apply his knowledge of mathematics in a way that will clarify issues, determine relationships, and perhaps point up basic differences. Under such circumstances we have the third of man's three major activities with numbers: that of *comparison*.

Within the realm of commonplace mathematics—elementary arithmetic—there are two basic comparative devices. One expresses relationships in terms of deficiency or excess, while the other expresses relationships in terms of measurement or ratio.

2. *Deficiency or Excess Relationship—Difference Finding.* Problems involving insufficiency or superfluity usually involve such questions as "How many more are there?" or "How many more are needed?" In both cases we have basically a comparative situation involving two groups. Fundamental to the solution of problems such as these is the idea of one-to-one correspondence, the pairing off of the elements in one group with those of the other group. If one group is larger than the other, eventually the elements of the smaller group will be exhausted in this pairing process and the remaining elements of the larger group can be evaluated by counting.

Isolating and then evaluating a remaining part of one original group in this way suggests the process of *subtraction*. The rationalization attending this process will of course differ somewhat from that advanced in analysis, for here we have not one original group but two. Accordingly we identify the *minuend* with the larger group and the *subtrahend* with the smaller group. In effect the subtraction here separates the larger group into two subgroups, one subgroup being the size of the smaller original group and the other subgroup being that which is left over, the excess. This excess might well be characterized as the "difference" between the two original groups. Thus it becomes appropriate to use the word *difference* for the solution of a subtraction problem whose nature is that of comparison.

To illustrate, suppose A has $65 and B has $31. How much of a difference is there between their respective wealths? The problem is solved by subtraction.

$$
\begin{array}{lll}
\text{A's wealth:} & \$65 & \text{(minuend)} \\
\text{B's wealth:} & \underline{\$31} & \text{(subtrahend)} \\
& \$34 & \text{(difference)}
\end{array}
$$

The $34 difference here is open to two interpretations, depending upon point of view. From B's point of view the $34 represents a deficiency when compared to A's wealth; therefore it becomes the answer to the question, "How many more dollars does B need to raise in order to match A?" From A's point of view, the $34 represents an excess when compared to B's wealth and therefore answers the question, "How many more dollars does A have than B?" In either case the general situation is this: there is a $34 *difference* in their wealths.

3. *Graphs.* The difference concepts elaborated upon above find ready application in the use of graphs. The interpretation which one is expected to make as he views a bar graph, for instance, is essentially one of comparison. The implication is that the longer the bar, the greater the value for which it stands. Thus in Figure 15, the longest bar of the five shown is meant to indicate that in 1954 sales for XYZ Company were the greatest in the five-year span 1950–1954, while the shortest bar at 1950 is to be interpreted to mean that sales were least in that year. Extent of the sales can be roughly ascertained by reading the scale along the left-hand side expressed in thousands of dollars. Bar graphs are not meant to convey their information with any high degree of precision (which can be done

much more accurately by a table listing the actual dollar sales per year), but their chief purpose is to facilitate general comparisons. At a glance, for instance, we can learn that sales were better in 1953 than in 1950 and 1951, but not so good as in 1952 and 1954; or that sales in 1951 were poorer than sales in 1952, 1953 and 1954.

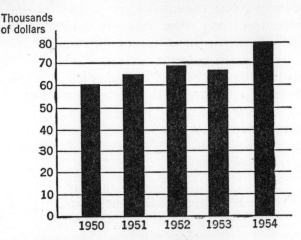

Figure 15. Yearly sales, XYZ Company.

In terms of the concepts developed in the previous section what we do when we visually compare, say, the 1952 bar with that of 1954 is to gauge the excess of the 1954 bar (minuend) over the 1952 bar (subtrahend) in terms of the scale on the left. In this case the excess exhibited is estimated as being roughly equal to $10,000; we therefore surmise that sales in 1954 exceeded sales in 1952 by about $10,000.

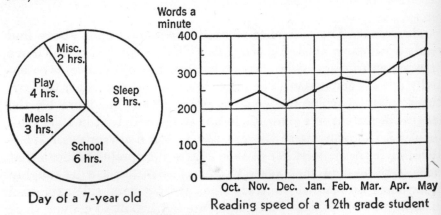

Figure 16. Circle and broken line graphs.

This same type of information is conveyed by broken line graphs and circle or pie graphs (see Figure 16). In the latter, however, the second of our methods of comparison, that of ratio, plays an important role in determining the size of each wedge or slice. In such cases we are able not only to compare one piece with another in the matter of excess or deficiency, but also to gain some idea of the size of the part in relation to the whole. Such important relationships come under the heading of measurement relationships.

4. *Measurement Relationships.* By way of distinction we might note that comparisons which employ the process of subtraction express differences in terms of the specific elements involved. For instance, where we use subtraction to compare the pocket money of A who has $10 with that of B who has $4, the result is in terms of *dollars;* where we compare the age of A who is 28 years old with that of B who is 7 years old, the difference is expressed in terms of *years.* In other words, subtraction produces the differences between the two things under comparison in terms of the basic scale used to measure each of these things. However, there is yet another important way by which to compare A to B, and that is to express A not in terms of the scale but in terms of B. Such a comparison is known as the *ratio of A to B.*

Ratio is essentially a measuring technique by which one thing (that which is compared) is measured by a "ruler" which is equal to the other thing (that which is the basis for comparison, the standard). This can be reversed so that what is originally compared becomes the basis for comparison and that which was the basis for the comparison becomes the thing compared. The result of such an interchange is a totally different ratio, unless, of course, the things are equal. Since these two comparisons are related, however, their ratios will also be found to be related: one will be the reciprocal of the other.*

To illustrate this ratio concept, suppose we wish to compare the yardstick (36 inches) and the foot ruler (12 inches). If we use the foot ruler as a unit of measurement we know from experience that it can be picked up and laid down three times in "measuring" the yardstick (see Figure 17). Thus we say that the yardstick, when compared with the foot ruler, is three times as long as the foot ruler. In other words, the ratio of the yardstick's length to that of the foot

---

* Any discussion, other than its mention here, of the term "reciprocal" will be best deferred until our work with fractions is under way.

ruler is 3 to 1. Symbolically, such a ratio is frequently expressed as (3:1).

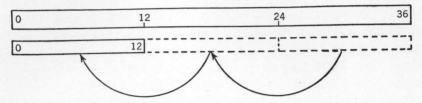

Figure 17. Foot ruler measuring the yardstick.

By extending this same line of reasoning, we compare in age a father of 28 to his son of 7. If we consider the son's 7 years as the measuring unit, we see that it will measure the father's age four times. Thus we say that the father is four times as old as his son, or that the ratio of ages of *father* to *son* (note that the son's age is the basis for comparison) is 4 to 1, or 4:1.

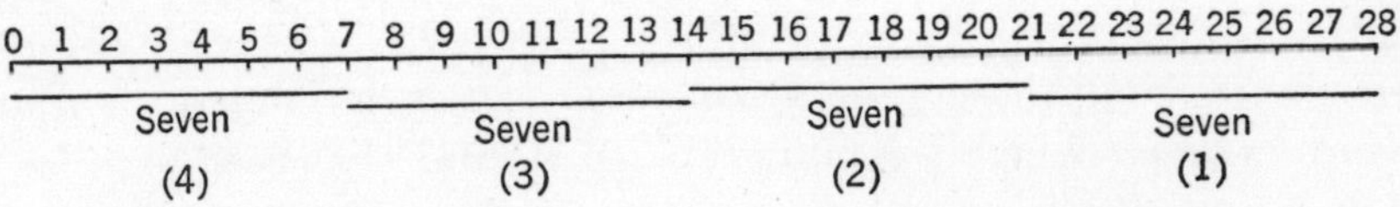

0 1 2 3 4 5 6 7 8 9 10 11 12 13 14 15 16 17 18 19 20 21 22 23 24 25 26 27 28

Seven	Seven	Seven	Seven
(4)	(3)	(2)	(1)

Figure 18. Father's age (28) measured by son's age (7).

It should be obvious that we have in each of these problems a case of measurement division. In both the yard-foot and the father-son age problems, that which is compared (the yard, the father's age) is the dividend and that which is the basis for the comparison (the foot, the son's age) is the divisor. Thus

$$12\text{ inches}\overline{)36\text{ inches}}^{\,3} \qquad 7\text{ years}\overline{)28\text{ years}}^{\,4}$$

From this it appears that the ratio value is embodied in the quotient, and since the quotient in measurement division is always abstract, it follows that ratios are always abstract values.

This brings up an interesting and sometimes useful approach to the process of division. Since we have seen that 36 inches compares with 12 inches as 3 does with 1, and that 28 years compares with 7 years as 4 does with 1, it might be concluded inductively that in every division the *dividend compares with the divisor as the quotient does with one.*

To state this relationship more succinctly, we might say (dividend : divisor) as (quotient : one).

Replacing "as" with the symbol (::) we have

dividend : divisor :: quotient : one

Here the reader undoubtedly recognizes, at least in the form of this expression, a *proportion*. Usually the topics of ratio, proportion, and variation receive their full treatment in the study of algebra, since within that framework they can best be rationalized and applied. This is not to say that some of the concepts of comparison inherent in proportion and variation are not to be met within the framework of elementary arithmetic, particularly in matters of per cent and measurement. But these are usually proportions of a direct type which can be handled adequately with only a knowledge of fractions and reductions. Meanwhile, it might be interesting for those with some experience with proportions to apply the well-known rule of proportions, "the product of the means equals the product of the extremes," to

dividend : divisor :: quotient : one

and see that

divisor $\times$ quotient = dividend $\times$ one = dividend

a relationship that was previously observed in our investigations of the division process.

Although our discussions of measurement comparison so far have involved only comparisons of the larger with the smaller quantities (36 inches with 12 inches, 28 years with 7 years), as stated earlier the concept is equally valid should we attempt to measure the smaller by the larger. Accordingly, it will be noted that the foot rule compares with the yardstick in the ratio of 1 to 3; the son's age compares with that of his father in the ratio of 1 to 4. Moreover, in terms of the division process this turnabout leads us to the following equally valid statement about division

divisor : dividend = one : quotient

Clearly this inverse notion takes us into the realm of fractions, making this point an appropriate one at which to call a temporary halt in our treatment of comparison. In the next chapter we shall introduce and explore the concept of fractions, and within that framework we shall find a highly convenient method for writing and working with ratios. This link will prove to be extremely beneficial in the solving of ratio and proportion problems; and a prior knowledge of the ratio concept will aid materially in the full understanding of that sometimes difficult number type, the fraction. For that reason, along with the fact that it completes our scheme of synthesis, analysis, and comparison, we have introduced the concept of ratio here.

PROBLEMS SET 18

1. Write out five word problems which use subtraction as a comparative process. Solve these problems and interpret your answers.

2. Enrollment at a certain college for the past 6 years was as follows:

1954–55:	862	1951–52:	804
1953–54:	800	1950–51:	780
1952–53:	825	1949–50:	720

Make a bar graph showing these data.

3. The following are the average daily temperatures recorded for the first ten days of March: 58, 59, 62, 64, 60, 59, 50, 49, 52, 57. Construct a line graph showing these data.

4. A school's annual budget is $180,000 distributed as follows: administration $45,000, faculty salaries $90,000, plant maintenance $15,000, heat, light and power $12,000, instructional materials $12,000, miscellaneous $6,000. Make a circle graph depicting the distribution of the annual budget.

5. In the budget data of Question 4, find the ratios which express the following comparisons:
    (a) Faculty salaries with administration
    (b) Plant maintenance with heat, light, power
    (c) Administration and faculty salaries with total budget
    (d) Instructional materials with faculty salaries
    (e) Faculty salaries with instructional materials

6. Write out five word problems which use division as the process of comparison. Solve these problems and interpret the answers.

7. State the problems of Question 6 in such a way as to reverse the ratios.

8. A 1–2–4 concrete mixture means 1 part cement, 2 parts sand, and 4 parts gravel. What is the ratio of
    (a) Sand to cement?
    (b) Gravel to sand?
    (c) Cement to sand?
    (d) Gravel to the total mixture?
    (e) Sand to the total mixture?
    (f) Cement and sand to the total mixture?

9. What are the scales (ratio of actual distance to map distance) for maps in which
    (a) Distance of 320 miles = 4 in.?
    (b) 1,000 miles is 10 in.?
    (c) 15 in. equals 240 miles?

10. What is the scale of a plan for an athletic field if its length is 840 ft and its width, represented as 13 in. on the plan, is 320 ft less than its length?

Chapter 5

FRACTIONS

Unit 19: The Concept of Fractions

1. *Origins*. We have said that even before recorded history, primitive man reacted to the multiplicity of things in his environment by inventing and using model groups. It is likely that at the same time he was equally conscious of parts of things as well. A piece of a broken spear, a fragment of a berry, a part of a journey were undoubtedly recognized for what they were. But it seems quite certain that whatever his ideas were about such partials, they were considerably more vague than his ideas about wholes. This is borne out by the fact that in cultures in which systems of number notation with respect to whole numbers were considerably advanced, attempts to systematize fractions were, if made at all, quite rudimentary. The major source of difficulty in systematizing fraction concepts apparently lies in the fact that a piece or a part of something is simultaneously a fragment of some whole and yet an entity or a whole in its own right. A system which incorporates both these ideas adequately and flexibly within a single framework is not a simple matter to grasp, let alone to invent. As a consequence, a workable system of notation for fractions has come to us more slowly and along a much more tedious route than that of whole numbers.

The derivation of the word *fraction* is strongly indicative of its early status. It comes from the Latin *frangere*, "to break." In its simplest setting, then, a fraction is merely a broken part of some whole. Consequently, in its earliest stages of use more attention was paid to the number of parts into which the whole was broken than to the respective sizes of the parts. At this point, a fraction was thought of much as the child thinks when he insists on having the

150

"biggest" half. To the child a "half" is simply one of two parts, with no thought whatever about equality of parts being vital to the term "half."

Eventually the systematic advantage of requiring the parts to be of equal size became evident, and at once the concept of unit fractions was born: the whole broken into two equal parts (the half), the whole divided into three equal parts (the third), the whole broken into four equal parts (the quarter), and so on.*

2. *Egyptian Fractions.* The method by which the ancient Egyptians employed their counting numbers to symbolize equal parts of the whole is illustrative of a system which is exclusively based upon unit fractions. Beyond the half, which was written as [, the characteristic feature of an Egyptian fraction symbol was the mark ⬭. Beneath this mark was written a number which expressed the number of equal parts into which the whole had been subdivided. For instance, in Egyptian hieroglyphics III was three, so ⬭ represented one of three equal parts, or one-third, ∩II = twelve, so ⬭ = one of twelve equal parts, or one-twelfth, ⬭ = one twentieth, ⬭ = one-hundredth, and so on.

With the exception of the frequently used fraction two-thirds, which had the special symbol ⬭, all Egyptian fractions were unit fractions. In order to understand how the Egyptian dealt with such nonunit fractions as our $\frac{5}{6}$, $\frac{9}{11}$, $\frac{23}{30}$, we must recall the two principles upon which the Egyptian system of notation operated, addition and repetition. By applying these principles the Egyptian expressed his nonunit fractions as a sequence of available unit fractions whose sum was the desired nonunit fraction. Thus

$$\frac{5}{6} = \frac{1}{2} + \frac{1}{3} = [\,⬭$$

$$\frac{9}{11} = \frac{1}{2} + \frac{1}{4} + \frac{1}{22} + \frac{1}{44} = [\,⬭\;⬭\;⬭$$

$$\frac{23}{30} = \frac{1}{3} + \frac{1}{6} + \frac{1}{10} + \frac{1}{10} + \frac{1}{15} = ⬭\;⬭\;⬭\;⬭\;⬭$$

There were no set ways available to these early mathematicians for determining the component unit-fraction parts of a given nonunit fraction. Some had worked out special techniques for certain cases,

* According to our present-day terminology, a unit fraction is one whose numerator is fixed at one and whose denominator is free to vary.

and these were jealously guarded as trade secrets. Otherwise, trial and error was the only approach.

The Egyptian method of expressing fractions seems tremendously cumbersome to us at first glance, and so it is when compared with ours. Yet we duplicate this technique nearly every day when we make change with our money. To illustrate, let us assume you are a clerk and someone makes a purchase from you worth seventeen cents. He hands you a dollar bill and it is your job to return to him, in value, a fraction or part of his dollar bill. Should you limit yourself always to giving back a minimum number of coins in change, you would in this case hand the customer a half dollar, a quarter, a nickel, and three pennies, though not necessarily in this sequence. In effect, you have established that

$$\frac{83}{100} = \frac{1}{2} + \frac{1}{4} + \frac{1}{20} + \frac{1}{100} + \frac{1}{100} + \frac{1}{100}$$

Obviously then, our whole system of coins is one of practical usable unit fractions of the dollar: the penny is $\frac{1}{100}$ dollar, the nickel is $\frac{1}{20}$ dollar, the dime is $\frac{1}{10}$ dollar, the quarter is $\frac{1}{4}$ dollar, and the half dollar is $\frac{1}{2}$ dollar.

Ordinarily, in the more complicated change-making problems we resort to the common denominator method (figuring everything in pennies), but this is a considerably more advanced technique which came into use only in the seventeenth century. So once again we are in a position to observe an instance of the evolution of thought. Since we are able to draw upon the experience and contributions of our predecessors, children of today are able to perform mentally many a problem which befuddled the best of scholars in an ancient day. This is not to say that the ancients were less intelligent than modern man, but that much of the efforts of ancient man had to be expended in uncovering many of the things which we today draw upon freely. It is almost banal to state that it takes infinitely more ingenuity to invent something than it does to recognize the merits of a good thing and to follow.

3. *Roman Fractions.* A diametrically opposite approach to fraction-thinking is best illustrated by a system used by the Romans, who took their lead from the Greek and Babylonian astronomers. These astronomers found it convenient to discuss parts of the whole in terms of sixtieths, which they referred to as the "first little parts," *partes minutiae primae.* The middle word indicates the de-

rivation of our word for the sixtieth part of the hour or degree, the *minute*. A subsequent subdivision of one of the "first little parts" into sixty smaller equal parts was referred to as the "second little parts," *partes minutiae secundae*, whence comes our word *second*, the sixtieth part of the minute. These fractions were known as the sexagesimals.*

Practically speaking, these small standardized parts, while satisfactory for the exact measurements of the astronomers, were far too refined for everyday use in the market place. So the Roman *uncials* came into being. The uncials followed the same pattern as the sexagesimals, only their part size was fixed at a smaller and more conveniently divisible twelve rather than sixty. It is from the Roman word *uncia*, which means "the twelfth part of something," that our words *inch* (twelfth part of a foot) and *ounce* (in those days the twelfth part of a pound) are derived.

The Roman of course had a symbolism to go with these fractional concepts, which is given here:

$$\frac{1}{12} \quad - \qquad\qquad \frac{7}{12} \quad S-$$

$$\frac{2}{12} \quad = \qquad\qquad \frac{8}{12} \quad S=$$

$$\frac{3}{12} \quad =- \qquad\qquad \frac{9}{12} \quad S=-$$

$$\frac{4}{12} \quad == \qquad\qquad \frac{10}{12} \quad S==$$

$$\frac{5}{12} \quad ==- \qquad\qquad \frac{11}{12} \quad S==-$$

$$\frac{6}{12} \quad S \text{ (after } semis, \text{ Latin for half)}$$

The closest parallel which we have in our modern arithmetic to the Roman fractions is that of per cent. This technique, however, stabilizes the whole at 100 rather than at 12 as the Romans did, and parts of the whole are referred to as parts of the hundred (per cent = *per centum* = per hundred) rather than the Roman parts of twelve.

4. *Summary.* We have presented here the Egyptian and Roman systems of fractions because they point up well two fundamental

* According to our present-day terminology a sexagesimal would be a fraction whose denominator is fixed at sixty or some power of sixty and whose numerator is free to vary.

concepts which are merged in the Hindu-Arabic system of fractions, concepts which must be properly appreciated if a thorough understanding of that system is to be had. Let us summarize briefly their merits and limitations.

We have seen that the Egyptians restricted their fractions primarily to those of unit fractions, fractions which would fit situations involving *one* part of a whole which had been subdivided into a given number of equal parts. Obviously, the *number* of these equal parts in which the whole is divided will vary inversely with the size of the resulting parts. (This is to say that the more pieces we cut the whole into, the smaller will be each individual piece; thus it follows that $\frac{1}{2} > \frac{1}{3} > \frac{1}{4}$, etc., where > means "is greater than.") As a consequence the Egyptians had produced a system of fractions which had great flexibility with regard to size of part; but when it came to coping with multiplicity of parts, it was singularly unwieldy (witness $\frac{11}{12} = $ ⌐ ⌣ ⌣). On the other hand, the concept behind the Egyptian system was relatively easier to grasp than ours, for the number of parts (our numerator) was steadfastly fixed at one and so the computer was free to concentrate on the remaining variable, the size of the part (our denominator).

The Roman concept of fraction was the very reverse of all this. By stabilizing the size of part at twelfths, the computer was concerned only with fixing the number of parts correctly, and so he was free to direct all his attention to that point. Consequently the Roman system was most flexible where the Egyptian system was least flexible (number of parts, numerator) and inflexible where the Egyptian system was most flexible (size of part, denominator).

Thus we see that both the Romans and the Egyptians had a system of fractions which met certain fraction situations well, but was seriously wanting in others. It was left to the Hindus, as we shall see in the next unit, to devise a system which successfully captured the flexibilities of both of these systems, while eliminating their inflexibilities; but unfortunately it had to be accomplished at the cost of added complexity.

PROBLEMS SET 19

1. Write the Egyptian equivalent for the following.

$$\frac{1}{5}, \quad \frac{1}{11}, \quad \frac{1}{23}, \quad \frac{1}{32}, \quad \frac{1}{100}, \quad \frac{1}{101}, \quad \frac{1}{24}, \quad \frac{1}{300}, \quad \frac{1}{1000}, \quad \frac{1}{100,000}$$

2. Write the following fractions in the Egyptian notation. (It is possible to write each of these without repeating any single fraction.)

$$\frac{3}{4}, \quad \frac{77}{100}, \quad \frac{41}{100}, \quad \frac{9}{20}, \quad \frac{12}{35}, \quad \frac{47}{60}$$

3. Compute how many seconds of time there are in a week.

4. If the sexagesimals had been extended to "third little parts" and "fourth little parts," how many "third little parts" would there be in the whole? How many "fourth little parts" would there be in the whole?

5. How does the metric system of linear measurement deal with parts of the whole? Look up the names of these metric parts and compare that system with that of the sexagesimals.

6. Compare the systematic qualities of our linear system of measurement (inch, foot, yard, mile) with that of the metric system. Which is more systematic?

7. Choose the larger fraction in the following pairs of fractions.

8. Formulate a rule for deciding which of two Egyptian fractions is the larger. Formulate a rule for deciding which of two Roman fractions is the larger.

Unit 20:   Common Fractions Today

1. *Origin.* Our modern system of fractions, like that of whole numbers, came from the Hindus. Unlike the Egyptians, whose approach to fractions permitted variation only in the size of the parts, or like the Romans, whose system permitted variation only in the number of parts, the Hindus developed systems which allowed for simultaneous variation in *both* the number of parts and the size of the part. Masters as they were of positional notation, the Hindus invented a vertical positioning of digits to represent these "broken numbers"; the horizontal positioning, as we have already seen, was reserved for whole numbers.

In order to symbolize, say, three parts of some whole which had been broken into seven equal parts (our three-sevenths), they wrote $\frac{3}{7}$. The top number was assumed arbitrarily to represent the number of parts and the bottom number the size of the part. The size of part was, of course, automatically determined by the number of equal parts into which the whole had been subdivided; hence this subdivision number makes an accurate index for the size of the part. Later the Arabs, the transmitters of the Hindu system, added the now familiar bar between the top and bottom digits, so that the fraction in question came to be symbolized as $\frac{3}{7}$, precisely as we write it today.* This bar disappeared in the early days of printing because it presented typesetting difficulties; later as printing techniques improved, it made a reappearance, now apparently for good.

2. *Interpretations of Fractions.* Fractions, in contrast to the natural numbers, are artificial numbers, the invention of man to satisfy certain requirements or needs. Initially the fraction was created to characterize but one thing: a part or parts of the whole. Thus the fraction $\frac{2}{3}$ meant only "two pieces of a whole broken into three equal parts." This single interpretation was made further evident by the names which the Latin writers attached to the two digits of the Hindu fraction symbolism. The top number they called *numerator* (the numberer of parts) and the bottom number *denominator* (*nom* = name, thus the "namer of the part by size"). Even the way in which a fraction is read reflects this concept: $\frac{2}{3}$ is read as "two-thirds," which is a contraction of "*two* pieces of the whole which has been divided into *thirds* or three equal parts." Although the underlying concept of the fraction has been broadened considerably, the terms numerator and denominator, as well as the numeration technique (reading of the fraction), have carried over into today's usage.

It will be recalled that initially the whole or natural numbers were cardinal. Later, when they were arranged in an orderly sequence, their ordinal uses became apparent, so that in matters of practice today, these numbers have many ordinal as well as cardinal interpretations. Fractions, too, began with a single definition, "so many equal parts of the whole"; later on new meanings and uses became apparent. Today any given fraction could mean any one of several things, depending upon the context. The fraction $\frac{3}{5}$, for instance, could be interpreted as:

    (a) Three parts of the whole which has been broken into five equal parts (the original concept).

    (b) *One* of five equal parts of *three* things.

    (c) A quotient of two numbers ($3 \div 5$).

    (d) A comparison or a ratio ($3:5$).

---

* Writing a fraction as $3/7$ has no historical significance. It is merely a more handy way to write fractions under certain circumstances. In the early grades this "slant," or solidus, symbolism can cause unnecessary confusion and is to be avoided.

3. *Unifying the Interpretation of Fractions*. At first glance the four fraction interpretations just enumerated appear to be somewhat divergent and unrelated. But we shall see that the division process with respect to whole numbers, as developed in Unit 15, will provide for them a unifying framework.

Let us begin by accepting as basic the third interpretation (c) above, that a fraction is one way of representing the quotient of two numbers.

When the two numbers happen to be integers, we have a type of fraction known as a *rational fraction*. These together with the integers (which can be represented easily as a rational fraction; for instance, $7 = \frac{7}{1} = \frac{14}{2}$ etc.) form an important set of numbers known as the *rational numbers*.* Rational numbers may be thought of as an extension of the set of whole numbers; consequently their operations are guided by the basic principles that have been established for operating with whole numbers. Of particular importance to us is the fact that this set of rational numbers is closed for all four of the basic operations of arithmetic, including division; they are therefore sufficient for the solution of any problem of elementary arithmetic.

Regarding the fraction as a quotient in this way implies a consistency with the basic definition of division: finding the value of the missing factor of a multiplication. This is to say that the fraction must satisfy the relationship:

$$\text{divisor} \times \text{quotient} = \text{dividend}$$

Therefore, if the fraction $\dfrac{A}{B}$ is to represent the quotient of number A divided by number B, it follows that $\dfrac{A}{B}$ must be such that

$$B \times \frac{A}{B} = A$$

From this the important identification of the divisor with the denominator and of the dividend with the numerator can be clearly seen.

We now push this fraction-division relationship one step further. It will be recalled from our discussions of division that at times the

---

* The negative integers and fractions are also included in this set of rational numbers, but for our purposes they will be ignored, since they are not of primary concern to elementary arithmetic.

quotient is concrete (when partitioning is involved) and at other times the quotient is abstract (when measurement is involved). Thus we conclude that some fractions may be partitive and some may be measurement, depending upon the situation. If we analyze the three remaining fraction interpretations above, (a), (b), and (d), we may note that interpretations (a) and (b) fit easily into our concept of partitioning, while the concept of ratio, interpretation (d), has already been identified with measurement division (see Unit 18).

Thus we have integrated all four fraction interpretations into one framework, that of division. Outlined below with illustrations are the main features of this unified classification of fraction interpretations.

Basic definition: *A fraction is an expression of the quotient of two numbers.* [*Interpretation* (c).]

1. *When the quotient is concrete,* which implies that the divisor (denominator) is abstract and the quotient (fraction) agrees with the dividend (numerator), the process is one of partitioning. The following fraction interpretations are included:

(a) ONE OR MORE EQUAL PARTS OF THE WHOLE:
   Example: Divide 1 yd of cloth into 7 equal pieces. Give Mary 3 of these pieces. How much cloth does Mary have?
      Answer: $\frac{3}{7}$ yd (3 × $\frac{1}{7}$ yd).

(b) ONE OF THE EQUAL PARTS OF SEVERAL UNITS:
   Example: Divide 3 yards of cloth equally among 7 children. How much does *each* child receive?
      Answer: $\frac{3}{7}$ yd ($\frac{1}{7}$ × 3 yd).

Note that in each case the result is a concrete number, a like number to the dividend or that which is subdivided. This is the distinguishing characteristic of partitive division.

2. *When the quotient is abstract,* which implies that the divisor (denominator) is concrete and agrees with the dividend (numerator), the process is one of measurement. This covers the following fraction interpretation:

(d) COMPARISON, OR RATIO:
   Example: A father is 29 years of age and his son is 7 years of age. Compare the son's age with that of the father.
      Answer: The son is $\frac{7}{29}$ his father's age.

This is the same as 7:29, or the result of measuring a 7-yr span with a "ruler" 29 yr in length. Note that the result here is *not* $\frac{7}{29}$ yr of age, but purely a ratio $\frac{7}{29}$, an abstract value, the distinguishing characteristic of measurement.

From a purely *computational* point of view, it will be recalled it does not matter at all whether the division is one of partitioning or measurement—the mechanics are the same; these distinctions are of importance, however, for interpretation and problem solving. So, too, it is with fractions: as far as computation is concerned, which of the foregoing interpretations is implied is immaterial to the ultimate calculations. But in a meaningful program, where interpretations and problem solving are important, a knowledge of these distinctions is essential.

4. *Other Classifications of Fractions.* Moving now from the interpretative aspects of fractions toward its computational or operational aspects, we find fractions classified in several ways.

Fractions, when written, may assume a variety of *forms*. When the fraction, say the half, is written in the form $\frac{1}{2}$, we call that *common fraction form*, and refer to the symbol as a *common fraction*. Originally, such expressions were referred to as *fractiones vulgares*, the fractions of the tradesmen. These were to be distinguished from the sexigesimals of the astronomer in which the half would be written as 30'. Later on in this text, when we see the decimal system of whole number notation extended to include fractions as well, the half, for instance, will be written as .5; this type of expression will be referred to as *decimal fraction form*.

Since our definition of fraction as the quotient of two numbers places no restriction upon the size of the numbers, fractions may be greater than one, equal to one, or less than one, depending upon the relative sizes of the numerator and denominator. Fractions which represent magnitudes less than one (in which case the numerator is less than the denominator, for example $\frac{3}{4}$, $\frac{2}{7}$, etc.) are called *proper fractions*. Fractions which represent magnitudes greater than one (in which cases the numerator is greater than the denominator, for example, $\frac{7}{3}$, $\frac{5}{2}$, etc.) are called *improper fractions*.

Furthermore, the basic definition of a fraction as a quotient places no restriction upon the nature or form of the two numbers involved, so still another classification of rational fraction types is possible.

When the rational fraction is expressed with whole numbers for the numerator and denominator, we refer to it as a *simple fraction*. When either the numerator or denominator, or both, involve other than whole numbers, we call that type of fraction a *complex fraction*. Finally, when either the numerator or denominator, or both involve an operation, such fractions are called *compound fractions*. Of course each of these may be either proper or improper, since form and size are not basically related. Examples of these three types are given below.

Simple fractions:

$$\frac{2}{3}, \quad \frac{5}{2}, \quad \frac{3}{7}, \quad \frac{8}{92}, \quad \frac{17}{14}$$

Complex fractions:

$$\frac{\frac{1}{2}}{6}, \quad \frac{2}{\frac{3}{4}}, \quad \frac{\frac{1}{3}}{\frac{2}{5}}, \quad \frac{\frac{3}{4}}{\frac{5}{8}}, \quad \frac{\frac{3}{5}}{10}$$

Compound fractions:

$$\frac{5-4}{3}, \quad \frac{6 \times 7}{3+8}, \quad \frac{\frac{1}{2}+3}{\frac{3}{4}}, \quad \frac{3+\frac{1}{6}}{8-\frac{1}{2}}$$

Note that since these are basically rational numbers, each of these types of fraction may be transformed by one or more reductions to a fraction whose numerator and denominator are whole numbers.

Sometimes we indicate or abbreviate the sum of a whole number and a proper fraction (because they are "unlikes" and therefore not additive in their present forms) and consider it a new number type known as a *mixed number*. For instance, the sum of $8 + \frac{2}{3}$ may be expressed without the $+$ sign as the mixed number $8\frac{2}{3}$, although in reading it, the word "and" which verbalizes the indicated addition is retained: eight and two-thirds. Similarly, we often omit the $+$ sign in expressing the sum of two unlike denominate numbers: 4 feet $+$ 7 inches becomes 4 feet 7 inches; 6 hours $+$ 18 minutes becomes 6 hours 18 minutes, etc. Thus the term "mixed number" means literally "an expression of the sum of mixed (unlike) numbers."

5. *Basic Principle of Fractions.* Division's principle of compensation (D-2, Unit 15) stated that if the dividend and divisor are both multiplied (or divided) by the same number, not zero, the quotient remains unchanged. Since fractions have been defined as the quotient of two numbers, and since the numerator has been identified with the dividend and the denominator with the divisor, we are led easily to the *principle of compensation with respect to fractions:*

Principle F-1: *If the numerator and denominator of a fraction are both multiplied (or divided) by the same number, not zero, the value of the fraction is unchanged.*

The effects of this principle are far-reaching and extremely useful. Cancellation, for instance, when properly used, draws its authority from this principle. With respect to the various interpretations of fractions, the principle of compensation may be explained more specifically as follows:

(a) *Partitioning.* Let us assume the fraction $\frac{6}{9}$ to mean the whole is divided into 9 equal parts, and our concern is with 6 of these parts. We are assured by the principle of compensation that if the whole is divided into twice as many equal parts (multiply denominator by 2), we will have the same amount as before if we take twice the number of parts (multiply numerator by 2). Thus

$$\frac{6}{9} = \frac{2 \times 6 \rightarrow 12}{2 \times 9 \rightarrow 18}, \quad \text{or} \quad \frac{6}{9} = \frac{12}{18}$$

An illustration of this, using scales, is given below.

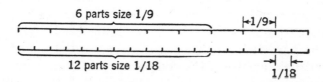

On the other hand, if we should triple the size of each part (divide denominator by 3) and take only one-third the number of parts (divide numerator by 3), we are again assured by the principle of compensation that we will have the same amount as before. Thus

$$\frac{6 \div 3 \rightarrow 2}{9 \div 3 \rightarrow 3}, \quad \text{or} \quad \frac{6}{9} = \frac{2}{3}$$

This too is illustrated.

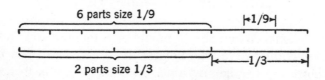

(b) *Measurement.* Within the framework of measurement, the principle of compensation with respect to fractions might be interpreted as a change in calibration with no change in position of the

standard or measuring device. To illustrate this, let us compare the
length of a two-foot piece of pipe with the length of a yardstick.

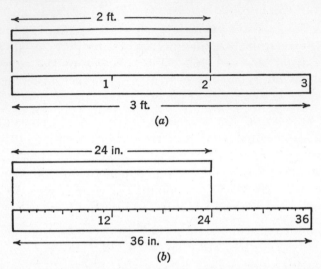

(a)

(b)

If, as in (a) above, we use the foot calibrations of the yardstick
(the basis or standard for the comparison), the pipe length (the
thing compared) is 2 feet. Hence the ratio of the pipe length to
that of the yardstick is $2:3$ or $\frac{2}{3}$. If we use the inch calibrations
of the yardstick, as in (b), the comparison of the pipe length to that
of the yardstick is $24:36$ or $\frac{24}{36}$. Applying the principle of compensation, and dividing the numerator and denominator of the
fraction $\frac{24}{36}$ by 12, the result will be $\frac{2}{3}$, the same ratio as before.
Furthermore, had we used the quarter-inch calibrations of the yard-
stick, the ratio of pipe length to yardstick length would have come
out to $96:144$ or $\frac{96}{144}$. Again, by an equal division of numerator
and denominator, $\frac{96}{144}$ can be shown to equal $\frac{2}{3}$. Hence we see that
the ratio of the length of the thing compared with the length of
whatever is the basis or standard for the comparison remains constant regardless of the calibration employed.

6. *Reductions.* When the principle of compensation with respect
to fractions is operative, the net result in each case is a change in
form without any change in value. This we recognize as a *reduction*.
At the time we first introduced the concept of reduction, it was
stated that the ultimate result of a reduction is *not* necessarily a
simpler expression or even a more abbreviated one. Consequently,
within the realm of fractions reductions are classified in two ways:

(a) *Reduction to lower terms.* This is the more appropriate use of the term "reduction," since both numerator and denominator are expressed in smaller numbers than before. It is accomplished computationally by dividing out common factors in both the numerator and denominator. When this elimination is done without the formality of a division setup, the process is known as *cancellation.* By the process of cancellation

$$\frac{60}{90} = \frac{\overset{6}{\cancel{60}}}{\underset{9}{\cancel{90}}} = \frac{6}{9}$$

and we say that the original fraction $\frac{60}{90}$ has been reduced to *lower* terms. In this particular case a further reduction beyond $\frac{6}{9}$ is possible (by dividing both numerator and denominator by 3) and the fraction is thus reduced to still lower terms:

$$\frac{\overset{2}{\cancel{6}}}{\underset{3}{\cancel{9}}} = \frac{2}{3}$$

At this point ($\frac{2}{3}$) the fraction is said to be reduced to *lowest terms*, since there exists no common integral factor (except the identity element 1) which will divide evenly both the numerator and denominator. In other words, a fraction is in lowest terms when the numerator and denominator are *relatively prime* to each other.

(b) *Reduction to higher terms.* Here the reduction operates in the opposite direction of (a) and involves multiplying numerator and denominator by some value greater than one. For example, by multiplying the numerator and denominator of the fraction $\frac{2}{3}$ by four we have

$$\frac{2}{3} = \frac{4 \times 2}{4 \times 3} = \frac{8}{12}$$

The resulting expression, $\frac{8}{12}$, is the equivalent of the fraction $\frac{2}{3}$ in value, but it is in a different form. Hence we say the fraction $\frac{2}{3}$ has been reduced to $\frac{8}{12}$. Ability to transform a fraction to its equivalent in higher terms in this way, as we shall soon see, facilitates the addition and subtraction of certain fractions.

PROBLEMS SET 20

1. Make up three simple word problems for each of the three interpretations of fractions (a), (b), and (d), page 156. Solve the problems to

see if they meet the requirements of partitive or measurement division.

2. Identify the following fractions as proper or improper, simple, complex, or mixed numbers.

(a) $\dfrac{2}{3}$ (e) $\dfrac{\frac{1}{2}}{\frac{5}{6}}$ (h) $1\frac{2}{5}$ (k) $\dfrac{3}{97}$

(b) $\dfrac{8}{2}$ (f) $\dfrac{7}{5}$ (i) $\dfrac{\frac{5}{3}}{\frac{17}{3}}$ (l) $3\frac{1}{63}$

(c) $\dfrac{3}{172}$ (g) $\dfrac{\frac{3}{7}}{\frac{4}{7}}$ (j) $\dfrac{69}{68}$ (m) $\dfrac{3}{2}$

(d) $\dfrac{3}{5}$

3. Show by a diagram and explain why:
   (a) $\frac{2}{3}$ interpreted partitively equals $\frac{8}{12}$.
   (b) $\frac{16}{20}$ interpreted partitively equals $\frac{4}{5}$.

4. Show by a diagram and explain why:
   (a) $\frac{3}{4}$ interpreted as measurement equals $\frac{9}{12}$.
   (b) $\frac{20}{28}$ interpreted as measurement equals $\frac{5}{7}$.

5. Using the principle of compensation with respect to fractions, show that the following complex and compound fractions are essentially rational fractions (fractions which can be expressed with a numerator and denominator which are integers).

(a) $\dfrac{\frac{6}{7}}{8}$ (d) $\dfrac{\frac{3}{21}}{\frac{6}{7}}$ (g) $\dfrac{6+7}{4\times 2}$ (j) $\dfrac{5-3}{8+2}$

(b) $\dfrac{\frac{3}{5}}{\frac{6}{5}}$ (e) $\dfrac{\frac{3}{17}}{\frac{7}{21}}$ (h) $\dfrac{\frac{3}{4}}{8-7}$ (k) $\dfrac{16 \div (8\times 3)}{4+17-6}$

(c) $\dfrac{4}{\frac{3}{17}}$ (f) $\dfrac{8}{\frac{3}{91}}$ (i) $\dfrac{\frac{2}{3}}{6\times 2}$ (l) $\dfrac{(24 \div 5)\times 15}{\frac{3}{4}}$

6. Reduce the following to simple fractions in lowest terms.

(a) $\dfrac{36}{48}$ (c) $\dfrac{78}{102}$ (e) $\dfrac{186}{378}$

(b) $\dfrac{28}{56}$ (d) $\dfrac{99}{144}$ (f) $\dfrac{680}{2,520}$

7. Reduce the following fractions to fractions with denominator equal to the number in parentheses.

(a) $\dfrac{2}{3}$ (6)   (e) $\dfrac{7}{8}$ (240)   (i) $\dfrac{3}{21}$ (49)   (l) $\dfrac{3}{5}$ (10)

(b) $\dfrac{3}{5}$ (100)   (f) $\dfrac{3}{31}$ (93)   (j) $\dfrac{4}{16}$ (12)   (m) $\dfrac{1}{4}$ (10)

(c) $\dfrac{4}{9}$ (27)   (g) $\dfrac{24}{36}$ (15)   (k) $\dfrac{3}{5}$ (20)   (n) $\dfrac{3}{8}$ (100)

(d) $\dfrac{3}{4}$ (100)   (h) $\dfrac{15}{40}$ (24)

8. Reduce the following fractions to fractions with *numerators* equal to the number in parentheses.

(a) $\dfrac{3}{4}$ (6)   (e) $\dfrac{2}{3}$ (16)   (i) $\dfrac{3}{24}$ (7)   (l) $\dfrac{4}{9}$ (96)

(b) $\dfrac{5}{7}$ (25)   (f) $\dfrac{3}{7}$ (21)   (j) $\dfrac{5}{20}$ (2)   (m) $\dfrac{3}{4}$ (100)

(c) $\dfrac{9}{11}$ (63)   (g) $\dfrac{18}{21}$ (6)   (k) $\dfrac{3}{8}$ (10)   (n) $\dfrac{2}{15}$ (11)

(d) $\dfrac{5}{12}$ (35)   (h) $\dfrac{7}{21}$ (4)

9. (a) What part of a day is 4 hr; 6 hr; 12 hr? (b) What part of 2 days is 4 hr; 6 hr; 12 hr?

10. Write in fraction form the following ratios.
  (a) $72 to $360
  (b) 4 yd to 17 yd
  (c) 3 yd to 20 ft
  (d) 14 oz to 3 lb
  (e) 1 mile to 84,000 in.
  (f) 3 months 6 days to 8 months 12 days
  (g) 500¢ to $8

Unit 21: Synthesis with Fractions

1. *Sequence of the Operations.* There is a certain amount of debate as to the sequence in which the basic operations of addition, subtraction, multiplication, and division of fractions should be taught. From a purely mechanical point of view there is something to be said for teaching multiplication and division first, for it is possible, using the algorisms, to produce an answer directly from the numbers as given. On the other hand, addition and subtraction of fractions frequently require an intermediate step, that of finding a common denominator, before the operation can take place.

As long ago as the Renaissance, certain writers (Pacioli, 1494; Recorde, 1542) strongly advocated a multiplication, division, addition, subtraction sequence on the grounds that the operations so ordered represented a flow from the easiest to the most difficult. Mechanically speaking, this was undoubtedly true. On the other hand, when our concern is with concepts rather than mechanics, the arrangement of the operations from the easiest to the most difficult becomes addition, subtraction, multiplication, and division. Thus in schools where meaning receives the major emphasis, this latter sequence is found to be preferable.

In this we recognize values of choosing as a common denominator the least common multiple of the denominators, referred to in arithmetic as the Least Common Denominator (LCD).

The advantages of the LCD escaped many of the early mathematicians. They generally advised adding a string of fractions by pairs, using the product of the denominators as the common denominator, then reducing before going on to the next addend.

For example, to add

$$\tfrac{3}{4} + \tfrac{1}{6} + \tfrac{3}{8} + \tfrac{1}{3}$$

fifteenth and sixteenth century mathematicians would have added

(1) $\tfrac{3}{4} + \tfrac{1}{6} = \tfrac{18}{24} + \tfrac{4}{24} = \tfrac{22}{24} = \tfrac{11}{12}$

(2) $\tfrac{11}{12} + \tfrac{3}{8} = \tfrac{88}{96} + \tfrac{36}{96} = \tfrac{124}{96} = \tfrac{31}{24}$

(3) $\tfrac{31}{24} + \tfrac{1}{3} = \tfrac{93}{72} + \tfrac{24}{72} = \tfrac{117}{72} = \tfrac{39}{24}$

Let us contrast with this the simplicity of using the LCD method:

(1) $\tfrac{3}{4} + \tfrac{1}{6} + \tfrac{3}{8} + \tfrac{1}{3}$

(2) LCD = LCM of 4, 6, 8, 3 = 24

(3) By reduction, the problem is recast as $\tfrac{18}{24} + \tfrac{4}{24} + \tfrac{9}{24} + \tfrac{8}{24}$, which equals

$$\frac{18 + 4 + 9 + 8}{24} = \frac{39}{24}$$

It is left as an exercise for the reader to demonstrate that the two remaining principles, commutation and association, are compatible with the process for adding fractions as outlined here.

3. *Multiplication of Fractions.* The second synthesizing operation is that of multiplication. Essentially, as it was explained in Chapter 2, multiplication is a shortened process of addition (when all the addends are identical), and it rests upon three basic principles: (1) association, (2) commutation, and (3) distribution. Here, too, it was seen that when the definition of number was extended to include the realm of integers in other scales, no violence was done to the basic principles. Again using the extended definition of number, which now includes rational fractions, we attempt to deduce rules of procedure (algorisms) for multiplying with fractions.

The multiplication of fractions has had an interesting history. Of particular concern to writers of the Middle Ages was the fact that the multiplication of a number by a proper fraction invariably resulted in a number *smaller* than the multiplicand. This seemed to be contrary to Scripture, which directed man to "increase and multiply and replenish the earth." To multiply, yet not increase, seemed to be inherently contradictory. Even today, a person will sometimes balk at the use of the word "times" in connection with multiplication of fractions. He will say, "Three *times* something makes sense to me; but one-half *times* something does not." The difficulty here is one of semantics and not of mathematics, for here the word "times" must be understood to have taken on a technical meaning for use within the framework of multiplication, much the same as the word "reduction" has been appropriated to signify an equivalent transformation.

In a sense "times" and "is multiplied by" are inverse expressions of each other. To demonstrate, consider the problem

$$
\begin{array}{r}
8 \\
\times 3 \\
\hline
24
\end{array}
$$

This problem may be verbalized either as "8 (multiplicand) *multiplied by* 3 (multiplier)" or to reverse this and express the multiplier first, as "3 (multiplier) *times* 8 (multiplicand)." Thus we have two ways of saying the same thing.

(a) *Multiplication of a fraction by a whole number.* To develop the algorism of multiplication with respect to fractions, let us take a direction similar to the one taken in whole numbers. Our start is made by defining multiplication as a shortened process of addition in which the addends are all exactly alike. Thus in the addition problem

$$\frac{2}{19} + \frac{2}{19} + \frac{2}{19} + \frac{2}{19} + \frac{2}{19} = \frac{10}{19}$$

we find the sum by merely adding the numerators $2 + 2 + 2 + 2 + 2$, and expressing this sum over the typical denominator. Common denominator is no problem, since the addends by definition are identical. Now by applying the basic definition of multiplication we can transform this stated addition problem to one of multiplication in which the $\frac{2}{19}$ is the typical addend and the 5 is the abstract multiplier; the product, of course, remains identical with the sum at $\frac{10}{19}$. Hence, $5 \times \frac{2}{19} = \frac{10}{19}$. Since the denominator of the typical addend remains static at 19, and the numerator of the product is the result of adding the five 2's together (the result of which can be computed more quickly by multiplying 5×2), we get the following algorism: *To multiply an integer (multiplier) times a fraction (multiplicand) multiply the integer with the numerator of the fraction and express their product as the numerator of a new fraction whose denominator is that of the original fraction.*

This can be demonstrated rather easily. Let us picture the problem, How much bread is there all together if I have four pieces, each of which is $\frac{2}{3}$ of a loaf? Computationally, the problem is

$$4 \times \frac{2}{3} = \frac{4 \times 2}{3} = \frac{8}{3}$$

Visually, here are the pieces.

Multiplication involves putting things together, so if we "synthesize" the pieces, we have collectively eight thirds (or four two-thirds):

(b) *Multiplication of a whole number by a fraction.* One direct consequence of principle M-2, the commutative law with respect to multiplication, is that multiplier and multiplicand may be interchanged without changing the product. Therefore the algorism for multiplying an integer (multiplicand) by a fraction (multiplier) is the same as before: multiply the numerator of the fraction by the integer and express the result over the denominator of the fraction.

The demonstration of this second case (fraction × integer) is quite different from the previous one (integer × fraction). Here the partitive aspect of a fraction is clearly in evidence, and as a consequence the process *could* be considered as one of division. This reflects the fact that when the definition of number is extended to include both whole numbers and fractions, the processes of multiplication and division truly merge: multiplication of a number by a unit fraction produces the same result as dividing the number by the denominator of the unit fraction (e.g., $\frac{1}{3} \times 6 = 3\overline{)6}$).

Let us consider the problem, How much is $\frac{2}{3}$ of four acres? Computationally this would be

$$\frac{2}{3} \times 4 \text{ acres} = \frac{2 \times 4}{3} = \frac{8}{3} \text{ acres}$$

Graphically, let us represent the four acres as

After dividing these four acres into three equal parts we have

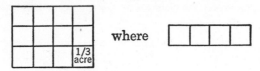

represents one-third of four acres. Crosshatching two of these three equal parts ($\frac{2}{3}$ of the four acres) we get

which is, collectively, eight one-third  acres, or $\frac{8}{3}$ acres.

(c) *Multiplication of a fraction by a fraction.* Whereas multiplication of a whole number by a fraction [(b) above] might be considered as determining a certain part of a whole or several wholes, multiplication of a fraction by a fraction might be considered as determining a part of a part.* Instead of having four acres as in (b), suppose we wish to find out how much land there is in $\frac{2}{3}$ of $\frac{4}{5}$ of an acre. First we designate the acre as

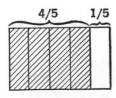

and then crosshatch $\frac{4}{5}$ of it as

---

* The algorism as developed, however, is equally valid when the fractions are improper.

Now if we subdivide this acre into thirds and crosshatch, in the opposite direction, two-thirds of it, the result is

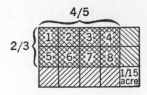

and we can see by the double crosshatched section the result of "putting together" multiplicatively $\frac{2}{3} \times \frac{4}{5}$. The horizontal and vertical lines have subdivided the original acre into 15 equal parts and the double crosshatched section contains 8 of these parts. Hence it follows that $\frac{2}{3} \times \frac{4}{5} = \frac{8}{15}$. Since the numerator of the ultimate product is the product of the numerators of the fractions, and the denominator of the ultimate product is the product of the denominators of the fractions, we have verified the basic algorism for multiplying a fraction by a fraction: *The product of two fractions is a fraction which has for its numerator the product of the two numerators, and for its denominator the product of the two denominators.*

In the development of these algorisms there have been several occasions for demonstrating the three basic principles of multiplication: association, commutation, and distribution. Specific verification of the fact that these algorisms are in full accord with these principles has been left as exercises.

4. *Cancellation in Multiplication.* Many of the early writers failed to recognize the advantages of cancellation in the multiplication of fractions. For instance, Smith* cites an illustration from the writings of Calandri (1491), who demonstrated the multiplication of

$$\tfrac{3}{4} \times \tfrac{4}{5} \quad \text{as} \quad \tfrac{3}{4} \times \tfrac{4}{5} = \tfrac{12}{20}$$

which was then reduced to $\frac{3}{5}$. As late as 1729, in the Greenwood American arithmetic, this method was still followed.

Actually cancellation in multiplication of fractions is nothing more than reducing to lower terms *before* the multiplications which lead to the ultimate numerator and denominator are undertaken. Since the factors in the multiplications concerned are going to be

* Smith, David Eugene, *History of Mathematics*, Vol. 2, Boston, Ginn & Company, 1925, p. 224.

the factors in the eventual product, cancellation merely anticipates ultimate reductions and simplifies prior to the formation of the product.

To illustrate, let us consider the problem $\frac{6}{35} \times \frac{20}{81}$, solved first without cancellation (a) and then with cancellation (b).

(a) $\dfrac{6}{35} \times \dfrac{20}{27} = \dfrac{6 \times 20}{35 \times 27} = \dfrac{120}{945}$

The highest common factor of 120 and 945 is 15. Hence

$$\frac{120 \div 15}{945 \div 15} = \frac{8}{63}$$

(b) $\dfrac{6}{35} \times \dfrac{20}{81}$

Divide 6 and 81 by 3, the 20 and 35 by 5.

$$\overset{2}{\underset{7}{\cancel{6}}} \times \overset{4}{\underset{9}{\cancel{\frac{20}{27}}}} = \frac{8}{63}$$

It is obvious that as more factors and larger factors are introduced the value of cancellation as a short cut increases.

PROBLEMS SET 21

1. Add the following; reduce answers to lowest terms.

(a) $\frac{3}{5} + \frac{1}{10}$ (c) $\frac{3}{8} + \frac{7}{40}$ (e) $\frac{3}{4} + \frac{1}{5}$ (g) $\frac{3}{8} + \frac{7}{20}$

(b) $\frac{3}{7} + \frac{2}{21}$ (d) $\frac{3}{7} + \frac{11}{63}$ (f) $\frac{2}{7} + \frac{1}{12}$ (h) $\frac{2}{9} + \frac{5}{12}$

2. Add the following, finding in each case the Least Common Denominator. Reduce answers to lowest terms.

(a) $\frac{3}{8} + \frac{1}{12} + \frac{2}{15} + \frac{3}{20}$ (d) $\frac{1}{12} + \frac{2}{32} + \frac{5}{48} + \frac{3}{64}$

(b) $\frac{1}{6} + \frac{1}{9} + \frac{1}{12} + \frac{1}{8}$ (e) $\frac{3}{20} + \frac{1}{60} + \frac{1}{90} + \frac{1}{160}$

(c) $\frac{2}{15} + \frac{7}{24} + \frac{1}{48} + \frac{3}{64}$ (f) $\frac{1}{3} + \frac{2}{17} + \frac{3}{11} + \frac{4}{5} + \frac{2}{13}$

3. Add (a) and (b) of Question 2 by the method advocated in the fifteenth and sixteenth centuries.

4. Use (c), (d), (e), and (f) of Question 2 to show that the commutative and associative law holds for the addition of fractions.

5. Multiply the following problems involving an integer and a fraction. Reduce answers to lowest terms.

(a) $\frac{3}{4} \times 2$ (c) $\frac{1}{5} \times 8$ (e) $18 \times \frac{5}{6}$

(b) $3 \times \frac{6}{13}$ (d) $\frac{3}{4} \times 12$ (f) $16 \times \frac{3}{8}$

6. Give a demonstration similar to the one in the text to show

(a) $2 \times \frac{3}{7} = \frac{6}{7}$ (c) $\frac{2}{3} \times \frac{3}{5} = \frac{2}{5}$

(b) $\frac{2}{3} \times 6 = 4$ (d) $\frac{3}{4} \times \frac{2}{9} = \frac{1}{6}$

7. Multiply the following using cancellation where possible. Reduce answers to lowest terms.

(a) $\frac{42}{63} \times \frac{5}{7}$ (c) $\frac{7}{9} \times \frac{63}{140}$ (e) $\frac{31}{79} \times \frac{43}{109}$ (g) $\frac{3}{5}(\frac{3}{9} \times \frac{5}{12})$

(b) $\frac{3}{27} \times \frac{15}{63}$ (d) $\frac{7}{12} \times \frac{3}{48}$ (f) $\frac{3}{4} \times \frac{37}{47}$ (h) $\frac{3}{5}(\frac{3}{9} + \frac{5}{12})$

8. Use the problem $\frac{3}{5} \times \frac{4}{15} \times \frac{5}{8} \times \frac{2}{3}$ to demonstrate the associative and commutative laws with respect to multiplication. Use the problem $\frac{3}{4}(\frac{1}{2} + \frac{1}{3})$ to demonstrate the distributive law.

9. A can paint a certain house in 5 days, B in 4 days, and C in 6 days. How much of the house would be painted in one day if all three painters worked together?

10. Using the three painters of Question 9, how many similar houses could be painted in 5 days?

11. If one hose fills a tank in 60 min and another in 45 min, how much of the tank would be filled after 10 min with both hoses running?

12. Three partners, A, B, and C, invested $33,000, $12,000, and $15,000, respectively, in a business, with the agreement to split profits in ratio to each partner's investment. What did each receive, if profits for the first year amounted to $14,400?

13. A family's income is $4,200 per year. If $\frac{1}{4}$ of the income goes for shelter, $\frac{5}{14}$ for food, $\frac{1}{8}$ for clothing, $\frac{1}{7}$ for miscellaneous, and the rest is saved, how many dollars are allocated to each of these categories? What fraction of the income is saved?

14. A survey shows that a cereal manufacturer's claim that "two-thirds of 3 out of 5 people eat our cereal" is in fact twice the true number. How many people out of every 100 *do* eat that cereal?

15. Discover the fallacy in this story: A farmer died and left a will which stated among other things that his eldest son was to receive one-half of the herd of cattle; the second son was willed one-third of the herd; and the youngest son one-ninth. Since there were 17 head of cattle at the time of the farmer's death, the sons were perplexed as to how to distribute the cattle. The problem was solved when a neighbor brought over one of his own cows and added it to the herd which then numbered eighteen. Whereupon the eldest son took one-half the eighteen, or nine; the second son took one-third, or six; and the youngest son one-ninth, or two head of cattle. Since nine, six, and two total seventeen, this left just one lone cow—which the neighbor led back into his barn.

Unit 22: Analysis with Fractions

1. *Subtraction of Fractions.* Analysis is the inverse or reverse process of synthesis, and subtraction is the specific inverse of addition. What addition puts together, subtraction takes apart. It can be shown that the principles of subtraction, likeness and compensation, which were first met in our discussion of whole numbers, remain equally valid when the scope of number is broadened to include fractions.

The principle of likeness, which holds that like numbers may be subtracted only from like numbers, when interpreted for fractions, implies that we may subtract fractions only when there is agreement in their denominators. When this is so, we proceed by simply reversing what we did in addition: *subtract the numerators and express the result as the numerator of a fraction whose denominator is the common denominator of the original fractions.* Thus

$$\frac{3}{8} - \frac{2}{8} = \frac{3-2}{8} = \frac{1}{8}$$

After our experience in adding unlike fractions, the technique for subtracting fractions in which the denominators differ should be obvious: *Find a common multiple of the denominators, reduce the given fraction(s) to fraction(s) having such a denominator, then proceed as in subtracting like fractions.* For example,

$$\frac{3}{4} - \frac{1}{8} = \frac{6}{8} - \frac{1}{8} = \frac{6-1}{8} = \frac{5}{8}$$

$$\frac{3}{4} - \frac{1}{6} = \frac{9}{12} - \frac{2}{12} = \frac{7}{12}$$

2. *Division of Fractions.* Today's computational techniques for division by fractions fall into one of two categories: the common denominator method or the inverted divisor method. The latter, the simpler of the two, was widely known by early Hindu and Arab mathematicians. Somehow or other, though, it was lost to most of the medieval and Renaissance scholars and its regeneration is a relatively recent event. These early European writers preferred either the common denominator method or one termed "cross multiplication" which has all the computational features of the inverted divisor method. To solve the division of one fraction by another fraction by "cross multiplication" the dividend was usually written to the right and the divisor to the left of it (the reverse of the way we do today). For example, to divide $\frac{3}{4}$ by $\frac{5}{6}$ (today $\frac{3}{4} \div \frac{5}{6}$) the fractions were written

$$\frac{5}{6} \qquad \frac{3}{4}$$

then "cross multiplied" (as indicated by the arrows):

$$\frac{5}{6} \diagdown \hspace{-0.6em} \diagup \frac{3}{4} \longrightarrow \frac{18}{20}$$

(Compare this with our "inverted divisor" approach following.)

Computationally both the common denominator and inverted divisor techniques can be justified by the principle of compensation (D-2). This principle, it will be recalled from Unit 15, holds that if the divisor and dividend are both multiplied (or divided) by the same number, not zero, the quotient remains unchanged. We shall now analyze these two currently used methods in light of this principle.

(a) *Common denominator method* (CD). Let us consider the problem $\frac{3}{4} \div \frac{5}{6}$. As in addition and subtraction, a common denominator is found for both terms before the operation is begun. In this case the LCD is 12, so the problem is reduced to $\frac{9}{12} \div \frac{10}{12}$. If we apply the principle of compensation and multiply dividend and divisor by 12, we would not affect the quotient which is the result of $9 \div 10$. Thus the denominators can be ignored once they are in agreement, and the division can be carried out by the numerators alone. To summarize:

$$\tfrac{3}{4} \div \tfrac{5}{6} = \tfrac{9}{12} \div \tfrac{10}{12} = 9 \div 10 = \tfrac{9}{10}$$

A slight variation of this approach would be to multiply both the divisor and the dividend immediately by the LCD of the two terms. This will reduce them to whole numbers, thereby transforming our division of fractions to the more familiar division of whole numbers, and yet, by our principle of compensation, not affect our ultimate quotient value. To illustrate:

$$\tfrac{3}{4} \div \tfrac{5}{6} = (12 \times \tfrac{3}{4}) \div (12 \times \tfrac{5}{6}) = 9 \div 10 = \tfrac{9}{10}$$

(b) *Inverted divisor method* (ID). Let us again consider the problem $\frac{3}{4} \div \frac{5}{6}$, but this time, in applying the principle of compensation, multiply the dividend ($\frac{3}{4}$) and the divisor ($\frac{5}{6}$) by the *reciprocal of the divisor* ($\frac{6}{5}$). A reciprocal of a fraction, or of any number for that matter, by definition is that specific number which when multiplied by the given number produces the identity element of multiplication (which is *one*). Thus $\frac{1}{3}$ is the reciprocal of 3, 7 is the reciprocal of $\frac{1}{7}$,

$\frac{3}{4}$ is the reciprocal of $\frac{4}{3}$. Accordingly our problem takes on this sequence:

$$\underbrace{\frac{3}{4} \div \frac{5}{6}}_{A} = (\frac{3}{4} \times \frac{6}{5}) \div (\frac{5}{6} \times \frac{6}{5}) = (\frac{3}{4} \times \frac{6}{5}) \div 1 = \underbrace{\frac{3}{4} \times \frac{6}{5}}_{B} = \frac{18}{20} = \frac{9}{10}$$

By ignoring what goes on in between, we can automatically get from phase A of this sequence to phase B by the widely known rule: *When dividing by a fraction, invert the divisor and multiply.*

3. *Descriptive Interpretation.* The foregoing rationalizations of the algorisms for division with fractions are entirely abstract; their logic stems directly from a mathematical framework of principles and interpretations. To repeat them in a more descriptive way—and for most a more meaningful way—requires a certain variety in illustration in order to increase the effects.

(a) *Division of a fraction by an integer.* This is best illustrated by choosing an example of partitive division. If $\frac{2}{5}$ ton of peat moss is to be shared by 3 neighbors, how much peat moss would each neighbor get? Computationally the problem is stated as $\frac{2}{5} \div 3$, and is solved, according to the two methods of the preceding section, as

CD: $\quad \frac{2}{5} \div 3 = \frac{2}{5} \div \frac{15}{5} = 2 \div 15 = \frac{2}{15}$ ton
ID: $\quad \frac{2}{5} \div 3 = \frac{2}{5} \times \frac{1}{3} = \frac{2}{15}$ ton

To demonstrate, let  represent the ton.

Subdivide it vertically into five equal parts:

Then shade two of these parts:

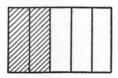

to represent $\frac{2}{5}$ of a ton. To illustrate division by 3, draw two horizontal lines cutting the original figure into three equal parts.

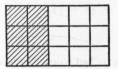

Thus 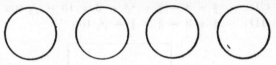 represents one of the 3 equal parts of $\frac{2}{5}$. Since there are 15 sections the size of ☐ in the whole ton, the resulting share per neighbor 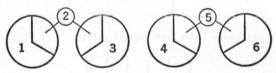 must equal $\frac{2}{15}$ ton.

    (b) *Division of an integer by a fraction.* This is best illustrated by measurement division. How many $\frac{2}{3}$-hour (40-minute) periods are there in a 4-hour interval? Solving this on an hourly basis, we would have

$$\text{CD:} \quad 4 \div \tfrac{2}{3} = \tfrac{12}{3} \div \tfrac{2}{3} = 12 \div 2$$
$$= 6 \text{ periods of } \tfrac{2}{3} \text{ hr (40 min) each}$$
$$\text{ID:} \quad 4 \div \tfrac{2}{3} = 4 \times \tfrac{3}{2} = \tfrac{12}{2}$$
$$= 6 \text{ periods of } \tfrac{2}{3} \text{ hr (40 min) each}$$

Visually, let the following circles represent the four hours.

Now, taking $\frac{2}{3}$ of a circle at a time,

we can see that there are collectively six two-thirds hours

in the four hours.

    (c) *Division of a fraction by a fraction.* Again let us draw our illustration from measurement division. If it takes $\frac{2}{9}$ pound of meat to make a hamburger, how many hamburgers can one get from $\frac{2}{3}$ pound of meat?

Computationally the problem can be solved as

CD: $\frac{2}{3} \div \frac{2}{9} = \frac{6}{9} \div \frac{2}{9} = 6 \div 2 = 3$ hamburgers

ID: $\frac{2}{3} \div \frac{2}{9} = \frac{2}{3} \times \frac{9}{2} = \frac{3}{1} = 3$ hamburgers

Graphically, let the shaded part represent $\frac{2}{3}$ pound of meat,

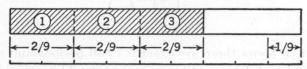

and let the scale below subdivide the pound into nine equal parts. Then with a unit equal to $\frac{2}{9}$ "measure" the existing $\frac{2}{3}$ pound of meat. Result: 3 hamburgers.

4. *Remainders.* For purposes of explanation, the division examples and illustrations chosen so far in this unit have been exact. We now turn to cases of inexact division, or division with a remainder.

Thinking in terms of repeated subtraction offers the best approach to an understanding of remainders in division. Let us begin with a problem similar to the one in the previous section, but involving a remainder—or as some refer to it, an undivided dividend —that must be interpreted.

How many $\frac{2}{3}$-hr (40-min) periods are there in a 5-hr interval?

As before, let the circles represent the full hours in the interval

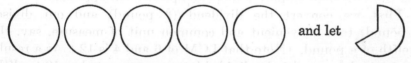 **and let**

represent a $\frac{2}{3}$-hour period. Again we form and remove as many $\frac{2}{3}$ circles as possible from the five circles (repeated subtraction). Thus we can see that there are in the five hours (circles) seven complete

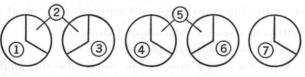

$\frac{2}{3}$-hour periods, 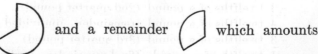 and a remainder   which amounts

to $\frac{1}{3}$ hour. But we must be careful in making our number statement of this situation: remember we are interested in *how many* $\frac{2}{3}$

hours there are in the five, and our remainder of $\frac{1}{3}$ hour is exactly half of the $\frac{2}{3}$-hour period:

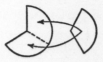

Hence, in five hours there are exactly 7 full periods and a $\frac{1}{2}$ period (or $7\frac{1}{2}$ periods) of $\frac{2}{3}$ hour (40 minutes) each. This coincides with a statement that was made in our discussion of remainders in Unit 15 to the effect that in measurement division (of which this is an instance) the remainder is expressed in the quotient as a part of the *divisor*.

Computationally this solution can be verified by

CD: $5 \div \frac{2}{3} = \frac{15}{3} \div \frac{2}{3} = 15 \div 2$
                    $= \frac{15}{2} = 7\frac{1}{2}$ periods of $\frac{2}{3}$ hr (40 min) each

ID: $5 \div \frac{2}{3} = 5 \times \frac{3}{2} = \frac{15}{2}$
                    $= 7\frac{1}{2}$ periods of $\frac{2}{3}$ hr (40 min) each

Let us consider another illustration involving a remainder, this time arising from division of a fraction by a fraction.

How many quarter pounds are there in $\frac{5}{6}$ lb?

Division in terms of repeated subtraction is still the most effective avenue to understanding and interpreting the remainder, although this time we shall employ a more computational approach.

First we convert the dividend ($\frac{5}{6}$ pound) and our divisor ($\frac{1}{4}$ pound) to a convenient and common unit of measure, say, the twelfth of a pound. (Note that LCM of 6 and 4 is 12.) As a result, our original $\frac{5}{6}$ pound to be divided is now represented as 10 twelfths of a pound and our quarter-pound divisor is now represented as 3 twelfths of a pound. In order to answer the question how many quarter pounds there are in the original amount, we proceed experimentally by removing quarter-pound equivalents one at a time.

     10 twelfths of a pound (the original amount)
    $\underline{-3}$ twelfths of a pound (1st quarter pound)
      7 twelfths of a pound (remainder—undivided dividend)
    $\underline{-3}$ twelfths of a pound (2nd quarter pound)
      4 twelfths of a pound (remainder—undivided dividend)
    $\underline{-3}$ twelfths of a pound (3rd quarter pound)
      1 twelfth of a pound (final remainder—undivided dividend)

By this successive removal of quarter-pound lots from the original $\frac{5}{6}$ pound, it was possible to realize 3 full quarter pounds and still have, as yet unremoved, 1 twelfth of a pound. Since our problem is interested in the *number of quarter pounds* in the $\frac{5}{6}$ pounds, the remaining twelfth of a pound represents a part $\left(\dfrac{1 \text{ twelfth}}{3 \text{ twelfths}} = \dfrac{1}{3}\right)$ of what would have been the next or fourth quarter pound. Hence in $\frac{5}{6}$ pound we state that there are $3\frac{1}{3}$ quarter pounds.

Computationally this can be verified by

CD: $\quad \frac{5}{6} \div \frac{1}{4} = \frac{10}{12} \div \frac{3}{12} = 10 \div 3 = \frac{10}{3} = 3\frac{1}{3}$ quarter pounds

ID: $\quad \frac{5}{6} \div \frac{1}{4} = \frac{5}{6} \times \frac{4}{1} = \frac{20}{6} = 3\frac{2}{6} = 3\frac{1}{3}$ quarter pounds

PROBLEMS SET 22

1. Subtract the following; reduce answers to lowest terms.

(a) $\frac{4}{5} - \frac{3}{5}$ (c) $\frac{3}{10} - \frac{3}{38}$ (e) $\frac{9}{35} - \frac{3}{14}$

(b) $\frac{3}{7} - \frac{2}{14}$ (d) $\frac{4}{25} - \frac{6}{50}$ (f) $\frac{17}{48} - \frac{11}{45}$

2. Perform the following divisions by the common denominator method; reduce quotients to lowest terms.

(a) $\frac{3}{8} \div \frac{3}{4}$ (c) $\frac{8}{17} \div \frac{3}{5}$ (e) $\frac{14}{27} \div \frac{7}{9}$ (g) $\frac{63}{360} \div \frac{28}{45}$

(b) $\frac{3}{7} \div \frac{5}{9}$ (d) $\frac{6}{27} \div \frac{12}{35}$ (f) $\frac{1}{2} \div \frac{7}{6}$ (h) $\left(\frac{3}{7} - \frac{1}{14}\right) \div \frac{35}{99}$

3. Perform the division problems of Question 2 by the inverted divisor method; reduce quotient to lowest terms.

4. Demonstrate with sketches (a) $\frac{3}{4} \div 4$, (b) $6 \div \frac{3}{4}$, (c) $\frac{2}{3} \div \frac{1}{6}$.

5. Demonstrate the following problems and interpret the remainder. Verify your solution computationally.

(a) How many autos can be repainted in 4 days if one can be painted in $\frac{3}{5}$ of a day?

(b) How many $\frac{2}{5}$ gal are there in $\frac{13}{15}$ gal?

6. How much must be added to $\frac{2}{7}$ of a number to equal $\frac{2}{3}$ of that number?

7. A worker filling bottles has completed $\frac{3}{5}$ of one lot. If he has 84 bottles more to fill, how many bottles are in the full lot?

8. A piece of cardboard is $\frac{3}{64}$ in. thick. How many pieces would there be in a pile $\frac{3}{4}$ in. high?

9. How many weights of $\frac{1}{8}$ pound are necessary to balance a weight of $\frac{3}{4}$ lb?

10. Will it be possible to balance $\frac{3}{4}$ lb, using only weights which are $\frac{1}{6}$ lb each?

11. Work this problem as a demonstration of the distributive law in two ways: A man, giving away samples, started with a full bag of 48. He gave out $\frac{1}{2}$ of them, then picked up another $\frac{1}{3}$ of a bagful, then gave away

$\frac{3}{8}$ of a bag, and finally picked up another $\frac{1}{8}$ of a bagful. How many samples did he have in his bag at this point?

12. How many canfuls of water must be dumped over the side of a boat if 35 gal must be bailed out with a can which has a capacity of $\frac{3}{4}$ gal, and a hole in the bottom which allows $\frac{1}{6}$ gal to escape each time before the contents are dumped over the side?

Unit 23: Mixed Numbers

1. *Reductions with Mixed Numbers.* In Unit 21 we defined mixed numbers as the indicated or abbreviated sum of an integer and a proper fraction. Since both integers and the proper fractions have been identified as being rational numbers, and since the rationals are closed for the process of addition, it follows that mixed numbers, as we have defined them, are also rational numbers. In terms of our number line the positive mixed numbers fall to the right of one and at points other than those which designate the positions of the integers. For example,

Since mixed numbers are rational numbers, it follows that they too should be ultimately reducible to a fraction of two integers. We now establish the technique for doing this.

(a) *Reduction of a mixed number to common fraction form.* A mixed number, we have said, represents the sum of two unlike numbers (integer and fraction); to add them, the principle of likeness requires a change in denomination of at least one of them so that they will be alike. For example, we know that the mixed number $8\frac{2}{3}$ can be interpreted as $8 + \frac{2}{3}$. In order to add them we reduce the 8 to thirds ($\frac{24}{3}$) and proceed as in addition of fractions.

$$8 + \tfrac{2}{3} = \tfrac{24}{3} + \tfrac{2}{3} = \tfrac{26}{3}$$

Because of the nature of mixed numbers, it is to be expected that their common fraction equivalents will invariably be improper fractions.

Notice that the common rule for converting a mixed number to an improper fraction, *"multiply the whole number by the denominator of the fraction part, then add the numerator of the fraction part, and express the sum over the denominator of the fraction part,"* is but an abbreviated version of this concept. Applied to our $8\frac{2}{3}$, it directs us to multiply the 8 by the 3, add the 2 for 26, then express the 26 over the 3.

Stated algebraically, this rule can be made even clearer. Thus if $a + \dfrac{b}{c}$ is a mixed number, then

$$a + \frac{b}{c} = \frac{ac}{c} + \frac{b}{c} = \frac{ac + b}{c}$$

Furthermore, since a, b, and c are integers and consequently rational numbers, and since the rationals are closed for addition, multiplication, and division $\left(\text{the operations implied by } \dfrac{ac + b}{c}\right)$ we verify that $\dfrac{ac + b}{c}$ must also be a rational number.

(b) *Reduction of an improper fraction to a mixed number.* Reducing an improper fraction to a mixed number is, of course, the inverse operation of (a). Here it is fruitful to use the basic interpretation of a fraction as a form of the quotient of two numbers. By dividing the larger numerator by the smaller denominator, expressing whatever the remainder happens to be as a part of the divisor, we have produced the same quotient value, only in mixed number form. (Provided, of course, the improper fraction was not reducible to an integer, as it is when the remainder is zero.) For instance, to reduce the improper fraction $\frac{29}{6}$ to a mixed number, we divide 29 by 6 and get a whole number quotient of 4 and a remainder of 5. Hence $\frac{29}{6} = 4\frac{5}{6}$.

2. *Synthesis with Mixed Numbers*

(a) *Addition.* In the addition of mixed numbers we hold to the principle of likeness for our direction. That is, we add fractions to fractions, whole numbers to whole numbers. When the denominators among the fractions are not alike, it is necessary first to reduce the given fractions to fractions with a common denominator. If after the fractions are added they result in an improper fraction (a value greater than one), this fraction is reduced to a mixed number; the proper fraction part is then written down, and the whole number part "carried" into addition with the wholes. To illustrate:

$$
\begin{array}{lll}
17\frac{2}{3} & = 17\frac{8}{12} & \left(\frac{8}{12} + \frac{5}{12} + \frac{6}{12} = \frac{19}{12} = 1\frac{7}{12}\right) \quad 17\frac{8}{12} \\
24\frac{5}{12} & = 24\frac{5}{12} & (17 + 24 + 16 = 57) \qquad\qquad\quad 24\frac{5}{12} \\
16\frac{1}{2} & = 16\frac{6}{12} & \qquad\qquad\qquad\qquad\qquad\qquad\quad \underline{16\frac{6}{12}} \\
& & \qquad\qquad\qquad\qquad\qquad\qquad\quad 58\frac{7}{12}
\end{array}
$$

(b) *Multiplication.* Since mixed numbers may be reduced to improper fractions, one approach for multiplying mixed numbers is to reduce both the multiplier and multiplicand to improper fractions and proceed according to the rules for multiplying fractions. For example,

$$3\frac{2}{5} \times 6\frac{5}{8} = \frac{17}{5} \times \frac{53}{8} = \frac{17 \times 53}{5 \times 8} = \frac{901}{40} = 22\frac{21}{40}$$

In certain cases a second approach, which adheres closely to the principle of distribution, is preferable. Let us consider two cases using this approach, first multiplication of a mixed number by a whole number, then multiplication of a mixed number by a mixed number.

(1) Multiplication of a mixed number by a whole number. Let

$$32\frac{2}{3}$$
$$\times 17$$

be the problem. This may be restated, expressing the mixed-numbered multiplicand as the sum which it is, as $17(32 + \frac{2}{3})$. By the principle of distribution this product is equal to

$$
\begin{array}{r}
32\frac{2}{3} \\
17 \\
\hline
224 \\
32 \\
11\frac{1}{3} \\
\hline
555\frac{1}{3}
\end{array}
\quad
\begin{array}{l}
\left.\vphantom{\begin{array}{c}224\\32\end{array}}\right\} \quad 17 \times 32 \\
\} \quad 17 \times \frac{2}{3}
\end{array}
$$

A second illustration of this type:

$$42(37 + \tfrac{3}{4}) = (42 \times 37) + (42 \times \tfrac{3}{4})$$

or

$$
\begin{array}{r}
37\frac{3}{4} \\
42 \\
\hline
74 \\
148 \\
31\frac{1}{2} \\
\hline
1585\frac{1}{2}
\end{array}
\quad
\begin{array}{l}
\left.\vphantom{\begin{array}{c}74\\148\end{array}}\right\} \quad 42 \times 37 \\
\} \quad 42 \times \frac{3}{4}
\end{array}
$$

(2) Multiplication of a mixed number by a mixed number. This algorism requires the double use of the principle of distribution (M-3). For example,

$$
\begin{aligned}
32\tfrac{3}{5} \times 45\tfrac{3}{4} &= (32\tfrac{3}{5}) \times (45\tfrac{3}{4}) \\
&= (32\tfrac{3}{5}) \times (45 + \tfrac{3}{4}) \\
&= (32\tfrac{3}{5} \times 45) + (32\tfrac{3}{5} \times \tfrac{3}{4})
\end{aligned}
\quad \left.\vphantom{\begin{array}{c}1\\1\\1\end{array}}\right\} \quad \text{M-3 once}
$$

$$= [(32 + \tfrac{3}{5}) \times 45] + [(32 + \tfrac{3}{5}) \times \tfrac{3}{4}] \longleftarrow \text{M-3 twice}$$

$$= [(32 \times 45) + (\tfrac{3}{5} \times 45)] + [(32 \times \tfrac{3}{4}) + (\tfrac{3}{5} \times \tfrac{3}{4})]$$

$$= 1{,}440 \quad\quad + \quad 27 \quad + \quad 24 \quad + \quad \tfrac{9}{20}$$

$$= 1{,}491\tfrac{9}{20}$$

Arranging this problem in a more familiar pattern we have

$$
\begin{array}{l}
45\tfrac{3}{4} \\
32\tfrac{3}{5} \\
\hline
90 \\
135 \\
27 \\
24 \\
\tfrac{9}{20} \\
\hline
1491\tfrac{9}{20}
\end{array}
$$

$$\left.\begin{array}{l}90\\135\end{array}\right\} \longrightarrow (32 \times 45)$$
$$27 \longrightarrow (\tfrac{3}{5} \times 45)$$
$$24 \longrightarrow (\tfrac{3}{4} \times 32)$$
$$\tfrac{9}{20} \longrightarrow (\tfrac{3}{5} \times \tfrac{3}{4})$$

3. *Analysis with Mixed Numbers*

(a) *Subtraction.* In the subtraction of mixed numbers, once again the principle of likeness is adhered to as we subtract fractions from fractions and whole numbers from whole numbers. When the denominators of the fractional parts disagree, a common denominator is again necessary before the operation can begin. Thus

$$
\begin{array}{l}
47\tfrac{2}{3} = 47\tfrac{4}{6} \\
12\tfrac{1}{2} = 12\tfrac{3}{6} \\
\hline
\phantom{12\tfrac{1}{2} = } 35\tfrac{1}{6}
\end{array}
$$

When the fractional part of the minuend is less than the fractional part of the subtrahend, the computational impasse is resolved as it is in whole numbers when a deficiency occurs in one of the orders of the minuend, i.e., by decomposition or by equal additions.

(1) *Decomposition method:*

(a) $47\tfrac{2}{5}$ (b) $47\tfrac{2}{5} = 40 + 7 + \tfrac{2}{5}$ (c) $46\tfrac{7}{5}$

$\;23\tfrac{4}{5}$ $= 40 + 6 + 1 + \tfrac{2}{5}$ $23\tfrac{4}{5}$

$\phantom{(a)\;23\tfrac{4}{5}(b)\;47\tfrac{2}{5}}= (40 + 6) + (1 + \tfrac{2}{5})$ $23\tfrac{3}{5}$

$\phantom{(a)\;23\tfrac{4}{5}(b)\;47\tfrac{2}{5}}= 46 + \tfrac{7}{5}$

The problem is stated in (a) with the fractional part ($\tfrac{2}{5}$) of the minuend being less than the fractional part ($\tfrac{4}{5}$) of the subtrahend. The units digit of the minuend, 7, is thereupon decomposed or reduced to $6 + 1$ as in (b) and the 1 is further reduced to $\tfrac{5}{5}$ and added to the deficient $\tfrac{2}{5}$ to make $\tfrac{7}{5}$. Thus the obstacle is removed and the subtraction can proceed as in (c).

(2) *Equal additions method:*

$$
\begin{array}{lll}
\text{(a)} \quad 47\frac{2}{5} & \text{(b)} \quad 47\frac{2}{5} + 1 = 47\frac{7}{5} & \text{(c)} \quad 47\frac{7}{5} \\
\qquad\; 23\frac{4}{5} & \qquad\; 23\frac{4}{5} + 1 = 24\frac{4}{5} & \qquad\; 24\frac{4}{5} \\
& & \qquad\; 23\frac{3}{5}
\end{array}
$$

In (a) the previous problem is repeated. By the compensation (S-2) principle, to add a like amount to minuend and subtrahend will not affect the remainder. So in this case we add one to both terms, only we add it to the minuend as $\frac{5}{5}$ and to the subtrahend as 1 unit, as in (b). Once more the impasse has been removed and the subtraction may proceed as in (c). (Note that each term in (c) is greater by one than that given in the original problem.)

(b) *Division.* The most effective attack upon division of mixed numbers is to reduce them to improper fractions and then proceed according to the rules laid down for division of fractions. Thus

$$6\frac{2}{3} \div 2\frac{3}{4} = \frac{20}{3} \div \frac{11}{4}$$

By CD: $\frac{20}{3} \div \frac{11}{4} = \frac{80}{12} \div \frac{33}{12} = 80 \div 33 = 2\frac{14}{33}$

ID: $\frac{20}{3} \div \frac{11}{4} = \frac{20}{3} \times \frac{4}{11} = \frac{80}{33} = 2\frac{14}{33}$

A variation is to treat the division problem initially as a complex fraction.

$$6\frac{2}{3} \div 2\frac{3}{4} \longrightarrow \frac{6\frac{2}{3}}{2\frac{3}{4}}$$

Then multiply numerator and denominator of this complex fraction by the least common denominator of the fraction parts.

$$\frac{6\frac{2}{3}}{2\frac{3}{4}} \xrightarrow{\;\;(\text{LCD}=12)\;\;} \frac{12 \times 6\frac{2}{3}}{12 \times 2\frac{3}{4}} \rightarrow \frac{80}{33} = 2\frac{14}{33}$$

For dividing mixed numbers there is no effective algorism which parallels the whole number algorism, (e.g. $2\frac{3}{4}\overline{)6\frac{2}{3}}$). Of course the problem could be done following the steps of the whole number algorism because the principles which give form to these algorisms are not influenced by the accidental nature of the numbers. From a practical point, however, the tedium involved in this approach makes it not worth the effort.

PROBLEMS SET 23

1. Convert the following mixed numbers to improper fractions.

(a) $6\frac{2}{3}$ (b) $7\frac{5}{8}$ (c) $16\frac{3}{16}$ (d) $4\frac{2}{7}$ (e) $1\frac{1}{8}$ (f) $12\frac{1}{4}$

2. Convert the following improper fractions to mixed numbers.

(a) $\frac{87}{9}$ (b) $\frac{46}{5}$ (c) $\frac{32}{7}$ (d) $\frac{1132}{75}$ (e) $\frac{424}{16}$ (f) $\frac{301}{150}$

3. Add:

   (a) $8\frac{2}{3} + 6\frac{5}{12} + 7\frac{3}{4} + 10\frac{1}{3}$

   (b) $146\frac{2}{5} + 32\frac{7}{18} + 46\frac{7}{9}$

   (c) $42\frac{3}{4} + 51\frac{7}{8} + 37\frac{2}{15}$

4. Subtract by decomposition:

   (a) $29\frac{2}{5} - 17\frac{3}{5}$ (d) $14\frac{3}{7} - 10\frac{5}{8}$

   (b) $32\frac{6}{7} - 14\frac{2}{5}$ (e) $32\frac{5}{8} - 16\frac{5}{7}$

   (c) $37\frac{1}{4} - 14\frac{3}{4}$ (f) $42\frac{4}{9} - 20\frac{5}{8}$

5. Subtract the problems of Question 4 using the equal additions method.

6. Multiply the following by converting to improper fractions. Express products as mixed numbers.

   (a) $16\frac{2}{3} \times 8\frac{3}{5}$ (c) $4\frac{4}{11} \times 9\frac{5}{8}$

   (b) $9\frac{4}{7} \times 4\frac{1}{5}$ (d) $2\frac{4}{7} \times 1\frac{7}{9} \times 10\frac{1}{2}$

7. Multiply the following *without* converting to improper fractions.

   (a) $14\frac{7}{9} \times 18\frac{2}{7}$ (c) $38\frac{2}{3} \times 462\frac{3}{10}$

   (b) $35\frac{3}{4} \times 864\frac{2}{5}$ (d) $66\frac{3}{11} \times 189\frac{2}{7}$

8. Divide the resulting products of the four multiplication problems of Question 7 by one of the factors. The quotient should be the other factor.

9. (a) What happens to the sum of two numbers if one is increased by $36\frac{3}{8}$ and the other by $18\frac{5}{14}$?

   (b) What happens to the remainder if the minuend is increased by $17\frac{2}{5}$ and the subtrahend is decreased by $3\frac{4}{7}$?

   (c) What happens to the product of two numbers if one is multiplied by $3\frac{1}{5}$ and the other is multiplied by $13\frac{1}{2}$?

   (d) What happens to the quotient of two numbers if the divisor is multiplied by $16\frac{2}{3}$ and if the dividend is multiplied by $16\frac{2}{3}$?

   (e) How many times larger will a number be if it is divided by $\frac{12}{57}$?

   (f) What change will there be in a number that is multiplied by $3\frac{1}{4}$ and divided by $\frac{4}{13}$?

   (g) What change will there be in the remainder if the minuend is increased by $37\frac{3}{8}$ and the subtrahend is increased by $19\frac{4}{5}$?

10. A board $7\frac{1}{8}$ ft long was cut into 3 pieces. One piece was $2\frac{1}{4}$ ft long and a second $3\frac{1}{3}$ ft long. Considering the fact that $\frac{1}{72}$ ft was lost in sawdust with each cut, how long was the remaining board?

11. John's uncle is $6\frac{1}{4}$ times as old as his nephew, who is $7\frac{1}{3}$ times as old as my little sister, who is $1\frac{1}{2}$ yr old. How old is John's uncle?

12. (a) What number multiplied by $6\frac{7}{8}$ yields a product of $114\frac{7}{12}$?

   (b) What number added to $18\frac{3}{8}$ equals $35\frac{6}{35}$?

(c) What number divided by $16\frac{2}{9}$ yields a quotient of $17\frac{1}{4}$?

(d) What number when multiplied by $4\frac{2}{5}$, then increased by $7\frac{1}{2}$, equals 24?

Unit 24: Decimal Fractions

1. *Origins.* In the several centuries before the advent of printing (mid-fifteenth century) computational arithmetic functioned on two levels, the mercantile level and the scientific level, the latter notably in astronomy. In the mercantile world practical considerations automatically restricted fractions to those of a relatively simple type. In the world of astronomy, where accuracy was important and small divisions and parts were frequent, a more accurate and flexible notation was necessary. Here the sexagesimals were used and were apparently sufficiently adequate, for they are still in use today (degrees, minutes, and seconds). Coincident with the advent of printing, excesses in fractions, far beyond all practical limitations, tended to mount. For instance, Smith* mentions a problem found in Coutereels' work (1658) which gives a result in days as

$$2\,\frac{1724912242}{3377560879}\ \text{days}$$

Gradually the need for a notation of fractions that was simpler and more manageable than either the common fraction or the sexagesimals became increasingly pressing. As far back as the time of the early Hindus there is evidence of some insight into the possibilities of extending the concept of the decimal system of whole number notation to include fractions, but nothing specific developed. Many of the early writers in the fifteen and sixteenth centuries showed by their works that they too had more or less hazy notions concerning decimals as we know them today, but still the total concept remained elusive. According to Smith,† Christoff Rudolff, in 1530 in his *Exempel-Buchlin*, showed the earliest comprehensive grasp of decimal fractions, but unfortunately his work was not fully promulgated or appreciated. Half a century later, in 1585, Simon Stevin, a Dutch mathematician, published a book on the subject which is usually credited with being at least the first formal introduction of man to decimal fractions. This book, written in Flemish, and best known in a French translation under the title of *La Disme*,

* Smith, D. E., *History of Mathematics*, Vol. 2, Ginn & Company, Boston, 1925, 1953, p. 235.

† *Ibid.*, p. 240.

outlined methods by which business calculations involving fractions could be computed as though they involved only integers. Stevin was so convinced of its merits that he proposed that the government adopt and require the use of such a system, thus foreshadowing what eventually occurred, as governments, by decree, established for their countries the metric system of measurement.

The work of Stevin was an attempt to associate the essential features of the astronomer's sexagesimal fractions with the place value principle of the Hindu-Arabic system. While this proved to be an extremely fruitful venture, Stevin's work did suffer the unfortunate lack of an adequate symbolism. In an attempt to overcome this defect, a variety of symbolisms ran rampant as the use of decimals became increasingly widespread. Below are a few of the suggestions made by some of these early writers. In each case the symbolism is intended to represent the number which would be written today in this country as 364.8231

$$\text{(a)} \qquad 364^\circ\ 8'\ 2''\ 3'''\ 1''''$$
$$\text{(b)} \qquad 364/8231$$
$$\text{(c)} \qquad 364,\ 8'\ 2''\ 3'''\ 1''''$$
$$\text{(d)} \qquad 3648231_{\textcircled{4}}$$
$$\text{(e)} \qquad \overset{0\,1\,2\,3\,4}{3648231}$$

As a matter of fact, even today there is by no means universal agreement throughout the world on the writing of a decimal fraction. In this country a point, known as the decimal point, is written at the lowest level between the last digit of the whole part and the first digit of the fractional part. In England a point is also used, but it is located a half space higher. Thus

$$\text{forty-six and three tenths} = 46.3 \text{ (U.S.)}$$
$$= 46 \cdot 3 \text{ (England)}*$$

In some countries of Europe (France, Belgium, Germany, Italy, and the Scandinavian countries) the comma is used in place of our decimal point.

2. *Fractions and the Decimal System of Notation.* As was stated in Unit 20, the terms *common fraction* and *decimal fraction* refer only to the *form* in which the fraction is expressed. Thus $\frac{3}{10}$ is the com-

---

* In the United States we use the dot, elevated one-half space, to represent multiplication: $3 \times 6 = 3 \cdot 6 = 18$; in England the reverse is true: there $3 \times 6 = 3.6 = 18$.

mon fraction expression of a certain part, while .3 is its equivalent in decimal fraction form.

Prior to the introduction of decimal fractions, the decimal system of notation commenced with units on the right and extended indefinitely to the left, as each successive place, counting to the left, represented a power of ten one greater than its neighbor to the right. To state this fact a bit differently, each successive place can be thought of as $\frac{1}{10}$ the size of its neighbor to the left. Thus the hundreds place (3rd order) is $\frac{1}{10}$ that of thousands (the 4th order and the one to the left of hundreds); tens are $\frac{1}{10}$ the size of hundreds; units are $\frac{1}{10}$ the size of tens. By extension, should we create a place to the right of units, it would logically represent a size $\frac{1}{10}$ that of unity, or simply *tenths*.

Once to the right of unity we move on to the second place, which would be $\frac{1}{10}$ of a tenth, or $\frac{1}{100}$ (*hundredth*); the third order to the right of unity would be $\frac{1}{10}$ of a hundredth (*thousandth*); and

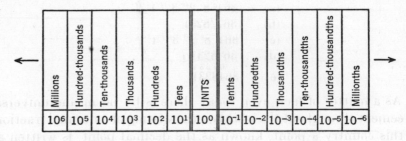

Figure 19. Decimal numeration scheme.

so on. Figure 19 gives schematically the value of the six places both to the right and to the left of unity together with their names and exponential equivalents.

Thus by this extension of the decimal system of notation, we have a system which extends indefinitely to the left and indefinitely to the right, with the units place occupying a center position. It is important to make a special note of the symmetry, or similarity of place names, in this system when it is viewed relative to the *units place*. For instance, thousands is the third order to the left of the units order and thousandths is the third order to the right of the units order; millions is the sixth order to the left and millionths is the sixth to the right of the units order.

Before the decimal system was extended into the realm of fractions, interpretation of a number's value hinged in a twofold way upon the value represented by each digit (face value) and its location relative to the units digit (place value). Then there was no need to specify what was what in, say, a three-digit number such as 438: clearly by virtue of their location the 8 represented 8 units, the 3 represented 3 tens, and the 4 represented 4 hundreds. Conversely, the sum of $(4 \times 100) + (3 \times 10) + (8 \times 1)$ can be simply written as 438. Now, suppose we wish to express the sum of $(4 \times 100) +$ $(3 \times 10) + (8 \times 1) + (7 \times \frac{1}{10}) + (3 \times \frac{1}{100})$ with our place value system of notation. So long as the scheme and headings are maintained the interpretation is obvious. Thus

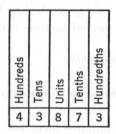

But when this scheme is removed and we depend upon relative place value only, the 43873 becomes meaningless unless we know which digit stands for unity. The need, therefore, for some sort of designator of the unit digit is obvious. In this country the designator is the dot known as the decimal point. Thus *the primary function of the decimal point is to designate the location of the units digit in a place value number expression.* By arbitrary convention it is placed at the lower level and *to the right* of the units digit. In view of its primary function it probably would have been more logical to place the decimal point either above the units digit or below it, as 43˙873 or 43.873.

Since the decimal point is in fact located to the right of the units digit, a *secondary* function can be ascribed to this dot: it separates the whole and the fractional parts of the number expression. Unquestionably far more people are conscious of this secondary role of the decimal point, that of a separatrix, than the primary one, that of a units designator. This is because most people are not fully conscious of the *systematic scheme* of our system of notation, but when the whole matter is put into its historical perspective, the essential and primary meaning of this designator becomes clear.

3. *Numeration.* Numeration, it will be recalled, is the technique of reading numbers. How to read whole numbers expressed in the decimal system of notation has already been discussed in Unit 4

and the usual way of reading fractions ($\frac{2}{3}$ as "two-thirds," $\frac{3}{10}$ as "three-tenths," and so on) in Unit 20. By definition a decimal fraction is one whose denominator is fixed at some power of ten. As a consequence, verbalizing such fractions will involve only so many tenths, so many hundredths, so many thousandths, etc.—nowhere is there to be heard a "so many thirds," or a "so many fifths," "so many seventeenths," etc., for 3, 5, and 17 are not powers of ten.

Let us proceed from what is known to what is new by a series of steps. Below are several common fractions whose denominators are powers of ten and which we can verbalize by the standard pattern. The denominators in the verbalizations are italicized.

$$\frac{3}{10} = \text{three } \textit{tenths}$$

$$\frac{47}{100} = \text{forty-seven } \textit{hundredths}$$

$$\frac{642}{1000} = \text{six hundred forty-two } \textit{thousandths}$$

$$\frac{74}{10000} = \text{seventy-four } \textit{ten-thousandths}$$

Let us now reconstruct our scheme of decimal fraction notation and put each of these four illustrative fractions in it. Note that there is no need for a decimal point as long as the scheme is present. The technique for reading from this scheme agrees with that which was established in our work with whole numbers (Section 7 of Unit 4).

Tens	*Units*	*Tenths*	*Hundredths*	*Thousandths*	*Ten-thousandths*		
		3				$\frac{3}{10}$	(three *tenths*)
	4	7				$\frac{47}{100}$	(forty-seven *hundredths*)
	6	4	2			$\frac{642}{1000}$	(six hundred forty-two *thousandths*)
			7	4		$\frac{74}{10000}$	(seventy-four *ten-thousandths*)

If the scheme is removed, and the principle of place value takes over, the need for the decimal point or units designator is seen. As has been stated, by convention in this country the decimal point lies after the units digit and before the tenths digit. And so our fractions become

$$.3 = \text{three tenths}$$
$$.47 = \text{forty-seven hundredths}$$
$$.642 = \text{six hundred forty-two thousandths}$$

In the case of $\frac{74}{10000}$ the need for two zero-spacers becomes evident and so

$$.0074 = \text{seventy-four ten-thousandths}$$

This duplication in numeration between common fractions and decimal fractions helps point up the fact that the difference between a common fraction and a decimal fraction is purely one of form. Thus, when the fraction is expressed in decimal form, the sequence of digits, which are read as though they represented an integer, corresponds to the common fraction's numerator; the position of the last digit to the right in this sequence determines the name (or size) of the fraction, and therefore corresponds to the common fraction's denominator.

Frequently a distinction is drawn between pure decimals and mixed decimals. A *pure decimal* is one which represents a number between 0 and 1 (or one whose equivalent common fraction expression is a proper fraction). The decimal expressions above are of this type. A *mixed decimal* is one which represents a number in excess of 1 (or one whose common fraction equivalent is an improper fraction) and is the counterpart of what we have defined earlier as a mixed number.

Numeration for the pure decimal, we have seen, coincides with the numeration for its common fraction equivalent. Similarly, numeration for the mixed decimal coincides with that for the mixed number. The word "and," which properly falls between the whole part and the fraction part, automatically marks the location of the decimal point. Thus $23\frac{7}{100}$ would be read as "twenty-three *and* seven hundredths"; its decimal form (23.07) is read in an identical manner.

Technically speaking, in reading a number, the word "and" is reserved for indicating the break between the whole and fractional part of the number expression. For the mixed decimal this implies that whatever number statement precedes the word "and" is the whole number part, and whatever follows the word "and" is the fractional part. Consequently such expressions as "four hundred *and* twenty" or "six hundred *and* twelve" are violations of a convention whose purpose is to remove ambiguity from number expression. To illustrate:

"one hundred sixty-four thousandths" is .164
"one hundred *and* sixty-four thousandths" is 100.064

It must be said, however, that this convention is rather roundly disregarded by all save the more mathematically precise.

Today there is an increasing trend toward the more modern numeration technique which states the digits in a number expression from left to right, using the word "point" to indicate the location of the decimal point. Thus 27.62 would be read as "two-seven-point-six-two" or .376 as "point-three-seven-six." While admittedly speedier and more easily learned, this modern numeration technique unfortunately does little to emphasize the schematic aspects of our decimal system of notation.

4. *Reductions.* Since common fractions and decimal fractions are but different forms of the same thing, it follows that it should be possible to move from one form to another without a change in value. Such transformations, of course, are known as reductions.

The method of changing from a decimal fraction form to a common fraction form should be obvious from our foregoing discussion of numeration. For instance, to change .28 to its common fraction form we need only read the fraction "twenty-eight hundredths" and express it in its common fraction form $\frac{28}{100}$. A reduction of this to lowest terms produces $\frac{7}{25}$, which is the equivalent of .28. By the same token

$$.48 = \frac{48}{100} = \frac{12}{25}$$

$$.008 = \frac{8}{1000} = \frac{1}{125}$$

$$.363 = \frac{363}{1000}$$

$$.075 = \frac{75}{1000} = \frac{3}{40}$$

$$.77 = \frac{77}{100}$$

Certain of these decimal fractions when converted to common fraction form were further reducible and some were not. With a little thought about potential common factors (those factors which are eliminated or divided out in reducing a fraction to lower terms) which exist between numerator and denominator, it will be seen that since the denominator is always a power of ten, the factors of such denominators are restricted to powers of two and five (the prime factors of ten being 2 and 5). Thus we need to size up the numerator only as to its divisibility by twos and fives. If the numerator is not exactly divisible by either 2 or 5 the fraction as it stands ($\frac{363}{1000}$, $\frac{37}{100}$) is in lowest terms.

Converting from common fraction form to decimal fraction form is somewhat more involved. We shall have to reserve discussion of the most frequently used method of dividing numerator by denominator until after our discussion of division with decimals. In the meantime an alternative method, the inverse of the method just described, which in certain cases can prove to be of considerable benefit to the calculator, may be described.

Let us start with something easy, such as $\frac{13}{25}$. To express this common fraction in decimal form a denominator which is a power of ten is necessary. By invoking our basic principle of fractions (see Unit 20) we multiply numerator (13) and denominator (25) by 4. Thus

$$\frac{13}{25} = \frac{4 \times 13}{4 \times 25} = \frac{52}{100} = .52$$

In the case of $\frac{17}{20}$ we would use 5 as the multiplier. Thus

$$\frac{17}{20} = \frac{5 \times 17}{5 \times 20} = \frac{85}{100} = .85$$

In the case of $\frac{11}{125}$ we would use 8. Thus

$$\frac{11}{125} = \frac{8 \times 11}{8 \times 125} = \frac{88}{1000} = .088$$

This method works well so long as the needed multiplier is readily recognized.

Sometimes we mix common fraction form with decimal fraction form in one expression. When this occurs, the common fraction part is assumed to be of the same order as the whole digit which precedes it. Some refer to this type of number expression as a *complex decimal*.

For example, to express $\frac{3}{8}$ in decimal form, the alert reader may recognize that $12\frac{1}{2} \times 8 = 100$ and apply the method explained above and get

$$\frac{3}{8} = \frac{12\frac{1}{2} \times 3}{12\frac{1}{2} \times 8} = \frac{37\frac{1}{2}}{100} = .37\frac{1}{2}$$

which in turn may be expressed schematically as

$$.37\tfrac{1}{2} = \begin{array}{|c|c|} \text{Tenths} & \text{Hundredths} \\ \hline 3 & 7\tfrac{1}{2} \end{array} = \frac{3}{10} + \frac{7\tfrac{1}{2}}{100}$$

Note that an expression of $.\tfrac{1}{2}$ has no meaning. If the number we wish to express is "$\tfrac{1}{2}$ tenth" then it should be expressed as $.0\tfrac{1}{2}$. In other words, in our decimal system a common fraction alone is not an adequate placeholder in the same sense that the numerals 0, 1, 2, 3, 4, 5, 6, 7, 8, 9 are. In some cases by extending the decimal expression into the next order the common fraction part can be eliminated.

Thus
$$\frac{7\tfrac{1}{2}}{100} = \frac{7}{100} + \frac{\tfrac{1}{2}}{100}$$

but
$$\frac{\tfrac{1}{2}}{100} = \frac{5}{1000} \quad \text{since} \quad \left(\frac{\tfrac{1}{2} \times 10}{100 \times 10} = \frac{5}{1000} \right)$$

so
$$\frac{7\tfrac{1}{2}}{100} = \frac{7}{100} + \frac{5}{1000}$$

and
$$.37\tfrac{1}{2} = \frac{3}{10} + \frac{7}{100} + \frac{5}{1000} = .375$$

At other times a similar extension, regardless of the number of orders to which it is carried, will not eliminate the common fraction part (e.g., $.33\tfrac{1}{3}$ or $.5\tfrac{2}{7}$). These fractions, while rational (can be expressed in common fraction form with an integral numerator and denominator) are known as unending (but repeating) decimals and will be treated more thoroughly in the next unit.

PROBLEMS SET 24

1. Make a list of the names, in sequence, used in the decimal notation for the orders starting with the twelfth order to the left of the units order (whole numbers) and continuing through to the twelfth order to the right of the units order (fractions).

2. Write the following fractions in decimal form.
   (a) fifty-six hundredths
   (b) two hundred seventeen thousandths
   (c) thirty-two thousandths
   (d) three hundred-thousandths
   (e) three hundred thousandths
   (f) one thousand two millionths
   (g) seventeen ten-millionths
   (h) one-seventh tenth
   (i) sixty-one billionths

  (j) four hundred and thirty-six thousandths
  (k) three and one-fifth tenth
  (l) two hundred and eight ten-thousandths
  (m) three and one-fifth tenths
  (n) sixteen and three-quarter hundredths

3. Express the following in words.

  (a) .362   (e) .4386274   (i) 3,400.0006
  (b) .0042   (f) .000004   (j) .34$\frac{3}{4}$
  (c) .100002   (g) .00000000007 (k) 200.007
  (d) .0$\frac{1}{9}$ (h) 100.027   (l) .207

4. Reduce the following from their decimal form to common fraction form in lowest terms.

  (a) .03   (e) .432   (i) .03$\frac{3}{4}$
  (b) .425   (f) .000375   (j) .007$\frac{2}{25}$
  (c) .0075   (g) .00375   (k) .0$\frac{1}{5}$
  (d) .333   (h) .8625   (l) .000$\frac{1}{4}$

5. Reduce the following to mixed numbers involving common fractions.

  (a) 16.02   (c) 37.5   (e) 14.3200
  (b) 3.75   (d) 14.32   (f) 6.03$\frac{3}{8}$

6. Reduce the following common fractions to decimal fraction form by appropriate multiplication of numerator and denominator.

  (a) $\frac{17}{50}$ (c) $\frac{74}{125}$ (e) $\frac{9}{40}$
  (b) $\frac{8}{25}$ (d) $\frac{7}{8}$ (f) $\frac{7}{16}$

7. Reduce:
  (a) .037 unit to tenths, hundredths, thousandths.
  (b) 4.62 units to tens, tenths, hundredths.
  (c) 37 units to hundreds, tens, tenths, thousandths.
  (d) 4.2 tenths to units, hundredths, thousands.
  (e) .0$\frac{1}{2}$ unit to tenths, hundredths, thousandths.

8. Extending our development of the decimal notation to other bases, what would be the base ten equivalent (in common fraction form) of

(a) .111 (scale two), (c) .3T4 (scale twelve) (e) 1.10101 (scale two)
(b) .1101 (scale five) (d) .666 (scale seven) (f) 32.13 (scale five)

Unit 25:   Operations with Decimals

1. *Introduction.* The most important reason for introducing the decimal fraction to elementary arithmetic was set forth by Stevin in the subtitle to his famous *La Disme.* He claimed that his method "teaches how all Computations that are met in Business may be performed by Integers alone without the aid of Fractions." The term "Fractions" here of course refers to common fraction form, at that time the prevalent method for expressing parts of things. Should one use the decimal notation exclusively, all the special techniques necessary for computing with common fractions could be eliminated and in their stead would be the familiar algorisms for operating with whole numbers, plus a few special rules for positioning the decimal point in the final solutions.

In our discussions of the various operations with decimals which follow, it should be noted that each algorism invariably consists of two distinct parts: (1) directions for handling the decimal point location in the solution, and (2) directions to compute as though working with integers or whole numbers. These rules tend to develop a highly automatic type of computation, commendable for its speed, but sometimes troublesome to understand clearly.

Again our approach will be to handle the four basic operations in our usual synthesis and analysis setting, reserving comparison until the following unit. As each of the operations is discussed an attempt will be made to build up an adequate rationale for its particular algorism. In general these rationales will rest heavily upon what we have learned in our discussions of common fractions; hence they tend to emphasize the link which exists between common fraction form and decimal fraction form. The reader will realize upon completion of this work that common fractions and decimal fractions are but two different ways for expressing the same set of numbers, each having its own set of peculiar advantages and disadvantages for particular situations.

The term "decimals," as it is used throughout this unit includes any number expression in decimal form, whether integer, pure decimal, or mixed decimal.

2. *Synthesis: Addition with Decimals.* Once more we shall rely upon the guidance offered by the basic principles of the additive process (likeness, commutation, association) to lead us to algorisms for handling numbers expressed in decimal form.

Let us assume that in an addition one addend is .152, which

consists of the several parts $\frac{1}{10} + \frac{5}{100} + \frac{2}{1000}$, and that another is
.834, which is $\frac{8}{10} + \frac{3}{100} + \frac{4}{1000}$. In order to combine the values of
these two addends, we are charged by the principle of likeness to add
tenths to tenths, hundredths to hundredths, thousandths to thousandths. Because of the principle of association we can rest assured
that the ultimate sum of these parts, though added piecemeal, will
be the true sum of the original numbers. Thus

$$.152 + .834 = \left(\frac{1}{10} + \frac{5}{100} + \frac{2}{1000}\right) + \left(\frac{8}{10} + \frac{3}{100} + \frac{4}{1000}\right)$$

$$= \left(\frac{1}{10} + \frac{8}{10}\right) + \left(\frac{5}{100} + \frac{3}{100}\right) + \left(\frac{2}{1000} + \frac{4}{1000}\right)$$

$$= \frac{9}{10} \quad + \quad \frac{8}{100} \quad + \quad \frac{6}{1000}$$

$$= \frac{900}{1000} + \frac{80}{1000} + \frac{6}{1000} = \frac{900 + 80 + 6}{1000}$$

$$= \frac{986}{1000} = .986$$

If we arrange these two addends in such a way that their respective orders align themselves vertically, as was done with whole
numbers, we can eliminate the necessity of expressing the component
parts of the numbers with their various denominators. Then by
adding the digits columnarly, we arrive at the sum and still remain
in conformity with the principle of likeness.

A consequence of this column-order arrangement is the fact that
the decimal points of the addends also fall into vertical alignment.
This fact is utilized in practice as a means of arranging digits of the
addends so that they are properly aligned by order. Thus we have
an algorism for adding decimals:

(1) *Arrange the addends to make the orders match by aligning
the decimal points vertically (and annexing zeros to the right
if needed to complete the columns); (2) add column by column
as with integers; (3) fix the decimal point in the sum so that
it aligns itself with those of the addends.*

To *illustrate:*

(a) 4.68 = 468 hundredths
    32.87 = 3287 hundredths
     5.23 = 523 hundredths
    42.78   4278 hundredths = 42.78 units

(b) Add 3.62 + 57.837 + 4.96 + .0043.

$$
\begin{array}{r}
3.6200 \\
57.8370 \\
4.9600 \\
.0043 \\
\hline
66.4213
\end{array}
$$

3. *Multiplication and Division by Powers of Ten.* Before we develop the general rule for multiplying and dividing decimals, let us first consider what happens to the decimal point in those cases in which we multiply by a power of the base, ten. It will be recalled from our discussion in Unit 10 that multiplication of a number by a power of the base had the effect of upgrading each of the component parts of the multiplicand a number of orders equal to the power of the multiplier. In the case of whole numbers, zero spacers were necessary to fill in the vacated orders. Thus

$$10 \times 64 = 10(6 \text{ tens} + 4 \text{ units}) = 60 \text{ tens} + 40 \text{ units}$$
$$= 6 \text{ hundreds} + 4 \text{ tens} = 640$$

Similarly it can be shown that

$$
\begin{aligned}
100 \times 863 &= 86{,}300 \\
1{,}000 \times 275 &= 275{,}000 \\
10 \times 4{,}200 &= 42{,}000
\end{aligned}
$$

Note that the product in such cases is the same as the multiplicand except for a relocation of the decimal point. To illustrate with more detail:

(a) 10×34.62
   = 10(3 tens + 4 units + 6 tenths + 2 hundredths)
   = 30 tens + 40 units + 60 tenths + 20 hundredths
   = 3 hundredths + 4 tens + 6 units + 2 tenths
   = 346.2

(b) $100 \times .0342$
   = 100(3 hundredths + 4 thousandths + 2 ten-thousandths)
   = 300 hundredths + 400 thousandths + 200 ten-thousandths
   = 3 units + 4 tenths + 2 hundredths
   = 3.42

From this we might derive a rule:

Multiplication by a power of ten has the apparent effect of moving the decimal point in the multiplicand a number of places to the right equal to the power of the multiplier.

For example:

(a) $10^3 \times 46.3275 = 1,000 \times 46.3275 = 46,327.5$
(b) $10^3 \times 5.6 = 1,000 \times 5.6 = 5,600$
(c) $10^4 \times .032 = 10,000 \times .032 = 320$

The term *apparent effect* in the rule above is an important one. Actually in this computation the decimal point remains systematically fixed, as it is on the keyboard or top panel of a desk calculator. It is the digits which really change position as they are upgraded (or downgraded, as we shall see in division). To cite a popular parallel, scientists long ago established that the earth rotates on its axis, yet for practical purposes—*since the apparent results are the same*—it is often convenient to consider the sun as revolving around the earth. Similarly with decimals we often find it practical to speak of "moving the decimal point" since the apparent results are the same.

Division by powers of ten, being the inverse of multiplication by powers of ten, reverses multiplication, and downgrades each of the component parts of the dividend a number of orders equal to the power of the divisor. Thus

$$420 \div 10 = (4 \text{ hundreds} + 2 \text{ tens} + 0 \text{ units}) \div 10$$
$$= 4 \text{ tens} + 2 \text{ units} + 0 \text{ tenths of a unit}$$
$$= 42$$

Similarly it can be shown that

$$543,000 \div 1,000 = 543$$
$$42,000 \div 10 = 4,200$$
$$4,000,000 \div 100 = 40,000$$

Note here that the downgrading of the various digits has also produced an apparent relocation of the decimal point. In the quotient it is to the *left* of its former position in the dividend a number of places equal to the power of the divisor. One might describe the decimal point as having "moved" to the left a number of places equal to the power of the divisor.

A further illustration of this effect is:

$$346.27 \div 100 = (3 \text{ hundreds} + 4 \text{ tens} + 6 \text{ units} + 2 \text{ tenths}$$
$$+ 7 \text{ hundredths}) \div 100$$
$$= \tfrac{3}{100} \text{ hundreds} + \tfrac{4}{100} \text{ tens} + \tfrac{6}{100} \text{ units} + \tfrac{2}{100} \text{ tenths}$$
$$+ \tfrac{7}{100} \text{ hundredths}$$
$$= 3 \text{ units} + 4 \text{ tenths} + 6 \text{ hundredths} + 2 \text{ thousandths}$$
$$+ 7 \text{ ten-thousandths}$$
$$= 3.4627$$

In a similar fashion it can be shown that

$$348.63 \div 10^1 = 348.63 \div 10 = 34.863$$
$$642.7 \div 10^3 = 642.7 \div 1{,}000 = .6427$$
$$.036 \div 10^2 = .036 \div 100 = .00036$$

From this we are able to derive the rule:

Division by a power of ten has the apparent effect of moving the decimal point in the dividend a number of places to the left equal to the power of the divisor.

4. *Synthesis: Multiplication with Decimals.* Consider the multiplication of 3.2×1.47. If we were to multiply 32×147, we would be using a multiplier which is 10 times larger ($32 = 10 \times 3.2$) and a multiplicand which is 100 times larger ($147 = 100 \times 1.47$). From our discussions and problems concerning multiplication of whole numbers we know that increasing or decreasing a multiplier a certain number of times increases or decreases the product that many times, and similarly for the other factor, the multiplicand. Consequently our product of 32×147, compared with the product of 3.2×1.47, will be 10 times larger because of the multiplier, and 100 times larger because of the multiplicand—or all told, the product of the former would be 1,000 times as great ($10 \times 100 = 1{,}000$ or $10^1 \times 10^2 = 10^3$) as that of the latter. Thus, if the product of $32 \times 147 = 4{,}704$, and 4,704 is a thousand times as large as the product of 3.2×1.47, then it follows that 4.704, which is one-thousandth the size of 4,704, must be the product of 3.2×1.47.

Another approach, patterned after the now familiar common fraction method of multiplication, ties in well with the foregoing and provides further insight into the algorism for multiplying decimals. For instance, if we consider 3.2 and 1.47 in their equivalent common fraction form, our multiplication problem of 3.2×1.47 can be translated to $\frac{32}{10} \times \frac{147}{100}$. The algorism for multiplying common fractions directs us to multiply numerators together and denominators together, expressing the former over the latter. Thus

$$\frac{32}{10} \times \frac{147}{100} = \frac{32 \times 147}{10 \times 100} = \frac{4704}{1000}$$

or

$$\frac{32}{10^1} \times \frac{147}{10^2} = \frac{32 \times 147}{10^{1+2}} = \frac{4704}{10^3}$$

Dividing the final numerator 4,704 by its denominator, which is a power of ten (the sum of the powers of the denominators of the multiplier and multiplicand, in this case 3), can be done easily by the "pointing off" method demonstrated in the previous section:

$$\frac{4704}{10^3} = 4.704, \text{ the product of } \frac{32}{10} \times \frac{147}{100} \text{ or } 3.2 \times 1.47$$

From this we derive a rule or algorism for multiplying decimals:

(1) *Ignore the decimal points in the multiplier and multiplicand and multiply these terms as though they were integers;*
(2) *compensate by locating the decimal point in the product to the left of as many digits as there are digits collectively to the right of the decimal point(s) in the multiplier and/or multiplicand.*

To illustrate: .453 × 78.2.

(1) Ignore decimal points, multiply 453 × 782, and get 354,246 for a product.

(2a) Count off collectively the number of digits to the right of the decimal points in the multiplier and multiplicand.

$$.4\ 5\ 3 \times 78.2$$
$$\underset{① ② ③}{\underrightarrow{\quad}} \qquad \underset{④}{\underrightarrow{\quad}}$$

(This corresponds to the power of ten by which the product of the original problem is exaggerated; or in terms of the fraction rationalization, the power of ten in the product of the denominators.)

(2b) Compensate by pointing off in the product, from the right, a number of digits or places equal to that of (2a).

$$3\ 5\ \cdot\ 4\ 2\ 4\ 6$$
$$\underset{④\ ③\ ②\ ①}{\underleftarrow{\qquad\qquad}}$$

5. *Analysis: Subtraction of Decimals.* The subtraction principle of likeness requires that we subtract likes from likes. For numbers expressed in a discrete sense this means that we subtract digits of like orders from digits of like orders. Again as a consequence of this order arrangement by columns, we note that the decimal point in the subtrahend falls beneath the decimal point in the minuend; once more the practitioner may utilize this condition to orient his figures properly before computation. Furthermore, since the remainder must be alike with the minuend and subtrahend, the decimal point in the solution to the subtraction should be in line with the decimal points for the two terms above it. Thus the algorism develops for the subtraction of decimals:

*(1) Arrange the minuend and subtrahend to make their orders
match by aligning the decimal points (and annexing zeros
to the right if needed to complete the columns); (2) subtract
column by column as with integers; (3) fix the decimal point
in the remainder so that it aligns itself with those of the other
terms.*

To *illustrate:*

(a) Subtract 4.372 from 8.643.

$$\begin{array}{r} 8.643 \\ \underline{4.372} \\ 4.271 \end{array}$$

(b) Subtract .00437 from 8.64.

$$\begin{array}{r} 8.64000 \\ \underline{.00437} \\ 8.63563 \end{array}$$

6. *Analysis: Division of Decimals.* In division, as in multiplication of decimals, there are several directions in which we might go
in quest of a rationalization for the process. In our discussion of
the division algorism with respect to whole numbers (Unit 15) we
emphasized division as repeated subtraction. Here let us vary our
attack and treat division in its alternative role, that of inverse
process of multiplication.

When division is looked upon as multiplication's inverse, it becomes that process by which we seek the missing factor of a multiplication in which the other factor and product are known. From
the previous section it should be clear that when one factor of a
multiplication is a whole number, the decimal point location in the
other factor and in the product will be in agreement. For instance,
in $23 \times 1.57 = 36.11$, the multiplicand as well as the product are
both expressed to hundredths; in $23 \times 15.7 = 361.1$, both multiplicand and product are expressed to tenths, and so on.

From this it follows that should the given factor in a division
(the divisor) be a whole number, there will be agreement (vertical
alignment of decimal points) between the known product (dividend)
and the missing factor (quotient). Thus

$$\begin{array}{cc} 1.57 & 15.7 \\ 23\overline{)36.11} & 23\overline{)361.1} \end{array}$$

A second rationalization, not at all unlike the above, is to interpret the division of a decimalized dividend by a whole number

divisor as one of partitioning; the hallmark of partitive division is, of course, its agreement between quotient and dividend. To illustrate, let us use the numbers of the two previous examples: $36.11 \div 23$ and $361.1 \div 23$.

$36.11 \div 23$ is interpreted here as

$$\frac{157 \text{ hundredths}}{23)\overline{3,611 \text{ hundredths}}} = 1.57$$

$361.1 \div 23$ is interpreted here as

$$\frac{157 \text{ tenths}}{23)\overline{3,611 \text{ tenths}}} = 15.7$$

Now the question logically arises, what happens when the divisor is either a pure or a mixed decimal and not a whole number? The answer comes by way of our principle of compensation with respect to division, which holds that should the divisor and dividend be multiplied by the same number, not zero, the quotient remains unchanged (Principle D-2, Unit 15). Consequently, by multiplying the decimal divisor by some power of ten (upgrading), that term can always be made into a whole number. So as not to influence the ultimate quotient, however, the dividend must also be subjected to a like multiplication upgrading. For instance:

$361.1 \div 2.3 \ = 3611 \div 23$ (multiplying both terms by 10)
$3.611 \div .23 \ = 361.1 \div 23$ (multiplying both terms by 100)
$36.11 \div .023 = 36,110 \div 23$ (multiplying both terms by 1,000)

Hence a division involving a decimal divisor can always be converted to an equivalent one in which the divisor is a whole number. This equal upgrading has the apparent effect of moving the decimal point in the divisor and dividend an equal number of places to the right. From this we derive the following algorism for dividing decimals:

(1) Upgrade the divisor so that it becomes a whole number. (In practice, move the decimal point so that it is to the right of all digits in the divisor.) (2) Compensate with an equal upgrading of the dividend, annexing zeros if necessary. (In practice, move the decimal point in the dividend to the right the same number of places that the decimal point in the divisor was moved.) (3) Divide as though working with integers. (4) Locate the decimal point in the quotient so that it aligns itself with the decimal point of the upgraded dividend. (In

practice, insert the decimal point in the quotient so that it aligns itself with the new location of the decimal point in the dividend.)

For example.

(a) $2.3\overline{)361.1}$ $\rightarrow$ $2.3_\wedge\overline{)361.1_\wedge}$ $\overset{157.}{}$

(b) $.23\overline{)3.611}$ $\longrightarrow$ $.23_\wedge\overline{)3.61_\wedge1}$ $\overset{15.7}{}$

(c) $.023\overline{)36.11}$ $\rightarrow$ $.023_\wedge\overline{)36.110_\wedge}$ $\overset{1570.}{}$

Many courses of study suggest that, instead of rewriting the problem or bothering with two sets of decimal points, the caret symbol ($\wedge$) be introduced to mark the new location of the decimal point in the divisor and dividend. The decimal point in the quotient is then aligned with the caret in the dividend. Thus

$$2.3_\wedge\overset{157.}{\overline{)361.1_\wedge}} \qquad .23_\wedge\overset{15.7}{\overline{)3.61_\wedge1}} \qquad .023_\wedge\overset{1570.}{\overline{)36.110_\wedge}}$$

Another well-known method of dividing decimals follows the usual pattern of carrying out the actual computation as though the digits represented integers, but differs in method of locating the decimal point in the quotient. The main steps in the rationalization of this decimal point location procedure are given below. Note that it rests heavily upon the multiplication algorism developed in the previous section.

(1) Quotient $\times$ divisor = dividend is a multiplication relationship.

(2) In multiplication of decimals the number of digits collectively to the right of the decimal points in the factors equals the number of digits to the right of the decimal point in the product.

(3) Consequently, the number of digits collectively to the right of the decimal point(s) in the divisor and quotient [the factors of (1) above] should equal the number of digits to the right of the decimal point in the dividend [the product of (1) above]. Or, to state this another way, the places to the right of the decimal point in the dividend minus the places to the right of the decimal point in the divisor equals the places to the right of the decimal point in the quotient. (When the number of digits or places to the right of the decimal point in the dividend is *less* than those of the divisor, annex zeros to the dividend until both are equal.)

Illustrations:

$$
\begin{array}{r}
157 \\
23{\overline{\smash{\big)}\,3611}} \\
\underline{23} \\
131 \\
\underline{115} \\
161 \\
\underline{161}
\end{array}
$$

$$3.611 \div .23 = 15.7$$
3 places − 2 places = 1 place

$$361.1 \div .23 \rightarrow 361.10 \div .23 = 157.$$
1 place − 2 places   2 places − 2 places = 0 places

$$.3611 \div 23. = .0157$$
4 places − 0 places = 4 places

Notice that in cases where the division is carried out beyond the original digits of the dividend, more care must be exercised with this method than in the previous one.

7. *Rounding Off*. As anyone experienced with division realizes, division problems are not typically so well behaved as many of the illustrations we have seen thus far. More frequently than not the division problem will be one in which a remainder of zero never will occur. To preserve absolute accuracy in dividing decimals of this type, we should carry our quotient to whatever degree of precision (order) desired, then express the remainder as the numerator of a fraction in that order whose denominator is the divisor. For instance, if we wish to carry out the following division, $53.8 \div 37$, to hundredths, we would first divide by 37 and carry the computation on to hundredths,

		Units	Tenths	Hundredths
		1 .	4	5
37)	5	3 :	8	0
	3	7		
	1	6	8	
	1	4	8	
		2	0	0
		1	8	5
			1	5

and then express the quotient as

Units	Tenths	Hundredths
1 .	4	$5\frac{15}{37}$

or simply $1.45\frac{15}{37}$.

This quotient is exact, for

$$37 \times 1.45\tfrac{15}{37} = 53.80$$

As stated previously, we do not usually mix common fraction form with decimal fraction form, so in most cases of this type we simply state the quotient *approximately* as 1.15. Thus this approximate quotient has been terminated, or *rounded-off* at hundredths, the remainder at that point having been ignored. The difference, or error, which exists between the exact quotient and the approximate one is of course exactly the amount of the ignored remainder. This is obvious when we "check" by multiplying 37×1.45 and get 53.65, which is exactly .15 shy of the dividend value 53.80.

Had the remainder been 19 or more instead* of 15, that is, more than half of the divisor (as in $53.84 \div 37$) we should have raised the 5 hundredths in the quotient to 6 hundredths, since in the latter case 1.16 would have been a closer approximation to the exact answer than 1.15.

Computationally this rounding off procedure is usually done by carrying the quotient to one place beyond that of desired precision. Then if the digit in this extra place is a 0, 1, 2, 3, or 4, it is ignored; if it turns out to be a 5, 6, 7, 8, or 9, then the digit in the last desired place is increased by one. This approximation technique is equally applicable in the rounding off of any decimal expression, no matter what its source. To illustrate this point, we offer the rounded-off values of the following numbers to the nearest hundredth and also to the nearest tenth.

	Nearest hundredth	*Nearest tenth*
$36.42793 =$	36.43	36.4
$427.6349 =$	427.63	427.6
$.34625 =$	.35	.3
$1.4962 =$	1.50	1.5

8. *Reduction of a Common Fraction to a Decimal.* Once we have developed an algorism for division of decimals, we are ready to take up an item deferred in Unit 24: the division method for reducing a common fraction to its equivalent in decimal form. If we adopt the interpretation of the common fraction as a quotient of numerator divided by denominator, then by carrying out this division on a

---

* Actually .19 and .15, but since we ignore the decimal point location while dividing and look upon the numbers involved as integers, we permit ourselves this liberty of expression.

decimal plane, the result is obviously the decimal equivalent of the original common fraction. For example:

$$\frac{1}{2} = 2\overline{)1.0} \qquad \frac{3}{4} = 4\overline{)3.00} \qquad \frac{2}{5} = 5\overline{)2.0}$$

$$\begin{array}{r} .5 \\ 2\overline{)1.0} \\ \underline{1\,0} \end{array} \qquad \begin{array}{r} .75 \\ 4\overline{)3.00} \\ \underline{2\,8} \\ 20 \\ \underline{20} \end{array} \qquad \begin{array}{r} .4 \\ 5\overline{)2.0} \\ \underline{2\,0} \end{array}$$

$$\frac{17}{20} = \begin{array}{r} .85 \\ 20\overline{)17.00} \\ \underline{16\,0} \\ 1\,00 \\ \underline{1\,00} \end{array} \qquad \frac{3}{8} = \begin{array}{r} .375 \\ 8\overline{)3.000} \\ \underline{2\,4} \\ 60 \\ \underline{56} \\ 40 \\ \underline{40} \end{array}$$

Hence

$$\frac{1}{2} = .5, \qquad \frac{3}{4} = .75, \qquad \frac{2}{5} = .4, \qquad \frac{17}{20} = .85, \qquad \frac{3}{8} = .375$$

It should be noted that in each of the illustrations above, the denominator of the given common fraction was invariably a number whose prime factors consisted entirely of 2's and/or 5's. As a consequence, the resulting decimal equivalent was invariably a terminating decimal expression; i.e., the division if carried sufficiently far eventually produces a zero remainder. In fact, by analyzing the denominator and ascertaining the highest power of 2 or 5 in it, we can predict the number of places to which the division must be carried before such a zero remainder will occur. Reasons why this is so are left to the reader as an exercise. Thus: ?

$$\frac{1}{2} = \frac{1}{2^1} = \text{one place (.5)}$$

$$\frac{3}{4} = \frac{3}{2^2} = \text{two places (.75)}$$

$$\frac{2}{5} = \frac{2}{5^1} = \text{one place (.4)}$$

$$\frac{17}{20} = \frac{17}{2^2 5} = \text{two places (.85)}$$

$$\frac{3}{8} = \frac{3}{2^3} = \text{three places (.375)}$$

On the other hand, if the fraction, expressed in lowest terms, has among the prime factors of its denominator a number which is *not* a 2 or 5, the ensuing division will never produce a zero remainder. The decimal equivalent of such common fractions (sometimes referred to as the *generating fractions*) is known as an *unending decimal*. However, there is something distinctive about these unending decimals: if the division is carried out sufficiently far, a recurring pattern of the digits will be evidenced. For instance (these should be verified by the reader):

$$\frac{1}{3} = .33333 \ldots$$

$$\frac{1}{6} = .16666 \ldots$$

$$\frac{1}{11} = .09090909 \ldots$$

$$\frac{1}{37} = .027027027 \ldots$$

$$\frac{1}{12} = .083333 \ldots$$

$$\frac{1}{88} = .011363636 \ldots$$

$$\frac{1}{7} = .14285714285714 \ldots$$

The three dots which follow the digits in these expressions are to be interpreted as "and so on indefinitely." Note that in some cases the division must be carried to several places before the repetition begins. The group of digits which repeat themselves is called the *repetend*. Some writers suggest that dots be placed above the first and last digit of the repetend to signify its repetitious or circular character. Thus, of the foregoing examples:

$$\frac{1}{11} = .\dot{0}\dot{9}$$

$$\frac{1}{12} = .08\dot{3}$$

$$\frac{1}{37} = .\dot{0}2\dot{7}$$

$$\frac{1}{7} = .\dot{1}4285\dot{7}$$

9. *Reduction of a Repeating Unending Decimal to a Common Fraction.* Since all common fractions have decimal equivalents, either of the ending or repetitiously unending variety, we have the final problem of reducing one of these repetitious unending decimals to its equivalent in common fraction form. (The reduction of the

ending decimal type to its equivalent common fraction was handled in Unit 24.) The method is best explained by two examples.

(a) Convert .090909 . . . to its common fraction equivalent.
   (1) Let $n = .090909 . . . .$
   (2) Multiply n by 100 (a power of ten equal to the number of digits in the repetend)........................... $100n = 9.090909 . . .$
   (3) Subtract n (equals subtracted from equals, results are equal)......... $\underline{\quad n = \quad .090909 . . .}$
   $99n = 9.000000 . . .$
   (4) Solve for n by dividing both terms by 99 $n = \frac{9}{99} = \frac{1}{11}$

(b) Convert .1351351351 . . . to its common fraction equivalent.
   (1) Let $n = .1351351351 . . . .$
   (2) Multiply n by 1,000 (10^3)........ $1,000n = 135.135135 . . .$
   (3) Subtract n.................... $\underline{\quad n = \qquad .135135 . . .}$
   $999n = 135.000000 . . .$
   (4) Solve for n.................... $n = \frac{135}{999} = \frac{5}{37}$

By inspection it can be seen that when the decimal in question contains only repetends, the common fraction equivalent (though not necessarily in lowest terms) will be one whose numerator is the repetend and whose denominator is a number consisting of as many 9's as places in the repetend. Thus

$$.333 . . . \quad \frac{3}{9} = \frac{1}{3}$$

$$.060606 . . . \quad \frac{6}{99} = \frac{2}{33}$$

$$.117117117 . . . \quad \frac{117}{999} = \frac{29}{333}$$

When the decimal in question contains digits other than those of the repetend, by utilizing the associative principle with respect to addition, we get, for instance:

$$.08333 . . . = .08 + .00\dot{3} = \frac{8}{100} + \frac{\dot{3}}{100} = \frac{8}{100} + \frac{\frac{3}{9}}{100}$$

$$= \frac{8}{100} + \frac{3}{900} = \frac{24}{300} + \frac{1}{300} = \frac{25}{300} = \frac{1}{12}$$

Similarly:

$$.62727 . . . = .6 + .02727 . . . = \frac{6}{10} + \frac{\dot{2}\dot{7}}{10} = \frac{6}{10} + \frac{\frac{27}{99}}{10}$$

$$= \frac{6}{10} + \frac{\frac{3}{11}}{10} = \frac{66}{110} + \frac{3}{110} = \frac{69}{110}$$

PROBLEMS SET 25

1. Add the following.
  (a) 3.68 + 4.975 + 1.3 + 16.42
  (b) 64.2 + .04 + 18 + 17.37
  (c) 8.637 + 492 + .003 + .1

2. In the following pairs of numbers subtract the smaller from the larger number.
  (a) 46.37, 18.48   (c) 60.42, 307
  (b) 2.004, 21.3   (d) 4.2, .00005

3. Using the following numbers as multiplicands: 4,368; 5700; 463.29, write the products without computation when the multipliers are (a) ten; (b) one hundred; (c) one thousand; (d) one million.

4. Using the same numbers of the previous question as dividends, write the respective quotients by sight when the divisors are (a) ten; (b) one hundred; (c) one thousand; (d) one million.

5. Using the same numbers as in Question 3 as multiplicands, find the products when the multipliers are (a) one-tenth; (b) one-hundredth; (c) one-thousandth; (d) one-millionth. Compare these products with the quotients of Question 4.

6. Using the pairs of numbers given in Question 2, multiply the larger by the smaller, using both methods of Section 4.

7. Divide the following, using both methods of pointing off as described in Section 6 of this unit.
  (a) 13.536 ÷ 3.2   (c) 9,433.6 ÷ 3.52
  (b) .15288 ÷ 63.7

8. Divide the following and express quotients accurate to the nearest thousandth.
  (a) 97.42 ÷ 86.3   (b) .49782 ÷ .031   (c) 2.639 ÷ 2.2

9. Identify which of the following common fractions will have terminating decimal equivalents (predict the number of places) and which will have unending decimal equivalents.

  (a) $\dfrac{7}{25}$ (c) $\dfrac{8}{15}$ (e) $\dfrac{7}{40}$ (g) $\dfrac{5}{13}$ (i) $\dfrac{73}{250}$

  (b) $\dfrac{3}{32}$ (d) $\dfrac{3}{24}$ (f) $\dfrac{3}{21}$ (h) $\dfrac{5}{205}$

10. Find the decimal equivalents of the common fractions given in Question 9.

11. Find the common fraction equivalents for the following repeating decimals.

(a) .030303 . . . (c) .3960396039 . . .
(b) .099099099 . . . (d) .13626262 . . .

12. Locate the decimal point in the rounded-off products and quotients of the following without working the problems.

(a) 46.2 × 60.2 = 27812 (e) 372 ÷ 60.52 = 6147
(b) 2.53 × 387.6 = 98063 (f) 4.002 ÷ 3.014 = 1328
(c) 61.9 × 98.6 = 61033 (g) .95474 ÷ 9.03 = 1057
(d) .3784 × 67.11 = 25394 (h) 3.235 ÷ 9.672 = 3345

13. A man travels 104.4 miles in 2.4 hr. What was his average speed per hour?

14. A draftsman made a mistake in choice of scale in preparing the blueprints of a house, with the result that 1.36 ft = 1 in. What are the dimensions of a room which measures on the blueprint 16⅜ by 12¼ in.? Of a closet which measures 2⅛ by ¾ in.?

15. An object traveling at 93.16 ft/sec overtakes another object traveling at 78.24 ft/sec. How far were they apart 2 sec before they met?

Unit 26: Comparison with Fractions

1. *Inequality of Common Fractions.* We have stated that two common fractions are equal to each other if they are identical in numerator and denominator (e.g., ¾ = ¾) or if one can be reduced to the other (e.g., ⅔ = 4/6). However, in many practical situations we are primarily interested in the inequality which exists between stated fractions. For instance, is ⅔ of a pound greater than ⅝ of a pound? Is 3/7 less than 2/5? and so on. Clearly these are cases of comparison and fall into our third major area of "things we do with numbers."

What causes difficulty in comparing numbers expressed in common fraction form is the fact that there are two variables operating simultaneously. The partitive interpretation of the common fraction makes this particularly clear. In comparing the relative magnitude, say, of ⅔ and ⅝, we note that in ⅔ there are fewer pieces (two) than in ⅝ (five), but on the other hand the size of the parts in ⅔ is much larger (whole divided into three equal parts) than the size of the parts represented by ⅝ (whole divided into eight parts). Therefore the problem is: Will fewer pieces of a larger size be greater than more pieces of a smaller size? Obviously, the answer depends upon the actual *number* of pieces and the actual *size* of the pieces under comparison.

From this we can see the necessity of either stabilizing the number of pieces and making our comparison on the relative size of each piece (recall the Egyptian system of fractions) or else stabilizing the size of each piece (recall the Roman system of fractions) and making our comparison on the relative number of pieces. In either case the medium by which we may make these comparisons numerically is our basic principle of fractions, compensation, which holds that multiplying (or dividing) both numerator and denominator of a fraction by the same nonzero number does not change the value of the fraction.

Most of us are aware of the application of this principle to the second of the two alternatives listed above, that of stabilizing denominators. Our familiarity with this approach undoubtedly stems from our experience with addition and subtraction of common fractions, in which the finding of a common denominator is a frequent first step. Accordingly, in order to compare the respective sizes of (a) $\frac{2}{3}$ and $\frac{5}{8}$, and (b) $\frac{3}{7}$ and $\frac{4}{9}$, we find a common denominator in each case and proceed thus:

(a) LCD for $\frac{2}{3}$ and $\frac{5}{8}$ is 24. By principle of compensation (actually a reduction),
$$\frac{2}{3} = \frac{16}{24} \quad \text{and} \quad \frac{5}{8} = \frac{15}{24}$$
Since denominators (sizes of parts) are alike, and 16 is greater than 15 ($16 > 15$), then $\frac{2}{3}$ must be greater than $\frac{5}{8}$ ($\frac{2}{3} > \frac{5}{8}$).*

(b) LCD for $\frac{3}{7}$ and $\frac{4}{9}$ is 63. By principle of compensation
$$\frac{3}{7} = \frac{27}{63} \quad \text{and} \quad \frac{4}{9} = \frac{28}{63}$$
Since denominators are stabilized at 63, and 27 is less than 28 ($27 < 28$), then $\frac{3}{7}$ must be less than $\frac{4}{9}$ ($\frac{3}{7} < \frac{4}{9}$).

Equally reasonable is the other alternative, that of stabilizing numerators (number of parts) and making our comparison on the basis of denominators (size of part). In such instances we find the least common multiple of the numerators and proceed thus:

(a) LCM of 2 and 5 (numerators of $\frac{2}{3}$ and $\frac{5}{8}$) is 10. By principle of compensation $\frac{2}{3} = \frac{10}{15}$ and $\frac{5}{8} = \frac{10}{16}$. Since the number of parts has been stabilized at 10, and the whole divided into 15 equal parts results in parts of a larger size than when the whole is divided into 16 equal parts, it follows that 10 fifteenths ($\frac{10}{15}$) is larger than 10 sixteenths ($\frac{10}{16}$); hence $\frac{2}{3} > \frac{5}{8}$.

(b) LCM of 3 and 4 (numerators of $\frac{3}{7}$ and $\frac{4}{9}$) is 12. By principle of compensation
$$\frac{3}{7} = \frac{12}{28} \quad \text{and} \quad \frac{4}{9} = \frac{12}{27}$$
Since 28 is greater than 27, then $\frac{1}{28}$ is less than $\frac{1}{27}$. Therefore $\frac{12}{28}$ is less than $\frac{12}{27}$, and $\frac{3}{7} < \frac{4}{9}$.

* The symbol $>$ means "is greater than," and the symbol $<$ means "is less than."

2. *Comparisons with Decimal Fractions.* Determining which of two decimal fractions is the larger is a relatively simple matter. It can be done at a glance, provided one fully understands the implications of decimal expression with respect to orders. First, any given order in a decimal expression is ten times greater than the one to its right, which in turn is ten times greater than the one to its right, and so on indefinitely. Second is the fact that the largest digit which can appear in any given order is 9, which means 9 times the value of that order. From these two facts it follows that no matter what digit occurs in a given order, it will represent a number *greater* than one represented by digits in *all* the orders to its right, regardless of the value of these digits. In other words, to cite an extreme case,

.1 > .099999999999999999999999999999999999999999 . . .

Consequently, in comparing two decimal expressions we make our comparison on an order-by-order basis. For example, .4 > .37 because the .4 represents more tenths (4) than the .37 (3), regardless of what each has in the way of hundredths (none for .4, 7 for .37) or beyond. Similarly .32 > .3199. Here both contain the same number of tenths (3), but the former has more hundredths than the latter (2 to 1 or 1 hundredth more). Note that the combined value of the latter's 9 thousandths ($\frac{9}{1000}$) and 9 ten-thousandths ($\frac{9}{10000}$) is still not enough to make up its deficiency of 1 hundredth ($\frac{9}{1000} + \frac{9}{10000} = \frac{90}{10000} + \frac{9}{10000} = \frac{99}{10000} < \frac{100}{10000} = \frac{1}{100}$).

Likewise:

$$.003 > .00299999999999 \ldots$$
$$6.03 > 5.98$$
$$.000712 > .00008$$
$$.7 > .6382$$

These and others may be verified by reducing each decimal to its common fraction equivalent, then making the comparison by one of the two methods described in Section 1 of this unit.

3. *Per Cent.* Most people in daily life when confronted with a problem situation of comparing common fractions similar to those of the first section will use neither of the two methods outlined in that section; instead they will elect another, that of per cent. Per cent, since its very invention at some time prior to the sixteenth

century, has always been the fraction of business and commerce, and as a consequence a firm possession of the practical layman.

In reality, per cent is but a special case of the first of the two methods discussed in the first section, the one in which denominators are stabilized at some common size. But here, instead of the choice of common size coming as a consequence of the particular fractions under comparison (the LCD of the two fractions), one hundred is chosen as the common denominator for *all* fractions. Thus each common fraction, when expressed in hundredths ($\frac{2}{5} = \frac{40}{100}$, $\frac{1}{2} = \frac{50}{100}$, $\frac{3}{4} = \frac{75}{100}$, etc.) might be referred to as a "per cent," the term being an abbreviated version of the Italian *per cento* which means "by the hundred." Since it was used in certain parts of Italy in the fifteenth century, the concept of per cent obviously predated our decimal fraction notation.

Many Italian merchants, instead of writing their hundredth fractions in common fraction form, simply wrote the numerator and followed it by "per $\frac{0}{0}$" which represented the stabilized denominator of 100. Gradually this latter became "per $\frac{0}{0}$"; then the "per" dropped out of usage and left only $\frac{0}{0}$, which was but one step from the modern symbol for per hundred, the "%."

Thus we have now been introduced to the third form which modern man has at his disposal for expressing fractions. The first, the common fraction, possesses the greatest flexibility and has least restriction upon the number of parts and size of part. The second, the decimal fraction, possesses many advantages as the extension of our whole-number decimal notation, though having the disadvantage of restricting size of parts (denominators) to powers of ten. The last, the per cent, is a form of great practicability, though with even greater restrictions upon size of part than that of the decimal fraction, for here the denominator is restricted to but *one* power of ten, that of one hundred.

4. *Reductions.* Since there is choice of form by which to express a given fractional value, we need some accompanying technique for changing a fraction expression from one form to another. This change in form without a change in value has already been defined as a *reduction*, and in previous units we have outlined methods of reducing a common fraction to a decimal fraction and vice versa. Now we need to develop techniques for transforming a per cent to its equivalent value in common fraction form and decimal fraction form, and vice versa.

(a) *Reduction of a per cent to a common fraction.* Since "per cent" by origin is a substitute for the denominator of one hundred, to accomplish this reduction we need simply to reverse matters and reinstitute the denominator of one hundred in exchange for the % symbol. Thus

$$87\% = \frac{87}{100}, \quad 50\% = \frac{50}{100} = \frac{1}{2}, \quad 37\tfrac{1}{2}\% = \frac{37\tfrac{1}{2}}{100} = \frac{\overset{3}{\cancel{75}}}{2} \times \frac{1}{\underset{4}{\cancel{100}}} = \frac{3}{8}$$

(b) *Reduction of a per cent to a decimal fraction.* Again the per cent symbol represents "hundredths," which is also the term for the second order to the right of unity (or to the right of the decimal point) in the decimal notation. Thus

$$8\% = \quad 8 \text{ hundredths} = .08$$
$$87\% = \quad 87 \text{ hundredths} = .87$$
$$50\% = \quad 50 \text{ hundredths} = .50 = .5$$
$$37\tfrac{1}{2}\% = 37\tfrac{1}{2} \text{ hundredths} = .37\tfrac{1}{2} = .375$$
$$3.6\% = 3.6 \text{ hundredths} = .036$$

From this we can induce the general rule that in order to change a per cent to its decimal equivalent we merely drop the per cent symbol and "move" the decimal point two places to the left of its previous location.

(c) *Reduction of decimal fraction to a per cent.* This, of course, is the inverse of (b). For instance, the fraction .32 is read 32 hundredths; by substituting the % symbol for "hundredths" we have transformed the decimal fraction to a per cent. On the other hand, while .6 is 6 tenths, it is also .60, which is 60 hundredths. Again substituting the % for the word "hundredths" we get .6 = 60%. Generally speaking, then, we merely express the decimal fraction as "hundredths" and then substitute the % symbol for the word "hundredths." In effect, this will appear (looking at the first and last steps only) to be a two-step operation: move the decimal point two places to the right and affix the % symbol. To illustrate:

$$.64 \quad = \quad 64 \text{ hundredths} = 64\%$$
$$.7 \quad = \quad 70 \text{ hundredths} = 70\%$$
$$.035 \quad = 3.5 \text{ hundredths} = 3.5\% \ (3\tfrac{1}{2}\%)$$
$$.0004 = .04 \text{ hundredths} = .04\%$$

(d) *Reduction of a common fraction to a per cent.* Sometimes a common fraction can be easily transformed to a per cent by reducing the given common fraction to one having a denominator of 100.

In such cases we need only to write the numerator and substitute the % symbol for the denominator of 100. Thus

$$\frac{1}{2} = \frac{50}{100} = 50\% \qquad \frac{4}{5} = \frac{80}{100} = 80\% \qquad \frac{7}{25} = \frac{28}{100} = 28\%$$

Theoretically this approach is always possible, since it is always possible to find some number which, when multiplied with the denominator of the given fraction, will yield 100 (making this multiplier the fraction

$$\frac{100}{\text{given denominator}}$$

will always turn the trick). At times, however, this can produce rather complicated results. The alternative, then, is the decimal fraction approach: (1) convert the common fraction to its decimal equivalent by dividing numerator by denominator, and (2) as in the case of reduction (c) above, "move" the decimal point two places to the right, and affix the per cent symbol. Thus

$$\frac{3}{8} = \frac{.375 \text{ units} = 37.5 \text{ hundredths} = 37\frac{1}{2}\%}{8\overline{)3.000}}$$

$$\frac{17}{80} = \frac{.2125 \text{ units} = 21.25 \text{ hundredths} = 21\frac{1}{4}\%}{80\overline{)17.0000}}$$

$$\frac{5}{12} = \frac{.41\dot{6} \text{ units} = 41.\dot{6} \text{ hundredths} = 41.\dot{6}\% = 41\frac{2}{3}\%}{12\overline{)5.000}}$$

5. *Comparing Fractions by Per Cent.* At the risk of belaboring the obvious, we return now to our earlier problem of comparing fractions by the per cent method. The problem, it will be recalled, involved the comparison of $\frac{2}{3}$ and $\frac{5}{8}$, $\frac{3}{7}$ and $\frac{4}{9}$. Here we simply convert both pairs of fractions to their per cent equivalents and make the comparison. Thus

$\frac{2}{3} = 66\frac{2}{3}\%$, while $\frac{5}{8} = 62\frac{1}{2}\%$. Since $66\frac{2}{3}\% > 62\frac{1}{2}\%$ it follows that $\frac{2}{3}$ is greater than $\frac{5}{8}$

$\frac{3}{7} = 42 + \%$ and $\frac{4}{9} = 44 + \%$. Since $42 + \% < 44 + \%$, it follows that $\frac{3}{7}$ is less than $\frac{4}{9}$

6. *Extended Use of Per Cent.* Like the term "fractions," the term "per cent" in its earliest connotation represented only a part and consequently could not exceed the whole. That is to say, by this definition, numerators of fractions could never exceed their denominators, and per cents had to be less than 100%. But just as man found extended uses for the fraction concept by removing this restriction (result—improper fractions), so too has he found uses

for expressions which exceed 100%. This results in no basic mathematical contradiction whatever; it merely involves a broadening of the basic definition while keeping fixed that which is mathematically pertinent. Consequently, statements such as "150% increase in cost," "200% rise in population," and the like, are not only perfectly valid statements but also extremely useful applications of the per cent concept as conceived today.

PROBLEMS SET 26

1. Using three methods: (1) equating denominators, (2) equating numerators, (3) decimal equivalents, show which fraction of the following pairs is the larger.

(a) $\frac{4}{5}, \frac{21}{25}$ (c) $\frac{3}{7}, \frac{5}{9}$ (e) $\frac{7}{12}, \frac{6}{11}$

(b) $\frac{3}{5}, \frac{5}{8}$ (d) $\frac{3}{5}, \frac{5}{7}$ (f) $\frac{3}{19}, \frac{5}{24}$

2. Determine the missing equivalent entries.

	Common Fraction	Decimal Fraction	Per Cent
(a)	$\frac{2}{5}$		
(b)	$\frac{3}{24}$		
(c)		.06	
(d)		.875	
(e)			48%
(f)			$16\frac{2}{3}\%$
(g)	$1\frac{4}{5}$		
(h)	$\frac{7}{4}$		
(i)		.0005	
(j)		1.08	
(k)			$\frac{1}{2}\%$
(l)			160%
(m)	$\frac{5}{2}$		
(n)		$.2\frac{1}{2}$	
(o)			$2\frac{1}{2}\%$
(p)	$\frac{2}{9}$		
(q)	$\frac{5}{16}$		
(r)		.1313 . . .	
(s)		.8686 . . .	
(t)			.004%
(u)	$\frac{37}{16}$		
(v)		$.0052\frac{1}{2}$	
(w)			$\frac{1}{8}\%$

3. Arrange the following numbers in the order of their magnitudes, from least to greatest.

(a) $\frac{13}{18}$, $\frac{13}{9}$, $\frac{13}{14}$, $\frac{26}{42}$, $\frac{13}{43}$, $\frac{13}{17}$, $\frac{26}{19}$

(b) $\frac{3}{4}$, $\frac{1}{6}$, $\frac{15}{28}$, $\frac{7}{12}$, $\frac{5}{21}$, $\frac{71}{84}$, $\frac{1}{2}$

(c) .37, .038, .375, .369, 3.7, .3084

(d) .36, .972, .478, .8, .63, .359

4. Arrange the following in the order of their magnitudes, from greatest to least.

(a) .374, $\frac{3}{8}$, 37%, $\frac{39}{99}$, .376

(b) .0$\frac{3}{4}$, .07, 7.4%, $\frac{1}{13}$, $\frac{7}{8}$%

(c) 121%, $\frac{5}{4}$, $1\frac{17}{98}$, 1,260 tenths, .125

5. Compare the present value of each of the numbers below with its changed value should we erase denominators.

$$\frac{1}{6}, \quad \frac{1}{15}, \quad \frac{2}{13}, \quad \frac{4}{9}, \quad \frac{6}{5}$$

6. Compare the present value of each of the numbers below with its changed value should we erase numerators.

$$\frac{1}{7}, \quad \frac{2}{3}, \quad \frac{3}{5}, \quad \frac{13}{17}, \quad \frac{6}{5}$$

7. Arrange the following numbers in terms of nearness to unity (1), from nearest to most distant.

(a) $\frac{3}{5}$, $\frac{5}{3}$, $\frac{4}{3}$, $\frac{7}{8}$, $\frac{9}{10}$, $\frac{4}{5}$

(b) 1.02, .97, .909, 1.2, .979

(c) $\frac{7}{8}$, 86%, 1.09, $\frac{8}{7}$, 1.1, 102%

8. What happens to the value of the fraction (answer for both proper and improper), if we

(a) Double the numerator?

(b) Halve the denominator?

(c) Halve the numerator and double the denominator?

(d) Increase the numerator by twice its value?

(e) Increase both the numerator and denominator by three?

(f) Divide the numerator and denominator by three?

Unit 27: Percentage

1. *Per Cent as a Ratio.* In the previous unit, it was noted that the concept of per cent was of value in the formation of comparative judgments involving more and less. We turn now to explore the role of this fraction form in the other phase of comparison, that of ratio or measurement. Problems which come under this heading are known as "percentage" problems.

It will be recalled that within the framework of common fractions it was valid to identify the numerator and denominator with the principle elements of a ratio. For instance, the common fraction $\frac{3}{5}$ might be interpreted as meaning "3 compared to 5" or "the ratio of 3 to 5." The ratio interpretation of the per cent form of a fraction is immediately evident in the reading of the term: $16\% = 16$ *per cento* $= 16$ per hundred, thus, 16 compared to 100.

The per cent has become an extremely useful tool in the realm of business. As early as the sixteenth century it was used extensively for computing interest. Gradually its utility spread to matters of profit and loss, taxation, commission, discount, and a host of other business situations. The fact that we in the United States have a decimal monetary system in which the two major denominations are the cent and the dollar (100 cents) increases for us the potential value of the per cent form, for it affords an easy translation from per cent to "cents on the dollar." To illustrate this, suppose a company declares bankruptcy and can claim in assets only 83% of its liabilities or indebtedness. The just share for each creditor then is 83% of what was due him or 83¢ on each dollar he is owed by the bankrupt company.

2. *Elements of a Percentage Problem.* Fundamentally, all percentage problems are comparison problems and involve three basic elements:

(a) the *base:* the quantity which is the basis or standard for the comparison.
(b) the *percentage:* the quantity which is compared.
(c) the *rate:* the expression of the comparison of percentage to base in the form of per cent.

The great versatility of the percentage concept stems from the fact that it is amenable to so many other basic concepts. Within these different conceptual frameworks, the elemental terms, of course, take on a variety of interpretations. In fact, any one of the concepts which we shall mention here might well be made the vehicle for rationalizing the concept of percentage.

In the case of measurement, the percentage would represent the magnitude to be measured, the base the unit of measurement, and the rate the number of times the base measures the percentage.

In terms of common fractions, the percentage would be identified with the numerator, the base with the denominator, and the rate would become merely the per cent equivalent of such a fraction.

In terms of division, the percentage would be the dividend, the base the divisor, and the rate the quotient.

In terms of a proportion, we would have (percentage : base = rate : 100%).

In terms of a part-whole relationship, the percentage would be identified as a part of the whole, while the base would be the whole; the rate, then, would be the per cent expression of this part-whole relationship.

Thus we see that there are many ways to interpret percentage; and within each of these interpretations there are an infinite number of potential problems. But basic to all of them are the three fundamental elements: the base, the percentage, and the rate.

3. *Rationale for the Solution of Percentage Problems.* Basic to every percentage problem is the concept of comparison. Fundamentally these problems always involve a comparison of one quantity to another, with the expression of the ratio of these two quantities as a per cent. In terms of the elements defined in the previous section, this is to say that every problem fundamentally involves the comparison of a percentage to a base, with the expression of their ratio as a rate. Expressed as a formula:

$$\frac{\text{percentage}}{\text{base}} = \text{rate}$$

If two of these three elements are known, the third can be determined. This can be verified by identifying this comparison or ratio problem as a case of measurement division in which the rate is associated with the quotient, the base with the divisor, and the percentage with the dividend. Thus

$$\frac{\text{percentage}}{\text{base}} = \text{rate} \qquad \text{base}\overline{)\text{percentage}}^{\,\text{rate}}$$

From this we can see that *if the base and percentage are known*, division of the percentage by the base will yield a quotient, which can in turn be translated to the rate. A translation is necessary here, since the rate is expected to be in per cent form, and since the per cent form is not a computational form, it can not result directly from the division of two numbers. What does result is a ratio which must be translated or reduced to per cent form.

On the other hand, *if both the base and rate are known*, what we have learned about division should indicate the way for finding the third element, the percentage. Here the divisor (base) and quotient (rate) are known, and the dividend (percentage) is sought. Since the dividend is actually the product of the divisor and quotient, the percentage must be the product of the base and rate. Once more, the rate as given is likely to be in per cent form, so a reduction of this element to a computational form (either common fraction or decimal) is necessary before multiplication of base and rate can take place.

Finally, *when the rate and percentage are known* and the base is sought, our knowledge of the two operations, which are inverses of each other, multiplication and division, will again indicate the way. Since, as we have stated, the percentage is the product of two factors, the base and the rate, if one of these factors is missing or unknown (base), dividing the product (percentage) by the known factor (rate) should yield the missing or unknown factor. And once more it will be necessary to reduce the rate to one of the computational forms before the computation can take place.

4. *Solving Percentage Problems.* The rationale for all problem solving, whatever the nature of the problem, involves two fundamentals. The first is an understanding of the problem. This means careful reading and analysis to determine what you want to know, what is given, and, most important, what relationship there is between what you do know and what you want to know. Then, second, you must decide what tool or device will serve to extract that which you want to know from what you already know. Both these phases are necessary and equally important.

Bringing these generalizations to bear upon our particular type of problem, the percentage problem, the direction toward their solution is clear.

1. Analyze the problem thoroughly; get its sense, and establish what you are looking for: a base, a percentage, or a rate.

2. Identify in the problem the expressions of the base, rate, percentage. This can be facilitated by getting clear in your mind what is being compared to what in the problem.

3. Bring your computational tools to bear upon the problem and solve for the unknown element in terms of its relationship with the known elements.

By way of illustration we present three problems.

(a) *Percentage and base known, rate unknown:*
  Example: An investment of $425 netted an annual interest payment of $13.60. What was the annual rate of return for this investment?

Here we are asked to compare the interest payment with the investment; the ratio of this comparison, expressed in per cent form, is the rate of return for this investment. Consequently, the investment itself is the basis for our comparison ($425) and the interest payment is the quantity compared ($13.60). The rate is sought. Thus

$$\frac{\text{percentage (\$13.60)}}{\text{base (\$4.25)}} = \text{rate (?)} \quad \text{or}$$

$$\text{base (\$425))}\overline{\text{percentage (\$13.60)}}^{\text{rate (?)}}$$

To find the rate, the quotient, *we divide the percentage by the base.* The result, .032 expresses the ratio of this comparison; when .032 is expressed as a per cent (3.2%) we have the required rate.

$$\$13.60 \div \$425 = .032 = 3.2\%$$

(b) *Base and rate known, percentage unknown*

Example: To what commission is a salesman entitled for selling $1,750 worth of goods if his rate of commission is 12%?

The ratio or comparison of a salesman's actual commission to his total sales is his *rate* of commission (and not his percentage as it is sometimes wrongly referred to). In this problem we know the basis for the comparison ($1,750) and the ratio of the comparison (12%), but not his actual commission, the quantity which is compared. Thus:

$$\frac{\text{percentage (?)}}{\text{base (\$1,750)}} = \text{rate (12\%)} \quad \text{or}$$

$$\text{base (\$1,750))}\overline{\text{percentage (?)}}^{\text{rate (12\%)}}$$

Here we seek the dividend, the product of the divisor and quotient; so after reducing the 12% to either its decimal equivalent (.12) or to its fractional equivalent ($\frac{3}{25}$) we *find the percentage by multiplying the rate with the base.*

$$.12 \times \$1,750 = \$210 \quad \text{or} \quad \tfrac{3}{25} \times \$1,750 = \$210$$

(c) *Percentage and rate known, base unknown*

Example: Forty students from one school attended a convention. If this represented 5% of the total enrollment of that school, what is the total enrollment?

This problem involves the comparison of a certain subgroup (40 students) to the whole group. The ratio of this comparison is given (5%). Thus

$$\frac{\text{percentage (40 students)}}{\text{base (?)}} = \text{rate (5\%)} \quad \text{or}$$

$$\text{base (?))}\overline{\text{percentage (40 students)}}^{\text{rate (5\%)}}$$

Here the divisor, a factor of the dividend, is unknown and can be found by dividing the dividend by the known factor (the quotient). So, after reducing the rate to either its decimal equivalent ($5\% = .05$) or to its common fraction equivalent ($5\% = \frac{1}{20}$), we *find the base*, the missing factor, *by dividing the percentage by the rate.*

$$40 \text{ students} \div .05 = 800 \text{ students}$$
$$\text{or} \quad 40 \text{ students} \div \frac{1}{20} = 800 \text{ students}$$

Throughout these problems a consistency with what we have stated about measurement division can be noted. The ratio is always abstract; the dividend and divisor (percentage and base) when stated in concrete terms are always in agreement. This will be further evident in the other percentage problems that follow. In other words, if the base is expressed in dollars, or people, or years, then the percentage will also be expressed in dollars, or people, or years, and conversely. In view of this, our earlier statement that a salesman's rate of commission (which is perforce an abstract number) should not be referred to as a percentage (which must agree with the base) might take on added meaning.

5. *Rates Greater than 100%.* Our basic definition identifies the percentage with that which is to be compared and the base with the basis or standard of the comparison; there is no restriction upon the relative sizes which these two terms might take. When the percentage is less than the base, the ratio expressed fractionally is bound to be less than 1; hence its per cent equivalent will be less than 100%. On the other hand, when the percentage (that which is to be compared) exceeds the standard of the comparison, the ratio in its fractional expression obviously will be greater than 1, therefore its per cent equivalent will be greater than 100%.

But, whether the percentage is greater than the base or less than the base, the rationales for the three types of percentage problems remain inviolate. The problems which follow demonstrate the point.

1. The elementary school population in a certain city was 64,000 in 1949. In 1954 it was 96,000. Compare the 1954 school population with that of 1949.

This problem is similar to our first illustration in the previous section in which the percentage (that which is compared, the 96,000) and the base (64,000) are known. The comparison is expressed by a rate. Thus

$$\frac{\text{percentage (96,000)}}{\text{base (64,000)}} = \text{rate (?)}$$

$$64{,}000)\overline{96{,}000.0} ^{1.5} = \frac{150}{100} = 150\%$$

2. In 1947, a market basket of certain groceries cost $12. Today that same basket of groceries costs 130% of what it did in 1947. How much does it cost today?

In this problem the base of the comparison ($12) and rate (130%) are known. Our task is to find the percentage, the quantity which is compared. So:

$$\frac{\text{percentage (?)}}{\text{base (\$12)}} = \text{rate (130\%)}$$

$$(130\% = 1.3) \qquad : 1.3 \times \$12.00 = \$15.60$$
$$\text{or} \quad (130\% = 1\tfrac{3}{10} = \tfrac{13}{10}) : \tfrac{13}{10} \times \$12.00 = \$15.60$$

3. In a certain locality the mean summer temperature in degrees Fahrenheit is 220% of the winter mean temperature. Find the winter mean if the summer mean is 77°.

In this problem the rate (220%) and percentage (77°) are known. The element desired is the standard for the comparison, the base. Thus

$$\frac{\text{percentage (77°)}}{\text{base (?)}} = \text{rate (220\%)}$$

$$(220\% = 2.20) \qquad : 77° \div 2.20 = 35°$$
$$\text{or} \quad (220\% = 2\tfrac{1}{5} = \tfrac{11}{5}) : 77° \div \ \tfrac{11}{5} = 35°$$

6. *Percentage Problems Involving More or Less.* Percentage problems which involve more or less can be particularly troublesome if the analytic and identification phases of problem solving are not performed with care. Frequently one or two words can change the sense of the problem and lead to considerably different solutions. To illustrate this, we shall repeat the problems of the preceding section with a slight change in wording and see that we are led to different solutions. (Word changes in the statement of the problem are underlined.)

1. The elementary school population in a certain city was 64,000 in 1949. In 1954 it was 96,000. Compare the increase in the 1954 population with that of 1949.

Here the "quantity compared," the percentage, is not given explicitly. If the school population jumped in 1954 to 96,000 from 64,000 in 1949, the increase was 96,000 − 64,000 = 32,000. To compare this increase to the school population of 1949, we have

$$\frac{\text{percentage (32,000)}}{\text{base (64,000)}} = \text{rate (?)}$$

$$\begin{array}{r} .5 \\ 64,000\overline{)32,000.0} = 50\% \end{array}$$

From this it can be said that the elementary school population of that city increased 50% over that of the base year 1949 (which is of course an equivalent statement to "the school population in 1954 is 150% of that of 1949.)

2. In 1947 a market basket of certain groceries cost $12. Today that same basket of groceries costs 130% more than it did in 1947. How much does it cost today?

If the groceries cost 130% more than they did in 1947, then today they must cost what they cost in 1947 plus 130%. In other words, in this problem the groceries today cost (100% + 130%) or 230% of what they did in 1947. So,

$$\frac{\text{percentage (?)}}{\text{base (\$12)}} = \text{rate (230\%)}$$

$$(230\% = 2.3) : 2.3 \times \$12 = \$27.60$$

3. In a certain locality the mean summer temperature is 220% more than the winter mean temperature. Find the winter mean if the summer mean is 77°.

As in the previous problem, 220% more than the winter mean temperature implies that the average summer temperature is the "winter mean plus 220% of the winter mean" or 330% of the winter mean. So

$$\frac{\text{percentage (77°)}}{\text{base (?)}} = \text{rate (330\%)}$$

$$(330\% = 3.3) : 3.3\overline{)77°} \quad 23+° \text{ (winter mean)}$$

Since those three problems all involve rates greater than 100%, it follows that it would be impossible to adapt them as illustrations of "less than" percentage problems. (You cannot decrease something more than 100%, though some advertisements have been known to read "Prices slashed 150%!") Here are two illustrations of "less than" percentage problems.

1. A salesman earned $6,000 last year and only $4,500 this year. What per cent less did he earn this year than last?

Here the "difference" between last year's earnings and this is $6,000 − $4,500 = $1,500. Comparing this difference with last year's salary of $6,000, we get

$$\frac{\text{percentage (\$1,500)}}{\text{base (\$6,000)}} = \text{rate (?)}$$

$$6,000\overline{)1,500.00} \quad .25 = 25\%$$

Hence his earnings were 25% less than those of last year. To state this another way, we might say, "His salary this year is 75% (100% − 25%) of last year's."

2. Attendance at a school play was 400 the first night, but a decrease of 20% was expected the second night. How many people were expected the second night?

Here we seek the percentage when the base (400 people) is known directly and the rate implicitly. If there will be 20% less the second night, the attendance will only be 80% (100% − 20%) of that of the first night. So:

$$\frac{\text{percentage (?)}}{\text{base (400)}} = \text{rate (80\%)}$$

$$(80\% = .8) : .8 \times 400 \text{ people}$$
$$= 320 \text{ people (expected second night)}$$

An alternative approach to this problem would be to find the percentage in terms of <u>numbers who are expected *not* to attend</u> (20% of 400 = 80) and then subtract (400 − 80 = 320) to find how many <u>are</u> expected to attend.

PROBLEMS SET 27

1. Complete the following.

(a) 30% of 400 is ——. (h) 38.5 is ——% of 3.85.

(b) ——% of 64 is 32. (i) $162\frac{1}{2}$% of —— is 91.

(c) —— is 10% of 452. (j) 4000% of 220 is ——.

(d) 125% of 800 is ——. (k) .0002 is ——% of .008.

(e) $37\frac{1}{2}$% of 64 is ——. (l) $333\frac{1}{3}$% of .06 is ——.

(f) .03% of —— is 36. (m) 17% of —— is 34.

(g) ——% of 96 is 144. (n) ——% of $\frac{1}{9}$ is .3.

2. If payment is made on electric bills within five days, a 4% saving can be realized. How much can be saved on a bill of $18.50?

3. An automobile is advertised at $2,125 cash or $318.75 down, the balance in easy monthly payments. What is the per cent of down payment?

4. A salesman works on a 35% commission basis. What were his total sales for the month of May if his commission came to $162.12?

5. Jones, an employee earning $100 per week, was given a 10% raise in salary. One year later business difficulties necessitated a 10% cut in salary to all employees. What was Jones' weekly salary after this cut?

6. The average rent in a certain apartment house ten years ago was $45. Since then rents have increased 110%. What is the average rent today?

7. An unschooled merchant advertised "prices reduced 100% on all coats." What would you expect to pay for a coat originally priced at $87?

8. A boy has 35 cents and finds 7 cents. Later he loses 12 cents. What per cent gain did his findings represent? What per cent decrease did his loss represent?

9. A new item is expected to boost sales next year to 120% over this year's sales. If sales this year amounted to $25,000, what are next year's anticipated sales?

10. Early in the season a baseball player has got 5 hits in 20 times at bat ($\frac{5}{20} = .25$); therefore his batting average is .250. How many hits must he get in the next 30 times at bat to bring his batting average up to .340?

11. A man borrowed $500 and repaid $525 one year later. What annual rate of interest did he pay?

12. An article, bought in a state which has a 3% sales tax, cost the buyer $701.43, tax included. What was the cost of the article before taxes?

13. A piece of machinery is considered to have seen 68% of its usefulness. What was the machine worth when new, if its present value is $305.92?

14. An article lists in the catalog for $75. If it costs 16% to have it delivered and I sell it for $116, what is my rate of profit compared to the selling price?

15. If 36% of the books in a certain library are novels, and 20% of the novels have been published in 1945 or later, how many books are there in the library if there are 10,512 novels dated *prior* to 1945?

Chapter 6

APPROXIMATE
NUMBERS

Unit 28: Measurement

1. *Denominate Numbers.* As was pointed out in Chapter 1, physicists are still much unsettled as to the fundamental nature of the universe, that is, whether it is discrete (atomic) or continuous. In any case, at the layman's level of comprehension, reality is in some cases continuous and in other cases discrete. Evaluating quantitively a whole which consists of discrete, or separate, elements can be accomplished easily by putting each of these elements into one-to-one correspondence with the set of natural numbers. This process, which evaluates the whole in terms of "how many," we already know as *counting*.

On the other hand, when the whole is fluid and continuous, there are no visibly discrete elements which can be placed into one-to-one correspondence with the natural numbers. So, in order to evaluate such magnitudes, it becomes necessary to *invent* some "typical element" which we call a *unit of measure*. Then, by subdividing the whole into so many parts, each equal to this unit of measure, we can place these parts in one-to-one correspondence with the set of natural numbers and thus obtain a quantitive evaluation of the whole. This process, which answers for us the question "How much?" is referred to as *measurement*. Numbers which are used to express such measurements are called *measurement numbers* or *denominate numbers*.

In a sense, counting the discrete objects in a group also provides a measure of the group or whole, though generally the term "measurement number" is reserved for only continuous wholes. To avoid any ambiguity in this respect, we shall use the term "counting number" exclusively to characterize the "how many" of discrete quantities, and the term "denominate number" exclusively to characterize the "how much" of continuous quantities. This implies that both counting numbers and denominate numbers may be referred to as measurement numbers.

We are now ready for an important distinction between counting numbers and denominate numbers. When counting numbers express the measure of a whole which consists of discrete elements, they express the true measurement of that whole *exactly*. When denominate numbers express the measurement of a whole which is continuous, they express the true measurement *approximately*. In this context denominate numbers are referred to loosely as approximate numbers.*

The reason for this difference in exactness is easily understood from an analysis of the differences between discrete wholes and continuous wholes. A pile of eggs, for instance, might be used as an example of a discrete whole. Although the eggs may differ somewhat in size, shape, color, etc., each element in the pile is an individual egg, a discrete element, distinct and separate from all the other members of the pile. Consequently, no matter how many times these eggs are counted, or by whom, each time the answer to the question "How many?" will be the same.

In contrast, consider a certain volume of water which is fluid and continuous, and which does not lend itself to any particular subdivision into discrete elements. In order to provide the answer to "How much?" here, we need to select some unit of volume—a cup or a dipper, perhaps—then, by extracting from the original volume these unit volumes, while keeping their account by setting up a one-to-one correspondence with our counting numbers, we can eventually evaluate or measure the original volume of water as the equivalent of "so many cupfuls."

Now, about the exactness of such measurement: let us suppose that another person uses his own cup to measure this same volume of water. Will he get the same result? No, not exactly. The amount of difference between the two measurements will depend primarily upon how much larger or smaller his cup is than ours. Furthermore,

* Actually the numbers themselves are not approximate, they are exact, but as measures of some particular magnitude they are only approximately correct.

even if this person uses the same cup we did, his measurement will *still* differ from ours. In fact, any two independent measurements of a continuous whole will always differ to some degree. Causes of such discrepancies may be traced to differences in applying the unit measure (care in the act of measuring which, in this case, would involve judgment as to the fullness of each cup); small differences in the size of the volume and the size of the unit measure (caused by changes in temperature and pressure); differences in the evaluation of the remainder or residue, after all possible full unit measures have been taken. Consequently, in the realm of the continuous, which also includes weight, distance, area, time, and the like, true measurement answers are forever unknown, because absolute accuracy or exactness in this respect is humanly unattainable.

2. *History of Measurement.* The history of measurement is basically the history of certain units of measure. Since continuous magnitudes present no logical breaks or subdivisions, the choice of a unit of measure is purely arbitrary, a matter of convenience to the user. Consequently, it is no surprise to find the earliest attempts at measurement highly personal, with certain body measures serving as ready units of length and personally owned stones and containers serving for measures of weight and capacity.

Of frequent occurrence in antiquity were the following five units of linear measure: the width of the *finger*, the width of the *palm*, the *hand span* (the distance between the tip of the thumb and the tip of the little finger of a spread hand), the *cubit* (the distance from the tip of the elbow to the tip of the longest finger), and the *fathom* (the distance between the fingertips of each hand when the arms are outstretched to left and right). Despite the fact that these measuring units were personal and independent of each other, a certain interrelationship was generally held to exist among them: four fingers equaled a palm, three palms equaled a span, and two spans equaled a cubit. Thus we have an early attempt at a *system* of measures.

For measuring linear distances, the *foot*, the *step*, and the *pace* (*double step*)—again personal body measures—were frequent units of measure among the ancients. For greater distances, the Romans used the *mille passuum* which meant "one thousand paces." Since the pace was a double step, about 5 feet in length, the *mille passuum* was a unit of about 5,000 feet in length, thus the forerunner of our present comparable unit of distance, the *mile* (5,280 feet).

Later in medieval England a few other units of measure which have endured to the present made their appearances. For instance, the *yard* was originally a Saxon measure for the distance around a man's body at chest level. Generally speaking, this was about half a fathom, or the distance from the tip of the fingers of an outstretched hand to the middle of the body. Even though today the yard is standardized at 36 inches, drygoods clerks frequently can be seen to measure cloth by spanning the goods between chin and outstretched fingertips. The term *furlong*, used little today outside of horseracing, is a contraction of *furrow long* and originally meant the length of a furrow that could be plowed by an ox without a rest. Later, it was standardized at 40 rods.

The *rod* was originally a stick carried by the plowman as an ox goad, which doubled as a measuring aid in calculating the distance between furrows. Undoubtedly the plowman's rod was considerably shorter than our present rod, standardized at 16½ feet. In fact, our present rod more closely approximates that of sixteenth-century Germany, where the following rule served to establish the length and relationship between the foot and rod:

> If you stand at the door of a church on a Sunday, and have sixteen men stop—tall ones and short ones—as they leave after service and have them stand so that their left feet are toe to heel behind each other, the length obtained shall be the right and lawful *rod* with which to measure and survey land. Furthermore, the sixteenth part of that distance shall be the right and lawful *foot*.

The inch, as was previously pointed out, came to us from the *uncia* which in Roman parlance was the twelfth part of some whole. Thus the inch was, and still is today, the twelfth part of the foot.

The history of standard units of measure for weights and capacity is much more devious and involved than that of length.

The ancients anticipated the developers of the metric system by tying their system of weights in with that of linear measurement. Originally the *pound* was defined as one sixtieth of a cubic foot of water, which closely approximated our definition, since a cubic foot of water by our standards weighs 62.5 pounds. The Romans called their pound the *libra* (whence comes our abbreviation "lb") and subdivided it into their usual twelve parts (*uncia*) from which we derive our pound subdivision, the *ounce*. During the Middle Ages, a series of other pound definitions came into use, causing no little confusion in the marketplace and trading centers throughout the world. This disorder persisted for several centuries, resisting a variety of attempts at standardization, until 1878, when the Parliament of England legally established the avoirdupois pound weight at 7,000 grains as the only pound, and fixed the ounce at one-sixteenth of that pound. The grain was originally the weight of a grain of wheat, but today it is defined in relation to a cubic inch of distilled water: a cubic inch of distilled water at 30 inches of barometric pressure and 62°F is defined to weigh 252.458 grains. Thus the grain is the basic element for the whole system of Anglo-American weights.

In early England an attempt was made to standardize these measures by issuing officially minted weights, such as the pound and its subweights, the shilling ($\frac{1}{20}$ pound) and penny ($\frac{1}{12}$ shilling). These official weights were not only used to balance scales but were traded as well, thus taking on the function of money. As a matter of fact, the money system in England today follows this same scheme:

$$12 \text{ pennies (pence)} = 1 \text{ shilling}$$
$$20 \text{ shillings} \qquad = 1 \text{ pound}$$

Most confusing of all has been the history of measures of capacity or volume. Originally in England capacity measures were based on weight, which gave to the maxim "the pint's a pound the world around" a certain validity. But since the densities of wine and ale, for instance, differ, it follows that a gallon of ale will differ in volume from a gallon of wine, or for that matter, from a gallon of corn or wheat, because in England there is no distinction drawn between liquid and dry measures of volume such as we have in the United States. Eventually, in 1824, the English Weights and Measures Act did away with wine gallons, wheat gallons, ale gallons, and the like, and defined the imperial standard gallon as that volume occupied by ten pounds of distilled water at 62°F and 30 inches barometric pressure. A bushel was defined as a volume equal to 8 gallons, and a pint remained $\frac{1}{8}$ of the imperial gallon.

Shortly after the stabilization of measures in England, the Treasury Department of the United States recommended the wine gallon (231 cubic inches) as the basic unit of liquid measure. This was accepted by Congress, and, as a result, in the United States the gallon is standardized at a volume roughly $\frac{4}{5}$ of the imperial standard gallon. Since the British had defined their gallon by weight and the United States by volume, these two are not exactly interchangeable.

In the United States it is illegal to interchange dry measure and

liquid measure units. The bushel, for instance, is in no way con-
nected with the gallon as it is in England; in this country the volume
of a dry pint equals 33.6 cubic inches, while that of a liquid pint
equals 28.9 cubic inches.

On the whole, conditions with respect to dry measures in the
United States today are especially chaotic. Not only does the bushel
differ in capacity for such diverse items as charcoal, corn, and
potatoes, but the bushel also varies from one part of the country to
another. It is reported that there are eight kinds of tons and nine
different volumes for barrel;* the U.S. National Bureau of Standards
uses over 500 pages of fine type to define all units of measure extant.

Below, in Table XII are given standard measures, their subdivisions and multiples, as generally accepted in the United States
today with respect to measurement of distance, weight, and capacity.

TABLE XII. SYSTEM OF MEASURES USED IN THE UNITED STATES

Length

12 inches	= 1 foot
3 feet	= 1 yard
16½ feet	} = 1 rod
5½ yards	
5,280 feet	
1,760 yards	} = 1 mile
320 rods	

Dry Measures

2 pints	= 1 quart
8 quarts	= 1 peck
4 pecks	= 1 bushel
(1 bushel	= 2,150.42 cubic inches)

Avoirdupois Weight

2,000 grains	} = 1 pound
16 ounces	
100 pounds	= 1 hundredweight
2,000 pounds	= 1 ton
2,240 pounds	= 1 long ton

Liquid Measure

2 gills	= 1 cup
2 cups	= 1 pint
2 pints	= 1 quart
4 quarts	= 1 gallon
(1 gallon	= 231 cubic inches)
31½ gallons	= 1 barrel
2 barrels	= 1 hogshead

3. *Computations with Denominate Numbers.* Actually the various
units of measure within a system of measures can be thought of as
so many different calibrations, each bearing a specific ratio to the
other. Therefore it is possible to express a given measurement in
many different ways. For example, a distance of one mile may be
expressed variously as 320 rods, 1,760 yards, 5,280 feet, or 63,360
inches. When a measurement is inexact with respect to any of these
specific denominations, instead of expressing the measurement with

*Twentieth Yearbook of the National Council of Teachers of Mathematics, National
Council of Teachers of Mathematics, 1201 Sixteenth St., N.W., Washington, D.C.,
1948, p. 11.

a mixed number coefficient (e.g., $5\frac{1}{3}$ yards) we often use a compounded expression with the fractional part of the original expressed
in terms of a smaller calibration or denomination (e.g., 5 yards
1 foot). Consequently in the realm of measurement we are constantly running into such compound denominate expressions as
6 hours 32 minutes 20 seconds, 16 yards 2 feet 7 inches, 7 pounds
8 ounces.

We are here concerned with a change in form without any change
in value. This of course is a reduction. For example, 3 pounds 2
ounces can be expressed as 50 ounces $[(3 \times 16) + 2]$, or in the
reverse direction, 50 ounces may be expressed as 3 pounds 2 ounces:

$$\frac{3R2}{16)\overline{50}}$$

or, 2 days 4 hours 22 minutes can be reduced to 52 hours 22 minutes
or to 3,142 minutes and vice versa; and so on. Computation with
denominate numbers makes constant use of reductions in both directions.

To compute with these denominate numbers, the same basic
principles that were developed in our discussions of whole number
algorisms are again our guides. Here, however, instead of the orders
being powers of ten as they were in our decimal notation, the orders
in our English-American system of weights and measures follow no
specific pattern of ratios. For instance, the ratio which exists between adjacent orders in the decimal scale is invariably 1 : 10 or
10 : 1, depending upon the direction. In our systems of weights
and measures, not only do we get a variation of ratios between
systems, but frequently a variation with each pair of orders within
the system. To illustrate this, in our system of linear measure it
takes twelve units of one order to equal one unit in the next higher
order (inches to feet), while it takes only three units of that order
to equal one unit in the next higher order (feet to yards), and so on.

In addition of denominate numbers, as in our algorism for whole
numbers and fractions, the principle of likeness is again of vital
importance and is responsible for the specific arrangement of the
addends. Thus, in order to add together compound denominate
numbers we add likes to likes and reduce the final sum "to simplest
terms." For example, suppose we wish to find the total length of two
boards, one 2 feet 5 inches long and the other 4 feet 10 inches long.
We arrange the addends as follows and add likes to likes.

$$2 \text{ ft} \quad 5 \text{ in.}$$
$$+4 \text{ ft} \ 10 \text{ in.}$$
$$6 \text{ ft} \ 15 \text{ in.} = 7 \text{ ft } 3 \text{ in.}$$

(or, if desired, 2 yd 1 ft 3 in.)

In multiplication of denominate numbers the principle of distribution is most important. For instance, a measurement of time such as 3 hours 42 minutes 28 seconds means a time lapse equal to the sum of 3 hours + 42 minutes + 28 seconds; if we wish to triple this time, by the principle of distribution the product can be found by multiplying the component parts piecemeal, reducing where necessary, either at the end or en route. Thus

$$3 \text{ hours} + 42 \text{ minutes} + 28 \text{ seconds}$$
$$\times 3$$

Reducing en route:

1. $3 \times 28 = 84$ sec $= 1$ min $+ 24$ sec. Write 24 sec and carry 1 min.

2. 3×42 min $= 126$ min; plus carried 1 min $= 127$ min $= 2$ hr $+ 7$ min. Write 7 min and carry 2 hr.

3. 3×3 hr $= 9$ hr; plus carried 2 hr $= 11$ hr. Write 11 hr.
   Total product: 11 hr 7 min 24 sec.

Reducing at the end:

Multiply 3 hr + 42 min + 28 sec by 3 and get 9 hr + 126 min + 84 sec. This can be reduced to 9 hr + 126 min + (1 min + 24 sec) which equals 9 hr + 127 min + 24 sec. In turn, this can be expressed as 9 hr + (2 hr + 7 min) + 24 sec, or 11 hr + 7 min + 24 sec.

In the subtraction of denominate numbers the principle of likeness again dominates the operation, as we subtract likes from likes. In cases where order impasses are met, they are removed as usual by either decomposition or equal additions. For example, if we wished to subtract 4 weeks 5 days from 9 weeks 2 days, we would solve the problem by either:

(a) Decomposition (in the minuend decompose 1 of the 9 weeks to 7 days):

$$9 \text{ weeks 2 days} \rightarrow 8 \text{ weeks 9 days}$$
$$\underline{4 \text{ weeks 5 days} \rightarrow 4 \text{ weeks 5 days}}$$
$$4 \text{ weeks 4 days}$$

(b) Equal additions (add equally to minuend and subtrahend: 1 week to subtrahend and 7 days to minuend).

$$9 \text{ weeks 2 days} \rightarrow 9 \text{ weeks 9 days}$$
$$\underline{4 \text{ weeks 5 days} \rightarrow 5 \text{ weeks 5 days}}$$
$$4 \text{ weeks 4 days}$$

Methods for handling division of denominate numbers may be classified in two ways. When the division is partitive, that is, the divisor is abstract, the most effective technique is one similar to the long division algorism (or if many of the steps are done mentally, short division). In either case the method rests heavily upon the principle of distribution. To illustrate, if we should cut a length of rope 7 yards 1 foot 8 inches long into 4 equal pieces, how long would each piece be?

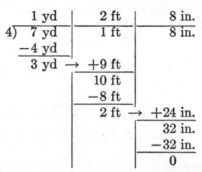

Steps in the computation:

1. 7 yd ÷ 4 = 1 yd and a remainder of 3 yd.
   Convert the 3 yd to feet and add to the 1 ft already in the dividend. Result, 10 ft.
2. 10 ft ÷ 4 = 2 ft and a remainder of 2 ft.
   Convert the remainder of 2 ft to inches and add to the 8 in. already in the dividend. Result, 32 in.
3. 32 in. ÷ 4 = 8 in. exactly.

To check, we of course multiply the quotient 1 yd 2 ft 8 in. by 4 and see that the product equals the dividend 7 yd 1 ft 8 in.

When the division is measurement division, that is, both divisor and dividend are denominate numbers, usually the best approach is to convert both terms to the smallest denominate part of either. In this way we get both the divisor and dividend expressed in like terms (homogeneous with each other) and can solve as any other division of like terms. By way of example:

How many bags of sugar, each weighing 1 lb 6 oz, can I get from one large quantity weighing 6 lb 14 oz?

$$\overset{5}{\overline{}}$$
$$\text{1 lb 6 oz})\overline{\text{6 lb 14 oz}} \rightarrow \text{22 oz})\overline{\text{110 oz}}$$
$$\phantom{\text{1 lb 6 oz})\text{6 lb 14 oz} \rightarrow \text{22 oz})}\underline{\text{110 oz}}$$

Answer, 5 bags.

This technique of reducing all measurements to the lowest ordered denomination of course can be used for any operation involving denominate numbers.

4. *The Metric System.* The outstanding fact in the history of weights and measures in the United States and England is that the basic units are personal in origin and traditional in maintenance. All efforts at standardization have involved the regulation and control of measures of long standing. The most remarkable thing about the decimalized metric system is the fact that it is based entirely upon science and logic and represents a clean break from custom.

The metric system, as we know it today, originated in France during the last decade of the eighteenth century, an outgrowth of the French Revolution. Under this system, certain basic unit measures of distance, capacity, and weight are defined. Its respective multiples and subdivisions (orders or denominations) are not related to each other by the haphazard ratios of our systems of measure, but follow the strict ratio of 1 : 10. Thus, there is produced a decimal system of weights and measures which is perfectly compatible with our decimal system of number notation.

The basic unit of length is the *meter*, by definition the distance between two marks on a platinum bar deposited in the Archives of State in France. It represents the best estimate of the time (1799) of one ten-millionth part of a terrestrial meridian running through Paris and stretching between the equator and the north pole. The basic unit of capacity in this system, which is employed for both dry and liquid materials, is the *liter*, a cube with edge dimension one-tenth of a meter. The basic unit of weight is the *gram*, originally the weight of a cube of pure water, at the temperature of melting ice, whose dimension is one-hundredth of a meter. Also in the Archives of State, along with the platinum meter, is a platinum weight equal to 1,000 grams (a kilogram) which since 1799 has been the standard for all metric weights.

Once the meter, liter, and gram were defined, the system provided multiples and subunits for each of these in powers of ten. Greek prefixes for ten (deca-), hundred (hecto-), thousand (kilo-) and ten thousand (myria-) have been appropriated to designate the various multiples; Latin prefixes are used to designate the subunits: tenths (deci-), hundreds (centi-), and thousandths (milli-). Tables of the basic metric units of distance, capacity, and weight follow.

1 myriameter	=	10,000 meters	1 myrialiter	=	10,000 liters
1 kilometer	=	1,000 meters	1 kiloliter	=	1,000 liters
1 hectometer	=	100 meters	1 hectoliter	=	100 liters
1 decameter	=	10 meters	1 decaliter	=	10 liters
1 meter	=	1 meter	1 liter	=	1 liter
1 decimeter	=	.1 meter	1 deciliter	=	.1 liter
1 centimeter	=	.01 meter	1 centiliter	=	.01 liter
1 millimeter	=	.001 meter	1 milliliter	=	.001 liter

1 myriagram	=	10,000 grams
1 kilogram	=	1,000 grams
1 hectogram	=	100 grams
1 decagram	=	10 grams
1 gram	=	1 gram
1 decigram	=	.1 gram
1 centigram	=	.01 gram
1 milligram	=	.001 gram

5. *Computations with Metric Measures.* The fact that the various orders or denominations in the metric system involve ratios which are powers of ten simplifies computations with these numbers tremendously. For instance, a distance of 3 meters 5 decameters 7 centimeters can be written as 3.57 meters and vice versa. If we wish to add this distance with another which is, say, 5 meters 8 decimeters 6 centimeters (5.86 meters) we simply add 3.57 to 5.86 as though they were the usual decimal expressions:

$$\begin{array}{r} 3.57 \\ +5.86 \\ \hline 9.43 \end{array}$$

The sum may be interpreted directly as 9.43 meters or as 9 meters 4 decimeters 3 centimeters. No specific reductions are necessary after the computation is completed, for all reductions are automatically taken care of in the normal process of "carrying."

Reductions from one metric denomination to another present no difficulty whatever. For instance, our resulting 9.43 meters can be expressed alternatively by a "movement" of the decimal point to read 94.3 decimeters, 943 centimeters, 9,430 millimeters, or in the other direction .943 decameters, .0943 hectometers, or .00943 kilometers.

Multiplication of these metric measures is also relatively simple. For example, suppose we are interested in the total volume of 8 jars, each with a capacity of 7 liters 4 deciliters.

$$7 \text{ liters } 4 \text{ deciliters } = \quad 7.4 \text{ liters}$$
$$\underline{\times 8}$$
$$59.2 \text{ liters}$$

which equals 59 liters 2 deciliters or 5 decaliters 9 liters 2 deciliters.

Or perhaps we may wish to first convert the contents of each jar to the smallest denomination involved, deciliters. The reduction is accomplished immediately upon removal of the decimal point. Thus

$$8 \times 74 \text{ deciliters } = 592 \text{ deciliters}$$

which also can be reduced to 59.2 liters or 5.92 decaliters, etc.

Similarly with subtraction and division, the computations follow along the lines of the usual algorisms for decimal operations; in the process reductions from one denomination to another are automatically taken care of and the interpretation of the component parts of the solution is immediately possible. For example,

1. If a weight of 1 gram 2 decigrams 9 centigrams is removed from a weight of 4 grams 7 centigrams, how much is left?

   4 grams 7 centigrams $\rightarrow$ 4.07
   1 gram 2 decigrams 9 centigrams $\rightarrow$ $\underline{-1.29}$
                                               2.78

                        = 2 grams 7 decigrams 8 centigrams (or 2.78 grams)

2. What is one-fifth of a total weight of 2 grams 3 centigrams 5 milligrams?

   2 grams 3 centigrams 5 milligrams = 2.035 grams
   $2.035 \div 5 = .407 = 4$ decigrams 7 milligrams (or .407 gram)

6. *Arguments For and Against Adoption of the Metric System.* England and the United States are the only two major nations of the world which do not fully use the metric system of weights and measures. In 1866 the Congress of the United States officially recognized the metric system as a legal means of measurement, but not to the exclusion of all others (whereas in France and other countries it is illegal to use any system other than the metric). The establishment of a permanent International Bureau of Weights and Measures in 1875, located near Paris and subscribed to by the United States, in effect made the metric system "official" for international transactions.

As has been pointed out, the metric system is scientific in origin and is especially adaptable to the computations of science. Because of its general world-wide acceptance it is also highly convenient for international use. Thus, as might be expected, we find among its strongest advocates the scientists, educators, diplomats, and consuls. Those resisting any change are notably the manufacturers, engineers, professional men, and the general public.

Proponents for the adoption of the metric system in the United States point out:

1. The metric system is of unquestioned superiority in the computations of science.
2. The world is becoming increasingly technological, and adjustment to its ways is necessary.
3. General acceptance of the metric system would facilitate the layman's consumption of scientific data.
4. Education would be speeded up if only one system were taught in the schools, and the metric system is more easily learned than the other.
5. Reluctance to change is unfounded. Few citizens of the United States would exchange their decimal money system for the confusing (for Americans) pound-shilling-pence system of the English. The decimal metric system of weights and measures possesses the very same superiority over the present English-American system of weights and measures.

Opponents to the metric system point out that, while systematically and logically sound, the metric system is unnatural. The general public can easily comprehend halves and quarters, they say but not tenths. The English system can trace its origin and endurance to convenience of use, and that must be the primary consideration in adopting a system of weights and measures. They also point out the fact that although for decades the metric system has been the only system taught in European schools, vestiges of former systems can still be found throughout the continent. Furthermore, within the metric system itself, people tend to halve and quarter the various measures. For instance, the most popular weight measure throughout Europe is the "half kilogram" because it comes closest to the "natural" pound (500 grams vs. 453.6 grams). If people had *really* adopted the principles of the metric system, that convenient weight would be stated as "five hectograms." * More-

---

* An interesting sidelight here is the fact that, particularly in the engineering field, there is a strong tendency to "decimalize" our basic units of measure. Expression of miles, feet, and inches in tenths and hundredths is frequent; likewise with pounds and tons; at the gas station gallons are registered in tenths.

over, the costs involved in changing such things as maps, machines, measuring instruments, standard containers, etc., would be prohibitive. Since the advantages to be gained are doubtful at best, these opponents contend, why change? Unfortunately much of the pressure for adoption of the metric system in this country has had all the earmarks of an organized propaganda campaign which, typically, has left the celebrated "man in the street" apathetic about the whole thing. What the future holds is still anybody's guess.

PROBLEMS SET 28

(To better illustrate computational techniques it may be assumed that the measurements given in the problems of this unit are exact. We shall see in the next two units that such an assumption in practical circumstances would be invalid.)

1. You are asked to measure the length of the front of a rectangular house with a yardstick. List all the possible sources of error that you can think of which could affect your measurement.

2. (a) Express 32 rods as inches, feet, yards, miles.
   (b) Express 11 bu as pecks, quarts, pints.
   (c) Express 224 lb as tons, ounces, grains.
   (d) Express $\frac{1}{63}$ bbl as hogsheads, gallons, quarts, pints, cups, gills.
   (e) Express $\frac{2}{3}$ yr as months, days, hours, minutes, seconds.

3. Express the following without using fraction coefficients for any denominator. Example: $2\frac{1}{2}$ yd = 2 yd 1 ft 6 in.

   (a) $4\frac{7}{9}$ yd   (e) $3\frac{5}{8}$ gal
   (b) $\frac{5}{3}$ miles   (f) $2\frac{23}{32}$ gal
   (c) $\frac{19}{4}$ lb   (g) $3\frac{53}{75}$ hr
   (d) $1\frac{3}{20}$ lb   (h) $2\frac{229}{504}$ weeks

4. Given 4 pieces of string of the following lengths: 3 ft 4 in.; 27 in.; $1\frac{1}{2}$ yd; $2\frac{3}{4}$ ft. How long a piece would they make if they were all tied together, assuming that each knot requires 1 in. from each piece?

5. Multiply the following by 3; by 8; by 52 and reduce to simplest terms.
   (a) 4 weeks 3 days 6 hr
   (b) 2 yd 2 ft 2 in.
   (c) 3 gal 2 qt 1 pint
   (d) 2 pecks 1 pint

6. A seaman wishes to cut a line that is 5 fathoms 4 ft 8 in. long into four equal pieces. How long will each piece be? (A fathom is 6 ft.)

7. If a horse trots a distance of 8 furlongs in 2 min, what is his average distance to the nearest inch per second?

8. How many trips must a truck make to the yard in order to haul 46 long tons of coal from a dock, provided the maximum load weight of the truck is $4\frac{3}{7}$ long tons?

9. (a) Express 42.3 meters in terms of all the denominations of the metric system of linear measurement.

(b) Express .032 liter in terms of all the denominations of the metric system of capacity.

(c) Express $2\frac{1}{4}$ kilograms in terms of all the denominations of the metric system of weights.

10. If we assume 1 kilometer equals .62136 mile,
(a) How many kilometers in a mile?
(b) How many miles in $12\frac{1}{2}$ kilometers?
(c) How many kilometers in $4\frac{1}{4}$ miles?

11. If we assume 1 liter equals 1.06 quarts,
(a) How many quarts in 1 liter?
(b) How many liters in 1 gallon?
(c) How many pints in 1 liter?

12. If we assume 1 in. equals 2.54 centimeters
(a) How many meters in 1 yard?
(b) How many inches in 2.54 meters?
(c) What part of an inch equals 1 centimeter?

13. What must be the total volume of liquid in a vat into which the following five amounts were dumped?
4 liters 3 centiliters; 46 deciliters; 1 hectoliter 20 centiliters; 4,200 milliliters; 2.14 decaliters.

14. For a scale balance we have a supply of only 1-gram, 1-decigram, 1-centigram, and 1-milligram weights. What minimum combinations of these are necessary to balance the following loads?
(a) $2\frac{3}{4}$ decagrams.
(b) 8 objects each weighing .217 grams.
(c) One-quarter of a substance which weighs 2 grams 3 decigrams 8 centigrams.

Unit 29: Approximate Numbers and Their Errors

1. *Sources of Approximate Numbers.* In the previous unit we discussed the greatest source of approximate numbers: measurement. It was noted that all measurements are stated in numbers which are approximate, because it is impossible to attain absolute accuracy in finding the number property of continuous situations. But before we investigate more fully the nature of approximate numbers, let us note a few more sources of their supply.

By definition, a *rational number* is one which can be expressed as a fraction whose numerator and denominator are integers—in effect, a simple fraction. Thus $\frac{1}{2}$, $\frac{9}{7}$, $\frac{5}{37}$, $\frac{5}{4}$, 2 ($= \frac{2}{1}$) are all rational numbers. If we attempt to express these numbers in decimal form, we know from Unit 25 that in the case of $\frac{5}{37}$, for instance, we will get a repeating, nonending decimal expression: $\frac{5}{37} =$ .135135135 . . . . Consequently, should it be necessary to use this decimal expression in some computation, a need for rounding off is clearly indicated. After this is done, the rounded-off version, say .135, would then be an *approximate decimal number* expression of the true value $\frac{5}{37}$.

Opposite this class of rational numbers is another class, known as *irrational numbers:* those real numbers which *cannot* be expressed as simple fractions. Basically, numbers in this classification fall into one of two types, the algebraic or the transcendental irrationals.

Algebraic irrationals arise as the numerical solutions of such algebraic equations as $x^2 = 3$, or $x^3 = 7$. Actually there is no rational number which when multiplied by itself equals 3 exactly, or one whose cube is exactly 7. Ordinarily we represent the exact solutions to such problems as $\sqrt{3}$ and $\sqrt[3]{7}$. However, when these irrationals are decimalized they take the form of an unending decimal *without* any specific pattern of repetition. Once again, if we wish to use their decimal expression in computation, we must round off and be satisfied with an approximate equivalent. Thus 1.732 is the approximate equivalent of $\sqrt{3}$, and 1.913 is the approximate equivalent of $\sqrt[3]{7}$.

Among the transcendental irrationals, probably the most widely known is π, that number which expresses the ratio of the circumference of any circle to its diameter (or the measurement of the circumference of any circle by a unit of measure equal to its diameter). As a matter of fact, the decimal equivalent of π has been carried to over 2000 places beyond the decimal point and, of course, the end was nowhere in sight. A five-digit approximation of this value is 3.1416; in common fraction form, we have another approximation for π, that is, $\frac{22}{7}$. Most logarithms and trigonometric functions, met in postarithmetic studies, are also examples of transcendental irrational numbers. Thus, with rare exception, the entries of trigonometric and logarithmic tables are but 4- or 5- or 7-place approximations of true values.

Convenience of interpretation is yet another source of approximate numbers. In this category we have numbers which involve data of an exact nature, but which for convenience are given expression with approximate numbers. For example, batting averages, because they are usually expressed in three digits only, would represent 9 hits in 32 times at bat (which is *exactly* .28125) as an approximate figure of .281. Other illustrations which might be cited here are those of an experienced shopper who interprets a $6.98 price tag as $7.00, a newspaper's account of a $3,467,985.68 budget as a "three and a half million dollar budget," or reference to an actual attendance of 4,047 as a "crowd of four thousand."

2. *Errors in Approximate Numbers.* An approximate number is inexact because of the error which exists between the approximate number and its true or correct value. In most cases, as we saw above, this correct value is either inexpressible or beyond our powers of comprehension. These errors may be analyzed in two different ways, as apparent errors and as relative errors.

The first, *apparent error*, has to do solely with the unit of measure employed. For example, in Figure 20 we have the measurement of

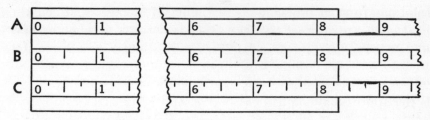

Figure 20. Card measured by three differently calibrated rulers.

the length of the same card by three differently calibrated rulers: ruler A is expressed in inches, ruler B is in half inches, and ruler C is in quarter inches. In terms of the three measuring devices, the length of this card would be stated as *approximately* 8 *inches* (according to ruler A); *approximately* 8½ *inches* (according to ruler B); and *approximately* 8¼ *inches* (according to ruler C). In each case, the measurement is stated according to the *nearest* exact unit of measurement on the ruler. By implication then, the *error* must be limited to within a *half unit* of the measurement as given. Thus, ruler A measured the card by inches, and its resulting measurement must be within a ±½ inch of the true value. Ruler B measured the card by half-inches (though stated as 8½ *inches*, it actually is "17 *half-inches*" since there are 17 half-inch units between the zero point and the $8\frac{1}{2}$ inch mark on the ruler), so its reading is within a $\pm\frac{1}{2}$ half-inch (or $\pm\frac{1}{4}$ inch) of the true value. Ruler C has the least apparent error of the three, because its unit measure is the quarter inch; because the end of the card falls between the 33rd ($8\frac{1}{4}$-inch) and the 34th ($8\frac{1}{2}$-inch) quarter-inch marks and nearer to the former, its reading is $8\frac{1}{4}$ inches—within $\pm\frac{1}{2}$ quarter inch ($\pm\frac{1}{8}$ inch) of the true value. In other words, the smaller our unit of measure, the nearer we can approximate the true value, and the smaller will be our apparent error. The term which is used to express this degree of apparent error is *precision*. It follows then that the smaller the apparent error, the more precise is the measurement. By the same token, the more refined our measuring instrument is, the more precise is its measuring capability. Consequently, a measurement expressed to the nearest hundredth of a meter (centimeter) is less precise than one expressed to the nearest thousandth of a meter (millimeter). On the other hand, the three measurements, $6\frac{1}{8}$ inches, $154\frac{3}{8}$ inches, and $1\frac{7}{8}$ inches all have the same degree of precision, since each is expressed to the nearest eighth of an inch.

Precision and apparent error are our chief concerns in working with tables of logarithms or trigonometric functions, in rounding off decimal equivalents of common fractions, and the like, because here we are certain of all the digits in our number except the very last (rounded off) digit. Note that our concern is not so much with this last digit itself as it is with its particular order or position; it is in terms of $\pm\frac{1}{2}$ the size of this order that we express our doubt or error. Thus the more "places" to which we extend our computation, the smaller becomes the value of the "last" place or order and the less will be our apparent error. This idea will prove to be an important and basic one in our discussion of *significance*, the subject of the following section.

Apparent error is sometimes referred to as *absolute* error, a term which contrasts particularly well with the second interpretation of this error, *relative error*.

By definition the *relative error* expresses a ratio of the apparent error (degree of precision) to the approximate number; thus relative error $= \dfrac{e}{A}$. For example, an error of $\frac{1}{4}$ inch in a measurement of $10\frac{1}{2}$ inches would have a relative error of

$$\frac{\frac{1}{4}}{10\frac{1}{2}} = \frac{1}{42}$$

while a greater absolute error of $\frac{1}{2}$ inch in a measurement of 70 inches

would mean a relative error of $\frac{1}{140}$ $\left(\frac{\frac{1}{2}}{70}\right)$.* When our error analysis
is based upon relative error, we say that the measurement involving
the smaller error is the more *accurate* measurement. In this case,
since $\frac{1}{140}$ is less than $\frac{1}{42}$, it follows that the second measurement
(70 inches correct to the nearest half inch) is the more accurate.
Note, however, that the first measurement ($10\frac{1}{2}$ inches to the nearest
quarter inch) was the more precise of the two because measurement
by quarter inches is more precise than measurement by half inches.
After our work with comparing fractions (Unit 26), we can readily
appreciate the generalization that "granted the same degree of precision in measurement, the greater the measurement the greater will
be the accuracy of that measurement."

3. *Significance.* In this section, let us restrict ourselves to expressing approximate numbers in decimal form only. Then if we
apply our discussion of apparent error to numbers so expressed, it
follows that whatever error there is in our number it is restricted
to $\pm\frac{1}{2}$ the denomination or order of the last (farthest to the right)
digit. For example, in each of the following numbers, 437.62, 82.04,
.03, and 1637.91, we have the same degree of precision (apparent
error); in each case it is $\pm\frac{1}{2}$ hundredth or $\pm.005$, which is to say
that the error occurs in the thousandth place or order. But we can
also see that the relative errors for each of these will be quite
different.

$$\frac{.005}{437.62} \qquad \frac{.005}{82.04} \qquad \frac{.005}{.03} \qquad \frac{.005}{1637.91}$$

Since these fractions all have the same numerators, it is possible
to arrange them by size according to their denominators (recall the
Egyptian system of fractions). Thus, from the largest to smallest,
we have

$$\frac{.005}{.03} \qquad \frac{.005}{82.04} \qquad \frac{.005}{437.62} \qquad \frac{.005}{1637.91}$$

Now since these ratios represent relative errors (degrees of accuracy)
and since the original numbers themselves occur in the denominators
of this sequence, it follows that the more digits there are to the left
of a given order in a given number, the larger that number is; and
when that number is compared with its apparent error, the smaller

---

* Sometimes these relative errors are expressed as per cents. Hence $\frac{1}{42}$ = 2.4%
and $\frac{1}{140}$ = .7%.

will be the result (its relative error). Hence there is a relationship between the number of digits in a number and its relative error. These digits in a number which occupy orders or places we are "sure of" are called *significant digits*. For instance, in 82.04 we have four significant digits, since we are sure of tens (the order occupied by 8), units (occupied by 2), tenths (occupied by 0), and hundredths (occupied by 4); the largest order we are unsure of is that of thousandths, since the 4, in the hundredths place, could be in error by $\pm \frac{1}{2}$ hundredth, or 5 thousandths.

To further illustrate, consider another number of four significant digits, 820.4, in which we are "sure" of hundreds, tens, units, and tenths. The apparent error is $\pm \frac{1}{2}$ tenth or .05 or 5 hundredths. Here again we have an opportunity to note that the relative error is actually a function of (related to) the number of significant digits in the number and has nothing to do with the specific places occupied by these digits.* The relative error of 82.04 we said was $\dfrac{.005}{82.04}$ and the relative error of 820.4 is $\dfrac{.05}{820.4}$; since the ratio of $\dfrac{.005}{82.04} = \dfrac{.05}{820.4}$, the relative errors of these two numbers are identical. Thus we see that the number of significant digits in a number is a valid index of the accuracy of that number. By extension, it follows that when two numbers are expressed decimally, the number which has the greater number of significant digits is always the more accurate, regardless of the location of the decimal point. When two numbers possess the same number of significant digits, the one with the greater leading digit is the more accurate.

In determining the number of significant digits in a given number, we must be cautious of the zeros. In numbers less than one, zeros which occur between the decimal point and the first nonzero digit (1, 2, 3, 4, 5, 6, 7, 8, or 9) to its right are purely spacers (which properly orient this first significant nonzero digit) and are not counted as being significant digits. Zeros anywhere interspersed between nonzero digits are always significant (as in 86.04, 800.02, 703.05). Zeros which are written to the right of the last nonzero digit of a decimal fraction (as in .3600, 4.20) are also significant, for these should not be written if there is no intention to show certainty to that order.

---

* On the other hand, precision and apparent error are concerned with the specific places occupied by the digits, notably the last digit; precision and apparent error are not concerned with the total number of digits in the number.

Zeros in whole numbers, however, sometimes present difficulty in determining which digits are significant. For example, 600 could mean six hundred to the nearest unit (599.5 to 600.5), or it could mean six hundred to the nearest hundred, putting the true value somewhere between $600 \pm \frac{1}{2}$ hundred, or between 550 and 650. In the former, we have in 600 a number of three significant digits, while in the latter, we have but one significant digit, the two zeros being spacers. Generally speaking, we must be guided by our knowledge of the situation giving rise to the number.

Some authorities have suggested writing the zero spacers of a rounded number in smaller script than those zeros which are significant. In this vein, 6oo would mean six hundred to the nearest hundred, while 600 would mean six hundred to the nearest unit. Others suggest writing out the denomination of smallest significance, in which case the first would be written as 6 hundred and the other as 600 units. About the only widely used solution to this difficulty of significant digits is that of scientific notation, the topic of the next section.

4. *Standard Form of Scientific Notation.* At various times in our discussions we have referred to alternate ways of expressing a given number. For instance, in Unit 4 we showed that 4 thousands = 40 hundreds = 400 tens = 4,000 units, and in Unit 24 this was further extended to additional alternative expressions such as 4,000 units = 40,000 tenths = 400,000 hundredths, etc. Now substituting the exponential form for these denominations (hundreds = 10^2, tens = 10^1, units = 10^0, tenths = 10^{-1}, hundredths = 10^{-2}, etc.) we get

$$4 \times 10^3 = 40 \times 10^2 = 400 \times 10^1 = 4,000 \times 10^0$$
$$= 40,000 \times 10^{-1} = 400,000 \times 10^{-2}, \text{ etc.}$$

By extension, it follows that an exact number such as 4,632 might be alternately expressed as

4,632 units or 4632×10^0
463.2 tens or 463.2×10^1
46.32 hundreds or 46.32×10^2
4.632 thousands or 4.632×10^3, etc.

Going in the other direction we get

46,320 tenths or $46,320 \times 10^{-1}$
463,200 hundredths or $463,200 \times 10^{-2}$, etc.

Thus we see that any rational number can be expressed in a variety of ways, each involving the product of some number and a power of ten. *Standard form of scientific notation* is a particular one of these; it is the expression of any number as the product of

(some number between 1 and 10) × (a power of 10)

To illustrate, the following numbers have been expressed in standard form of scientific notation.

$$36.42 = 3.642 \times 10^1$$
$$3{,}400 = 3.4 \times 10^3$$
$$36{,}000{,}000 = 3.6 \times 10^7$$
$$.046 = 4.6 \times 10^{-2}$$
$$.0000327 = 3.27 \times 10^{-5}$$
$$.0007 = 7. \times 10^{-4}$$

The value of this technique in expressing approximate numbers should be rather obvious. For instance, if the distance to Jupiter is 391,000,000 miles, expressed to the nearest million miles, we may express this number as 3.91×10^8 where only the significant digits are given in the first factor. If the measurement of this planet had been expressed correct to the nearest hundred thousand miles, the distance would have been expressed as 3.910×10^8.

Standard form is also advantageous for expressing precision in very, very small values. For instance $.000000703 = 7.03 \times 10^{-7}$, and .000300 (precision to the nearest millionth) $= 3.00 \times 10^{-4}$.

Over and above the values of precise expression, standard form of scientific notation is also useful in making comparisons among numbers which are either very large or very small. When numbers are expressed in standard form, the largest number will have the largest exponent attached to the 10, while the smallest will have the smallest exponent (for instance, 10^6 is smaller than 10^8, 10^{-5} is smaller than 10^2, and 10^{-8} is smaller than 10^{-7}). When two numbers expressed in standard form involve the same power of ten, then the decision of relative size depends, of course, upon the relative values of the first factors (for in effect denominations are alike), the ones which are expressed as a number between one and ten.

PROBLEMS SET 29

1. List seven specific instances other than those of the text in which number is used as an approximate measure.

2. State with what unit of measurement the following measures were obtained and give the apparent error for each.

(a) 13.6 in.   (e) 13.1 liters
(b) 2.16 lb   (f) 4.60 kilometers
(c) 14 lb 3 oz   (g) 3.602 miles
(d) 8 ft 4 in.   (h) 3 hr 22 min

3. A distance between two points is measured first to the nearest eighth of an inch and again to the nearest thirty-second of an inch.

(a) Which measurement has the greatest apparent error?

(b) Which measurement has the greatest relative error?

4. Arrange the following measurements in the order of their precision (from least to greatest). In (a) assume the denominator of the fraction part indicates the unit of measure used.

(a) $36\frac{1}{4}$ in., $27\frac{2}{7}$ in., $32\frac{3}{8}$ in., $46\frac{0}{16}$ in., $22\frac{1}{2}$ in.

(b) 4.62 in., 3.041 in., 3 in., 82.4 in., .3762 in.

(c) 3 gal ($\pm\frac{1}{5}$ gal), 14 gal ($\pm\frac{2}{7}$ gal), 23 gal ($\pm.22$ gal), 7 gal ($\pm\frac{3}{4}$ gal), 8 gal ($\pm.17$ gal)

5. Arrange the following measurements in order of their accuracy (from least to greatest): 6 ft ($\pm\frac{1}{2}$ ft), 3.2 in. ($\pm.05$ in.), 7.2 miles ($\pm.005$ mile), $3\frac{1}{2}$ in. ($\pm\frac{1}{2}$ in.), 3 yd 4 in. ($\pm\frac{1}{8}$ in.).

6. Arrange the three sets of measures of Question 4 in order of their accuracy (from least to greatest).

7. Count the number of significant digits in each of the following.

(a) 43.26   (e) .6070   (i) 76.000

(b) 4,607   (f) .0030   (j) 43,000

(c) 32.004   (g) 4.0030   (k) 0.036

(d) .0062   (h) .03624   (l) 200.00004

8. Convert the following common fractions to decimal fractions expressed with 5 significant digits.

(a) $\frac{2}{3}$ (b) $\frac{3}{11}$ (c) $\frac{3}{64}$ (d) $\frac{5}{19}$ (e) $\frac{1}{41}$ (f) $\frac{1}{11}$

9. Express the following in Standard Form of Scientific Notation.

(a) 463,000,000   (f) .0000400

(b) 327,000   (g) 36.8×10^5

(c) .000462   (h) $.8 \times 10^{-7}$

(d) 32.004   (i) 72 billion

(e) 2   (j) $3\frac{1}{4}$ million

10. By inspection arrange the following, by letter, in order of their magnitude, from least to greatest.

(a) 3.6×10^5 (f) 4.1×10^6

(b) 3.5×10^8 (g) 3.527×10^2

(c) $4. \times 10^{-6}$ (h) 3.55×10^8

(d) 3.527×10^8 (i) 3.4×10^{-7}

(e) 3.5×10^{-12} (j) 3.39×10^{-8}

11. Arrange the numbers of Question 10 in order of their distances from *unity or 1*, from least to greatest.

12. Check your answer to Questions 10 and 11 by expanding the numbers (express them as integers and decimal fractions) of Question 10.

Unit 30:   Computation with Approximate Numbers

1. *Introduction.* In the previous unit we saw that approximate numbers can be expressed with varying degrees of precision. When these numbers become involved in the operations of addition, subtraction, multiplication, and division, the results will also vary in precision. In fact the precision of these results will be limited by the least precise term involved, because, generally speaking, such results cannot produce more information (less error) than was contributed by any of the original terms.

In the sections to follow, certain rules will be developed for computing with approximate numbers. These rules are the consequence of the rationalizing which precedes them, and are assuredly valid in application only if the assumptions of these rationalizations are met. Although these rules have a high degree of applicability in arithmetic, they are by no means inflexible and all-powerful. Dr. Aaron Bakst in his *Approximate Computation,** probably the best single source of information on this subject, makes this important point:

> Generally speaking, the technique of Approximate Computation is not mechanical. The performance of numerical processes may be thought of as mechanical, but the arithmetic of Approximate Computation can be fully appreciated if and only if the interpretive processes are predominant. Only when a pupil is conscious of the nature of the data and can interpret the approximativeness and the meaning of the numerical results obtained by him, will he understand the importance of Approximate Computation as a fundamental part of applied mathematics.

2. *Addition with Approximate Numbers.* It will be recalled that one of the basic principles of addition is that of likeness (A-1): Only like numbers may be added. In terms of precision, numbers are alike when they possess the same degree of precision. Thus, the first step in the process of addition where the addends are of different degrees of precision is to round off all addends so that their precision is that of the least precise addend. To illustrate, if we were given the following approximate numbers (sometimes called ragged decimals) to add: 63.9 + 4.276 + 342.87 + 37.45, we would first round off each addend to the degree of precision of the least precise addend (63.9) thus: 63.9 + 4.3 + 342.9 + 37.5.

But before we attempt that particular four-addend addition, let

---

Twelfth Yearbook of the National Council of Teachers of Mathematics, National Council of Teachers of Mathematics, 1201 Sixteenth St., N.W., Washington, D.C., 1937, p. 18.

us start with cases of two and three addends in which the degree of precision is already uniform. This agreement of precision implies that the apparent error of each addend will be identical. In the specific example which follows we have precision to hundredths; so the apparent error is $\pm\frac{1}{2}$ hundredth or .005. If we express the two approximate numbers 62.47 and 31.38 with their apparent errors and add them,

$$\begin{array}{r} 62.47 \pm .005 \\ 31.38 \pm .005 \\ \hline 93.85 \pm .010 \end{array}$$

it follows that the apparent error of the sum of the two approximate numbers may be, at most, equal to the sum of the apparent errors of the addends. In this case the apparent error could be as much as a hundredth (.01). Consequently, in our sum (93.85) the hundredth place is open to question, which means our precision certainty in that number reaches only to the tenths order. Rounding off to that order, we get 93.9 as the sum of the two approximate numbers 62.47 and 31.38.

Now in the case of three addends we have

$$\begin{array}{r} 86.42 \pm .005 \\ 175.97 \pm .005 \\ 36.44 \pm .005 \\ \hline 298.83 \pm .015 \end{array}$$

Here the cumulative effect of the apparent error of the addends again reaches into the hundredths order, so once more we are limited in our sum to the precision of tenths. Hence the sum of the addition is 298.8.

Our earlier four-addend problem would be, according to these rules,

$$\begin{array}{r} 63.9 \pm .05 \\ 4.3 \pm .05 \\ 342.9 \pm .05 \\ 37.5 \pm .05 \\ \hline 448.6 \pm .20 \end{array}$$

Since the sum of the apparent errors here involves tenths, our sum must be rounded off to the next higher order, that of units: thus, 448.6 $\pm$ .20 becomes 449.

If we note that the maximum apparent error always amounts to 5 of some denomination or order (tenths, hundredths, etc.), it follows that the maximum cumulative effect of a quantity from 2 to 19 of these errors will involve an order of just one higher than that of the apparent errors. When the number of addends ranges from 20 to 199, the maximum cumulative effect of the apparent errors will extend to an order two higher than that of the individual errors. To illustrate:

$$19 \times .000\overset{\downarrow}{5} = .0095 \quad \begin{array}{l}\llcorner\!\!-\!\!-\!\!-\!\!-\!\!-\!\!-\!\!-\text{ten-thousandths}(10^{-4}) \\ \ \ \ \ \ \ \ \ulcorner\!\!-\!\!-\!\!-\text{thousandths}(10^{-3})\end{array}$$

$$20 \times .000\overset{\downarrow}{5} = .0100 \quad \begin{array}{l}\llcorner\!\!-\!\!-\!\!-\!\!-\!\!-\!\!-\!\!-\text{ten-thousandths}(10^{-4}) \\ \ \ \ \ \ \ \ \ulcorner\!\!-\!\!-\!\!-\text{hundredths}(10^{-2})\end{array}$$

$$199 \times .000\overset{\downarrow}{5} = .0995 \quad \begin{array}{l}\llcorner\!\!-\!\!-\!\!-\!\!-\!\!-\!\!-\!\!-\text{ten-thousandths }(10^{-4}) \\ \ \ \ \ \ \ \ \ulcorner\!\!-\!\!-\!\!-\text{hundredths }(10^{-2})\end{array}$$

$$200 \times .000\overset{\downarrow}{5} = .1000 \quad \begin{array}{l}\llcorner\!\!-\!\!-\!\!-\!\!-\!\!-\!\!-\!\!-\text{ten-thousandths }(10^{-4}) \\ \ \ \ \ \ \ \ \ulcorner\!\!-\!\!-\!\!-\text{tenths }(10^{-1})\end{array}$$

From this we can induce a general rule for adding approximate numbers:

(1) Round off all addends to a precision equal to that of the least precise of the addends.

(2) If the addends are less than twenty in number, add these rounded addends as though they were exact numbers, then round off the sum to an order one higher than its resulting state. If the addends number between 20 and 199, round off the sum to an order two higher than its resulting state.

It should be noted particularly that this discussion and most of the others which follow in this unit are based upon the assumption of maximum error in every measurement. This is to say that some of the digits which are discarded according to these rules are likely valid in some cases. To illustrate, let us reconsider for a moment the rule just stated for adding approximate numbers. It is true that *if* the error of each of, say, fifty addends were the maximum, and all errors were in the same direction, there would be reason to doubt the validity of the digits in the two lowest orders of the sum. On the other hand, by the laws of probability, such an array of maximum errors, all in the same direction, is unlikely. In fact, the more addends there are, the more likely it is that the actual errors will counterbalance each other. Hence, from a probability point of view, the last statement of the rule above, "If the addends number be-

tween 20 and 199, round off the sum to an order two higher than
its resulting state," is unnecessary. But when we are assuming a
maximum error, the rule should be applied. The reader will not find
these last two statements contradictory if he keeps clear the assumptions upon which each statement is made.

3. *Subtraction with Approximate Numbers.* Since we know that
subtraction is the inverse process of addition, it follows that much
of the logic used in developing the rules for adding approximate
numbers will have equal applicability in the subtraction of approximate numbers.

Likeness, it will be recalled, is also a basic principle of subtraction; it follows, then, that if there is a difference of precision existing
between the minuend and subtrahend, the term of greater precision
must first be rounded off to the precision of the less precise term.
Only then may the subtraction proceed.

Consider the subtraction of two approximate numbers 637.55
− 431.13. Expressed in algorismic form with their respective apparent errors, we have

$$637.55 \pm .005$$
$$\underline{-431.13 \pm .005}$$

However, if we are not careful in our thinking about the nature of
apparent error, there is a strong temptation to proceed with the
subtraction in a manner similar to that used in our work with excess
of nines (see p. 107) and perhaps decide that the apparent errors will
always subtract out to zero. This would be true if both errors
happened to lie in the same direction; but since we are uncertain of
this, we may assume the *worst* case, that of the errors lying in
opposite directions. Remember, all we know is that the correct value
of 637.55 lies somewhere between 637.545 and 637.555 and that the
correct value of 431.13 lies somewhere between 431.125 and 431.135.
If both errors are equal and lie in the same direction, we get the
effect of the errors subtracting out; thus

637.545		637.555
431.125	or	431.135
206.420		206.420

But if the errors happen to lie in opposite directions, we get a
cumulative effect, the extremes of which would be

$$
\begin{array}{ccc}
637.545 & & 637.555 \\
\underline{431.135} & \text{or} & \underline{431.125} \\
206.410 & & 206.430
\end{array}
$$

Therefore the potential range of our solution is from 206.410 to 206.430, and so the best we can say is that the solution is 206.4.

From this we can see that for maximum safety in subtracting approximate numbers, we must assume that the apparent errors of the minuend and subtrahend are cumulative. Coming back to the original statement of our subtraction problem, we have

$$
\text{Subtract} \left\downarrow \begin{bmatrix} 637.55 \pm .005 \\ \underline{431.13 \pm .005} \end{bmatrix} \right\uparrow \text{Add}
$$
$$
206.42 \pm .01
$$

Since the cumulative effect of our apparent errors reaches the next higher order (here hundredths) we round off our solution to tenths. Thus we get the solution 206.4.

Crystallizing the foregoing into a rule for subtracting approximate numbers, we have

(1) Round off the minuend or subtrahend to a precision equal to the less precise of the terms.

(2) Subtract the terms as though they were exact numbers, then round off the solution to an order one higher than its resulting state.

4. *Multiplication with Approximate Numbers.* Let us assume that we have two approximate numbers, a and b. Let us further assume that A and B are the correct values and that e_a and e_b are, respectively, the apparent errors which separate the approximate values from their correct values. Thus $A = a \pm e_a$ and $B = b \pm e_b$, and the product of $A \times B$ would become

$$
\begin{aligned}
A \times B = AB &= (a \pm e_a) \times (b \pm e_b) \\
&= ab \pm (e_a)(b) \pm (e_b)(a) + (e_a)(e_b)
\end{aligned}
$$

Remember that the term $A \times B$ is the true (but unattainable) result of our multiplication, while ab is the result we get from multiplying these approximate numbers as though they were exact numbers. The difference between AB and ab is obviously the error quantity $(\pm e_a b \pm e_b a + e_a e_b)$.

Let us illustrate this development by assuming that $a = 3.24$ and $b = 1.46$, both approximate numbers and both with an apparent error of $\pm.005$. Thus $e_a = e_b = .005$ and

$$A \times B = ab \pm e_a b \pm e_b a + e_a e_b$$
$$= (3.24)(1.46) \pm (.005)(1.46) \pm (.005)(3.24) + (.005)(.005)$$
$$= 4.7304 \pm (.00730) \pm (.01620) + (.000025)$$

For all practical purposes the final term of the error quantity ($e_a \times e_b$) can be discarded, since it is so small compared with the rest of the error quantity (the $e_a b$ and the $e_b a$). Once more we assume the worst and maximize the potential error by adding together the contributions of $e_a b$ and $e_b a$, getting $.00730 + .01620 = .02350$. Thus we see that potentially the error could have a corruptive influence all the way into the hundredths order; therefore our safest estimate of $A \times B$ would be 4.7.

Consider one other example. Let $a = 8.62$ and $b = 3.17$. Again the apparent error for each term will be .005. Then

$A \times B$ (the true product)
$$= (8.62)(3.17) \pm (.005)(3.17) \pm (.005)(8.62) + (.005)(.005)$$
$$= \quad 27.3254 \pm (.01585) \pm (.04310) + (.005)^2$$

Upon adding the major contributors to the error quantity $(.01585 + .04310)$, we get .05895, and again we note that the potential error could affect the solution as far as the hundredths order. Therefore our best guess at the true product is 27.3.

This technique for determining the precision of a product of two approximate numbers, while consistently rational, is rather time-consuming in practice. So let us consider an alternative approach which will lead us to a simpler rule of operation.

If we take the sum of the principle contributors to the error quantity of the product ab in its most erratic (cumulative) state $(e_a b + e_b a)$ and express it as a relative error, $\dfrac{e_a b + e_b a}{ab}$, we can see that this relative error of the product ab is actually the sum of the relative errors of each factor.

$$\frac{e_a b + e_b a}{ab} = \frac{e_a \cancel{b}}{a \cancel{b}} + \frac{e_b \cancel{a}}{\cancel{a} b} = \frac{e_a}{a} + \frac{e_b}{b}$$

From this we conclude that the relative error of the product $\dfrac{e_a b + e_b a}{ab}$ must be at least as great as the relative error of either factor $\dfrac{e_a}{a}$ or $\dfrac{e_b}{b}$. To state this in terms of accuracy, it follows that the accuracy of the product of two approximate numbers cannot exceed the accuracy of its least accurate factor. Since, as we saw in the preceding unit, significant digits offer a reliable index of accuracy, our previous conclusion takes on a new variation: The product of two approximate numbers cannot have more significant digits than the factor having the least number of significant digits.

Note that while this rule places only an upper limit on the number of significant digits in the product, there may be fewer. Recall our two earlier examples 3.24×1.46 and 8.62×3.17. In both cases the factors each had three significant digits, yet our analysis based on apparent error resulted in a product in the first case of 4.7 (two significant digits) and in the second case 27.3 (three significant digits).

The reason for this difference is that the product of two exact single-digit factors may possibly yield a single-digit result ($2 \times 4 = 8$) or a two-digit result ($5 \times 3 = 15$); the product of an exact single-digit factor and an exact two-digit factor may yield either a two-digit product ($4 \times 12 = 48$) or a three-digit product ($4 \times 81 = 324$); likewise, the product of two two-digit factors may result in products of either 3 or 4 digits ($30 \times 20 = 600; 80 \times 90 = 7,200$). Since our concern is basically a matter of precision—of distinguishing the last valid place to the right—digits to the left of it are of no consequence. But since we have elected this alternative approach involving relative error and accuracy, our interpretation requires counting off significant digits from the left; so:

To multiply two approximate numbers:

(1)   When one of the two numbers contains more significant digits than the other, round off the number of greater significance so that it contains one significant digit more than the number of lesser significance.*

(2)   Multiply the numbers as though they were exact numbers.

(3a)   If the product of the digits which occupy the highest order of each number equals or exceeds 10, or if the product of the digits in the two highest orders of each number equals or exceeds 1,000, round off the final product so as to have as many significant digits as the number having the least number of significant digits.

(3b)   In cases where (3a) does not apply, round off the final product to one *less* significant digit than the number having the least number of significant digits.

Illustrations:

Multiply 4.9×36.2:

$$
\begin{array}{r}
36.2 \\
4.9 \\
\hline
3258 \\
1448 \\
\hline
177.38 \rightarrow 180.
\end{array}
$$

* This simplifies the work, since these discarded digits do not increase the validity of the product.

Since 4×3 (highest ordered digits of multiplier and multiplicand) equals 12 (which is greater than 10) we round off the product 177.38 to *two* significant digits (after the multiplicand, the factor of least significance). Thus our 177.38 becomes 180.

(b) Multiply 1.24×4.17:

$$
\begin{array}{r}
4.17 \\
1.24 \\
\hline
1668 \\
834 \\
417 \\
\hline
5.1708 \rightarrow 5.2.
\end{array}
$$

Since $1 \times 4 = 4$ (which is less than 10) and $12 \times 41 = 492$ (which is less than 1,000) we round off the product 5.1708 to *two* significant digits, one less than the significance of the least significant factor. Thus our product becomes 5.2.

(c) Multiply 38.1×33.41:

$$
\begin{array}{r}
33.41 \\
38.1 \\
\hline
3341 \\
26728 \\
10023 \\
\hline
1272.921 \rightarrow 1,270.
\end{array}
$$

Since $3 \times 3 = 9$ (which is less than 10), but $38 \times 33 = 1,254$ (which is greater than 1,000) we round off the product 1,272.921 to *three* significant digits (after the factor of least significance, the multiplier) and get 1,270.

5. *Division with Approximate Numbers.* In the previous section we noted that the relative error of the product of two numbers $a \times b$ was approximately equal to the sum of the relative errors of these two numbers:

$$
\frac{e_a b + e_b a}{ab} = \frac{e_a}{a} + \frac{e_b}{b}
$$

We shall now show that the relative error of a quotient of two approximate numbers, $a \div b$, is also approximately equal to the sum of the relative errors of the two numbers.

Again let A and B be the correct but unattainable values, e_a and e_b their respective apparent errors, and a and b the approximate values we have to work with. Thus $A = a \pm e_a$ and $B = b \pm e_b$. In the previous section it was noted that the product of

$$
A \times B = ab \pm (e_a)(b) \pm (e_b)(a) + (e_a)(e_b)
$$

Should we divide through by B^2 and b^2, admittedly we destroy the equality, since B is not exactly equal to b (they differ by the amount of the error e_b). But this will not greatly affect our ultimate result which is approximate anyway—particularly since we shall again discard the $(e_a)(e_b)$ term as having too little an effect upon the error quantity ($e_a b$ and $e_b a$) to concern us. So we get

$$\frac{A \times B}{B^2} = \frac{A}{B} \approx \frac{a\!\!\!/}{b\!\!\!/^2} \pm \frac{(e_a b) + (e_b a)}{b^2} \qquad (\approx \text{ means "approximately equal"})$$

Thus the apparent error of the quotient of two approximate numbers (a/b) is approximately equal to

$$\frac{(e_a)(b) + (e_b)(a)}{b^2}$$

If we divide this apparent error by the quotient, we get the relative error of the quotient.

$$\frac{(e_a)(b) + (e_b)(a)}{b^2} \div \frac{a}{b} = \frac{(e_a)(b) + (e_b)(a)}{b\!\!\!/^2} \times \frac{b\!\!\!/}{a}$$

$$= \frac{(e_a)(b) + (e_b)(a)}{ab}$$

$$= \frac{(e_a)(b\!\!\!/)}{ab\!\!\!/} + \frac{(e_b)(a\!\!\!/)}{a\!\!\!/b} = \frac{e_a}{a} + \frac{e_b}{b}$$

From this we can see that for two approximate numbers a and b the relative error of their quotient is approximately the same as the relative error of their product. Hence the rules developed for multiplication of two approximate numbers have similar applicability to the quotient of two approximate numbers.

To divide two approximate numbers:

(1) When one of the two numbers contains more significant digits than the other, round off the number of greater significance so that it has just one digit more than the number of lesser significance.

(2) Divide the numbers as though they were exact numbers.

(3a) If the product of the digits which occupy the highest order of each number equals or exceeds 10, or if the product of the digits in the two highest orders of each number equals or exceeds 1,000, round off the quotient so as to have as many significant digits as the number having the least number of significant digits.

(3b) In cases where (3a) does not apply, round off the quotient to one *less* significant digit than the number having the least number of significant digits.

Illustrations:

(a) Divide 23.982 by 16.2.

$$1.\,48 \rightarrow 1.5$$
$$16.2_\wedge \overline{)23.9_\wedge 8}$$

Round off 23.982 to four significant digits 23.98 (one more than in the other number 16.2) and divide as though they were exact numbers. Since the product of the highest ordered digits of the two numbers is less than 10 ($1 \times 2 = 2$) and the product of the numbers formed by the digits in the two highest orders is less than 1,000 ($16 \times 23 = 368$), we carry the quotient to the number of places equal to the number of places in the number of least significance (16.2, three places) and round it off to one less place.

(b) Divide 6.879 by 3.43.

$$2.\,005 \rightarrow 2.01$$
$$3.43_\wedge \overline{)6.87_\wedge 9}$$

Since the product of the highest ordered digits of divisor and dividend ($3 \times 6 = 18$) exceeds 10, we carry the quotient out to one place more than the number of places in the number of least significance (divisor) and then round off to one less place.

(c) Divide 59 by 6.3685.

$$9.26 \rightarrow 9.3$$
$$6.37_\wedge \overline{)59.00_\wedge}$$

Round off 6.3685 to three significant digits 6.37 (one more than in the other number 59) and divide as though they were exact numbers. Since the product of the highest ordered digits of the two numbers exceeds 10 ($5 \times 6 = 30$), we carry the quotient to one digit more than in the number of least significance, then round off to the number of digits in that number of least significance.

6. *Multiplication and Division When One Number Is Exact.* When a multiplication or division involves an exact number and an approximate number, it must be remembered that the approximate number is always the number of lesser significance, because the exact number possesses, in effect, an infinite number of significant digits. For example, the natural number 6 is exactly

$$6.0000000000 \ldots$$

So if we wish, for example, to know the total weight of 42 rings, each weighing approximately 3.742 ounces, we multiply as though both numbers were exact, $42 \times 3.742 = 157.164$, and round off the product to four places (157.2 ounces) the number of places in the less significant factor (3.742).

An example of division in which one of the numbers is exact:

What weight of salt would there be in each pile if 5.62 g of the salt were divided equally into 4 piles? Dividing the 5.62 by 4 we get

$$1.405 \rightarrow 1.41$$
$$4\overline{)5.62}$$

The quotient is rounded off to three places; hence each pile will contain approximately 1.41 g of the salt.

PROBLEMS SET 30

1. Add the following approximate numbers.
   (a) $36.42 + 875.1 + 37.4 + 28.375 + .62$
   (b) $587.39 + 42.5 + 32.0 + 64.783 + 37.07$

2. Subtract the following approximate numbers.
   (a) $3.7 - 2.683$
   (b) $42.0 - 37.645$
   (c) 13 hundred $- 647$
   (d) $375 - .00421$

3. Multiply the following approximate numbers.
   (a) 4.2×36.8
   (b) 30.2×4.683
   (c) $3.7 \times 4,682$
   (d) $3.72 \times (2.8 \times 10^4)$

4. Divide the following approximate numbers.
   (a) $49.62 \div 3.74$
   (b) $3.642 \div .83$
   (c) $5.72 \div .13852$
   (d) $.000342 \div .000201$
   (e) $3.14 \times 10^7 \div 8,005$

5. Find the area of a rectangular field which is 826.5 rods long and 307 rods wide.

6. The monthly output of a mine is estimated at 32 hundred tons of ore. What will be the income for the month if the ore continues to sell at $32.27 a ton?

7. The circumference of a circle is stated $C = \pi d$, in which d is the diameter of the circle. If π is given as 3.141593, find the circumferences of the following circles whose diameters are:
   (a) 3.6 in.
   (b) .0032 in.
   (c) 46.37 ft
   (d) 7 miles

8. A machine stamps out parts each weighing .627 lb. How much weight is there to 74 of these parts?

9. Assuming that water weighs 62.5 lb per cu ft, what is the volume of 15,710 lb?

10. An automobile plant claims it turns out one new car every 3 min 42 sec. What is the plant's production for one week if the plant operates 24 hr per day?

11. Assuming that 1 lb is the exact equivalent of 7,000 wheat grains, how many pounds would there be in a supply of wheat grains that number 2.27×10^6?

12. Each bag of cement contains 92 lb of cement. How many bags can be obtained from a load of 64,000 lb of cement?

13. One inch is approximately equal to 2.54 centimeters.
    (a) How many centimeters are there in 108 in.?
    (b) How many inches are there in 1 cm?

14. In a town of 3,600 the average wealth per person is estimated at $647. What is your best estimate of the total wealth of the town?

15. If a bushel of sweet potatoes weighs 60 lb in Maryland and 46 lb in North Dakota, how many Maryland bushels are there in 875 North Dakota bushels?

ANSWERS (Selected)

Problems Set 1, page 5

5. (a) ordinal;   (e) ordinal;   (h) ordinal;   (k) ordinal;
   (b) cardinal;   (f) ordinal;   (i) cardinal;   (l) cardinal;
   (c) cardinal;   (g) cardinal; (j) cardinal; (m) ordinal.
   (d) ordinal;

Problems Set 2, page 11

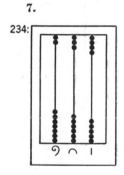

4.

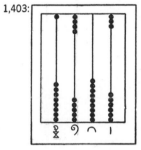

7.

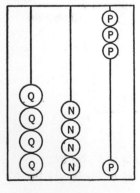

8. one I, two II, three III, four IIII, five ∩, six ∩I, seven ∩II, etc.

9.

Three:

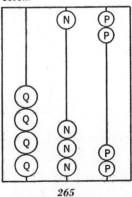

Seven:

Seven: and One hundred six:

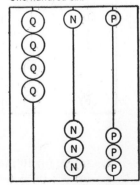

Problems Set 3, page 16

2. $\sigma\lambda\delta$ (234) CCXXXIV $\prime\alpha\psi\gamma$ (1,703) MDCCIII

    $\phi\xi\beta$ (562) DLXII $\prime\eta\nu\theta$ (8,409) $\overline{\text{VIII}}$CDIX

                                   $\lambda\delta$

    $\prime\alpha$ (1,000) M   M$\tau\kappa\beta$ (340,322) $\overline{\text{CCCXL}}$CCCXXII

3.   59   531   20,130

       888   2,012   52,284

       303   9,600   240,503

4.   Hint: consider numbers greater than ten-thousand.

5.   29   958   1,100,511

       46   949   410,003

       78   1,956   60,118

     202   1,646   1,500,009

7.   Principle of addition.

8.

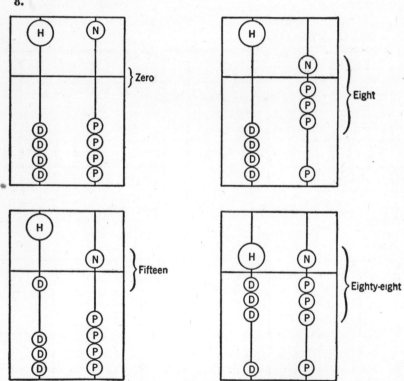

Problems Set 4, page 27

2.   (a) 6^4; (b) 10^4; (c) $3^3 \times 4^3$ or $(3 \times 4)^3$ or 12^3; (d) $2^4 \times 5^3$; (e) 2^{10}.

3.   (a) 3^{10}; (b) 5 (or 5^1); (c) 10^3; (d) 27; (e) k^{a+b}; (f) M^{a-b}; (g) 1; (h) 6^4; (i) 3^5; (j) 1.

5. $36,827 = a_4x^4 + a_3x^3 + a_2x^2 + a_1x^1 + a_0x^0$, in which $a_4 = 3$, $a_3 = 6$, $a_2 = 8$, $a_1 = 2$, $a_0 = 7$, and $x = 10$. Therefore, $x^4 = 10,000$, $x^3 = 1,000$, $x^2 = 100$, $x^1 = 10$, and $x^0 = 1$.
   $201 = a_2x^2 + a_1x^1 + a_0x^0$, in which $a_2 = 2$, $a_1 = 0$, $a_0 = 1$, and $x = 10$.

6. (a) three million, six hundred forty-two thousand, three hundred seven;
   (c) forty-two million, three hundred sixty-two thousand, eight hundred fifty-seven;
   (e) four billion, three;
   (g) six billion, three hundred million, twenty-seven.

7. (a) 307,004,068; (c) 7,250; (e) 16,750,000,000.

8. (e, Question 6): 4,000,000,003, or four thousand million, three;
   (e, Question 7): 16,750,000,000, or sixteen thousand, seven hundred fifty million

9. (a) 400,000 tens   (c) 87,200 tens   (e) 436,250 tens
       40,000 hundreds   872 thousands   43,625 hundreds
        4,000 thousands   4,362½ ⎫
                                                     or   4,362.5 ⎭ thousands

11. 6,327,498 contains 6,327 complete thousands, 63,274 complete hundreds, 632,749 complete tens;
    24,621 contains 24 complete thousands, 246 complete hundreds, 2,462 complete tens.

Problems Set 5, page 39

1. Spot checks:

Scale:	Two	Four	Seven	Eleven	Thirteen
Number concept:					
five	101	11	5	5	5
ten	1010	22	13	T	T
fifteen	1111	33	21	14	12
twenty	10100	110	26	19	17
thirty	11110	132	42	28	24

2. scale seven: four hundred;
   scale eight: five hundred eighty-five;
   scale twelve: one thousand eight hundred eighty-five;
   scale two: fifteen.

4. (a) five; (b) spot checks: five $(-\triangle)$, twelve $(<<)$, nineteen $(\leq \square)$, twenty-seven $(-\triangle<)$.

5. No, because (1) every system must have a null symbol, and (2) the number of symbols must equal the base value; consequently a "base one" scale of notation would be permitted but one symbol which would have to represent *both* absence and presence of quantity—an impossibility.

6. (a) nine;   (d) 10;   (g) 11;
   (b) sixteen;   (e) 10;   (h) 11;
   (c) thirty-four;   (f) 10;   (i) 11.

Problems Set 6, page 40

1. (a) 14; (b) 57; (c) 149; (d) 463; (e) 180; (f) 282; (g) 18; (h) 80; (i) 511; (j) 312; (k) 846; (l) 719; (m) 407; (n) 755; (o) 1715.
3. 96; 133; 176; 225; 280; 341; 408; 481.
4. 2,331 (five); 665 (seven); 418 (nine); 290 (eleven); 1,325 (six); 525 (eight); 341 (ten); 245 (twelve).
5. (a) 3,022 (five); (b) 1,150 (seven); (c) 1,403 (six); (d) 101,010 (two); (e) 6TE (twelve); (f) 31,241 (five); (g) EEE (twelve); (h) 100,110,100,100 (two).
6. (a) four; (c) seven; (e) eighteen.
7. (a) any odd scale greater than five;
   (b) any even scale greater than six.

Problems Set 8, page 58

1. (a) like; (b) unlike; (c) like; (d) unlike; (e) unlike; (f) unlike; (g) like; (h) unlike.
7. (a) 189 days; (b) 187 days.
8. (a) 409 miles; (b) 137 miles.
10. (a) G; (b) B; (c) $E + 17$; (d) $E + 3$; (e) twice E, or $2E$.

Problems Set 9, page 68

2. (a) 443; (c) 11,114; (e) 2,024.
3. (a) 9T4; (c) 20,509; (e) 2,080.
6. (a) five; (c) any scale above six; (e) twelve.
7. (a) 4 weeks, 2 days.
8. (a) 5 cartons, 3 bottles.
9. (a) 5; (c) 0; (e) 9; (g) 10.

Problems Set 10, page 77

1. (a) $1.25: multiplicand; 8: multiplier; $10.00: product.
   (c) 12 eggs (dozen): multiplicand; 15: multiplier; 180 eggs: product.
   (e) $.25: multiplicand; 7 (sixes in 42): multiplier; $1.75: product.
2. The proper unit of measure in area is the "square" foot. Actually the rectangle should be thought of as containing five rows of 6 square feet each, or six columns of 5 square feet each. In either case the resulting area is 30 square feet. Mechanically we arrive at the same result by multiplying length by width, or (thanks to the commutative law) width by length.
3. (a) $(50 \times 2) \times 8 = 100 \times 8 = 800$;
   (c) $13 \times (2 \times 50) = 13 \times 100 = 1,300$;
   (e) $2 \times 4 \times 7 \times 25 = 2 \times 7 \times (4 \times 25) = 14 \times 100 = 1,400$.
4. six ways.
12. (a) doubled; (b) halved; (c) unchanged; (d) A; (e) either A, or B, or both equal to zero; (f) one.

Problems Set 11, page 85

2. (a) 10,032; (c) 120,003.
3. (a) 14,125; (c) 63,331.

4. (a) 10,101; (c) 100,011,110.
6. (a) twelve; (c) forty-four; (e) nine.

Problems Set 13, page 103

6. (a) Jan., \$42.41; Feb., \$31.95; Mar., \$30.79; Apr., \$21.03. (b) 12,618 kilowatt-hours, 5,182 kilowatt-hours.
7. (a) 150 days; (b) 148 days; (c) 175 days; (d) same; (e) compensation (S-2).
9. (a) 95 students;
    (b) (1) $675 - 95, 17 + 203 + 181 + 179$
        (2) $675 - (17 + 203 + 181), 95 + 179.$
10. (a) unchanged; (b) doubled; (c) increased by M; (d) M; (e) K; (f) $R + G$; (g) R increased by 17.

Problems Set 14, page 110

1. (a) 1,7T9; (c) 7E2,227.
2. (a) 2,120; (c) 20,244.
4. (a) 2,8E4; (c) 2,TEE.
5. (a) five; (c) nine; (e) eight.
6. (a) 3 gross, 9 dozen, 9 units.
7. (a): (1) 4 ft 2 in. (2) 1 ft 9 in. (3) 8 in. (4) 5 ft 5 in. (5) 6 ft 5 in. (6) 6 ft 11 in.
8. (a) 100,011; (b) 114; (c) 213.

Problems Set 15, page 119

2. (a) not closed; (b) closed; (c) closed; (d) closed; (e) closed; (f) closed; (g) closed; (h) closed.
3. one.
4. Assume the division to be possible, yielding some real quotient K (e.g. $7/0 = K$); but then $0 \times K = 7$, which is absurd; therefore, division by zero is impossible.
5. (a) missing factor is multiplicand: partitioning;
    (c) missing factor is multiplier: measurement;
    (e) missing factor is multiplicand: partitioning.
8. twelve 13's.
10. (a) three trips; (b) five cartons.
11. (a) partitioning; (b) measurement.
12. (a) 1,624 parts;   (c) 9,009;   (e) 9,740;
     (b) 316;   (d) 318;   (f) 34,768.

Problems Set 16, page 132

1. 47) ‾‾ : (a) 49.15%; (b) 76.22%.
    85) ‾‾ : (a) 62.44%; (b) 62.44%.
2. (a) 598; (c) 224 R 372; (e) 789 R 581.
3.   207   *Ans.* 207 R 19
    24)4987
       187
        19

6.   (a) 13,872; (b) 54,180 R 3.

9.   (a) $2x^2 - 5x - 1$; (b) $x^2 + 2x + 4$; (c) $3a^{2x} - 3a^x + 2$.

10. (a) 36; (b) 36; (c) 19; (d) 16; (e) same: 18; (f) 32 times; (g) 2×576 = 1,152; (h) same: 576.

11. (a) $3 \times 24 = 72$; (b) $2 \times 24 = 48$; (c) $\frac{1}{2} \times 24 = 12$; (d) $\frac{1}{2} \times 24 = 12$.

Problems Set 17, page 141

1.   2, 3, 5, 7, 11, 13, 17, 19, 23, 29, 31, 37, 41, 43, 47, 53, 59, 61, 67, 71, 73, 79, 83, 89, 97.

2.   (a) prime; (b) composite; (c) prime.

3.   (a) $2 \times 2 \times 2 \times 3 \times 5 \times 5 \times 7$; (b) $2 \times 2 \times 2 \times 2 \times 3 \times 3 \times 11$.

4.   (a) 360; (c) 3,960; (e) 41,580.

7.   Hint: $73,864 = (73 \times 1,000) + 864$.

8.   Hint: similar to the rule for divisibility by four.

10. 2,340, 3,240, 3,420, 4,320.

11. (a) Certainly divisible by 2, 4, 5, 10; divisibility by 3, 6, 8, 12 would depend on values of the missing digits.

     (c) Certainly divisible by 2, 4, 5, 8, 10; unsure of 3, 6, 9, 12.

Problems Set 18, page 148

5.   (a) 2 : 1; (b) 5 : 4; (c) 3 : 4; (d) 2 : 15; (e) 15 : 2.

8.   (a) 2 : 1; (b) 2 : 1; (c) 1 : 2; (d) 4 : 7; (e) 2 : 7; (f) 3 : 7.

9.   (a) 1 in. = 80 miles; (b) 1 in. = 100 miles; (c) 1 in. = 16 miles.

10. 1 in. = 40 ft.

Problems Set 19, page 154

1. $\frac{1}{5} =$ ⌣ , $\frac{1}{23} =$ ⌣ ; $\frac{1}{100} =$ ⌣

2. $\frac{3}{4} =$ [⌣ ; $\frac{41}{100} =$ ⌣ ⌣ ⌣ ⌣ ; $\frac{12}{35} =$ ⌣ ⌣

3.   604,800.

4.   216,000 "third little parts"; 12,960,000 "fourth little parts."

Problems Set 20, page 163

2.   (a) proper, simple;   (i) proper, complex;

     (c) proper, simple;   (k) proper, simple;

     (e) proper, complex;   (m) improper, simple.

     (g) proper, complex;

5.   (a) $\frac{6}{56} = \frac{3}{28}$; (c) $\frac{68}{3}$; (e) $\frac{9}{17}$; (g) $\frac{13}{8}$; (i) $\frac{1}{18}$; (k) $\frac{9}{45}$.

6.   (a) $\frac{3}{4}$; (c) $\frac{13}{17}$; (e) $\frac{31}{64}$.

7.   (a) $\frac{4}{6}$; (c) $\frac{12}{27}$; (e) $\frac{210}{240}$; (g) $\frac{10}{12}$; (i) $\frac{7}{49}$; (k) $\frac{12}{20}$; (m) $\frac{2\frac{1}{2}}{10}$.

8.   (a) $\frac{8}{8}$; (c) $\frac{88}{77}$; (e) $\frac{16}{24}$; (g) $\frac{9}{7}$; (i) $\frac{7}{56}$; (k) $\frac{10}{26\frac{2}{3}}$; (m) $\frac{100}{133\frac{1}{3}}$.

9.   (a) $\frac{1}{6}$; $\frac{1}{4}$; $\frac{1}{2}$. (b) $\frac{1}{12}$; $\frac{1}{8}$; $\frac{1}{4}$.

10. (a) $\frac{1}{5}$; (c) $\frac{9}{20}$; (e) $\frac{133}{175}$; (g) $\frac{5}{8}$.

Problems Set 21, page 173

1. (a) $\frac{7}{10}$; (c) $\frac{11}{20}$; (e) $\frac{19}{40}$; (g) $\frac{29}{40}$.
2. (a) $\frac{89}{120}$ (LCD 120); (c) $\frac{473}{960}$ (LCD 960); (e) $\frac{53}{288}$ (LCD 1,440).
5. (a) $\frac{3}{2}$; (c) $\frac{8}{5}$; (e) 15.
7. (a) $\frac{10}{21}$; (c) $\frac{7}{20}$; (e) $\frac{1333}{8611}$; (g) $\frac{1}{12}$.
9. $\frac{37}{60}$.
10. $3\frac{1}{12}$ houses.
11. $\frac{7}{18}$.
12. A: \$7,920; B: \$2,880; C: \$3,600.
13. Savings \$525, or $\frac{1}{8}$ total income.
14. 20 out of every 100.
15. Hint: $\frac{1}{2} + \frac{1}{3} + \frac{1}{9} = \frac{17}{18}$.

Problems Set 22, page 181

1. (a) $\frac{1}{8}$; (c) $\frac{21}{65}$; (e) $\frac{3}{70}$.
2. (a) $\frac{1}{2}$; (c) $\frac{40}{51}$; (e) $\frac{2}{3}$; (g) $\frac{9}{32}$.
5. (a) $6\frac{2}{3}$ autos; (b) $2\frac{1}{6}$.
6. $\frac{8}{21}$.
7. 210 bottles.
8. 16 pieces.
9. Six.
10. No; $\frac{3}{4}$ is not exactly divisible by $\frac{1}{6}$.
11. $48 \times (1 - \frac{1}{2} + \frac{1}{3} - \frac{3}{8} + \frac{1}{8}) = 48 - 24 + 16 - 18 + 6 = 28$.
12. 60 canfuls.

Problems Set 23, page 186

1. (a) $\frac{20}{3}$; (c) $\frac{259}{16}$; (e) $\frac{9}{8}$.
2. (a) $9\frac{2}{3}$; (c) $4\frac{4}{7}$; (e) $26\frac{1}{2}$.
3. (a) $33\frac{1}{6}$; (c) $131\frac{91}{120}$.
4. (a) $11\frac{4}{5}$; (c) $22\frac{1}{2}$; (e) $15\frac{51}{56}$.
6. (a) $143\frac{1}{3}$; (c) 42.
7. (a) $270\frac{8}{9}$; (c) $17,875\frac{3}{5}$.
9. (a) increased by $54\frac{11}{56}$; (b) increased by $20\frac{34}{35}$; (c) $43\frac{1}{5}$ times larger; (d) no change; (e) $\frac{57}{12}$ or $4\frac{3}{4}$ times larger; (f) $10\frac{9}{16}$ times larger; (g) increased by $17\frac{23}{40}$.
10. $1\frac{37}{72}$ ft.
11. $68\frac{3}{4}$ years old.
12. (a) $16\frac{2}{3}$; (b) $16\frac{4}{7}$; (c) $279\frac{3}{8}$; (d) $3\frac{3}{4}$.

Problems Set 24, page 196

[handwritten: .00003]

2. (a) .56; (b) .217; (c) .032; (d) .0003; (e) .300; (f) .001002; (g) .0000017; (h) $.0\frac{1}{7}$; (i) .000000061; (j) 400.036; (k) $3.0\frac{3}{5}$; (l) 200.0008; (m) $.3\frac{1}{5}$; (n) $.16\frac{3}{4}$.
3. (a) three hundred sixty-two thousandths; *[handwritten: no supplied]*
   (c) one hundred thousand two-millionths;
   (e) four million, three hundred eighty-six thousand, two hundred seventy-four ten-millionths;

(g) seven hundred-billionths;

(i) three thousand four hundred and six ten-thousandths;

(k) two hundred and seven thousandths.

4. (a) $\frac{3}{100}$; (c) $\frac{3}{400}$; (e) $\frac{54}{125}$; (g) $\frac{3}{800}$; (i) $\frac{3}{80}$; (k) $\frac{1}{50}$.

5. (a) $16\frac{1}{50}$; (c) $37\frac{1}{2}$; (e) $14\frac{8}{25}$.

6. (a) .34; (c) .592; (e) .225.

7. (a) .037 units = .37 tenths = 3.7 hundredths
$\qquad\qquad\qquad\qquad\qquad\qquad = 37$ thousandths;

(c) 37 units = .37 hundreds = 3.7 tens
$\qquad\qquad\qquad\qquad = 370$ tenths = 37,000 thousandths;

(e) $.0\frac{1}{2}$ units = $\frac{1}{2}$ tenth = 5 hundredths
$\qquad\qquad\qquad\qquad\quad = 50$ thousandths.

8. (a) $\frac{7}{8}$; (b) $\frac{151}{625}$; (c) $\frac{139}{432}$; (d) $\frac{342}{343}$; (e) $1\frac{21}{32}$; (f) $17\frac{8}{25}$.

Problems Set 25, page 212

1. (a) 26.375; (b) 99.61; (c) 500.740.

2. (a) 27.89; (b) 19.296; (c) 246.58; (d) 4.19995.

3. (a) 43,680; 57,000; 4,632.9.

(c) 4,368,000; 5,700,000; 463,290.

4. (a) 436.8; 570; 46.329. (c) 4.368; 5.7; .46329.

5. (a) 436.8; 570; 46.329. (c) 4.368; 5.7; .46329.

6. (a) 856.9176; (b) 42.6852; (c) 18,548.94; (d) .00021.

7. (a) 4.23; (b) .0024; (c) 2,680.

8. (a) 1.129; (b) 16.059; (c) 1.200.

9. (a) terminate, 2 places;   (g) non-terminating;

(c) non-terminating;   (i) terminate, 3 places.

(e) terminate, 3 places;

10. (a) $.2\dot{8}$; (c) $.5\dot{3}$; (e) .175; (g) $.\dot{3}8461\dot{5}$; (i) .292.

11. (a) $\frac{1}{33}$; (b) $\frac{11}{111}$; (c) $\frac{40}{101}$; (d) $\frac{1349}{9900}$.

12. (a) 2,781.2; (c) 6,103.3; (e) 6.147; (g) .1057.

13. 43.5 miles per hour.

14. (a) 22 ft 3 in. $\times$ 16 ft 8 in.; (b) 2 ft 11 in. $\times$ 1 ft 0 in.

15. 29.84 feet.

Problems Set 26, page 219

1. (a) $\frac{21}{25} > \frac{4}{5}$;   (c) $\frac{5}{9} > \frac{3}{7}$;   (e) $\frac{7}{12} > \frac{6}{11}$;

(b) $\frac{5}{8} > \frac{3}{5}$;   (d) $\frac{5}{7} > \frac{3}{5}$;   (f) $\frac{5}{24} > \frac{3}{19}$.

2. (a) .4, 40%;   (m) 2.5, 250%;

(c) $\frac{3}{50}$, 6%;   (o) $\frac{1}{40}$, .025;

(e) $\frac{12}{25}$, .48;   (q) .3125, $31\frac{1}{4}$%;

(g) $.2\dot{6}$, $26\frac{2}{3}$%;   (s) $\frac{86}{99}$, $86\frac{86}{99}$%;

(i) $\frac{1}{2000}$, .05%;   (u) 2.3125, $231\frac{1}{4}$%;

(k) $\frac{1}{200}$, .005;   (w) $\frac{1}{800}$, .00125.

3. (a) $\frac{13}{43}, \frac{26}{42}, \frac{13}{18}, \frac{13}{17}, \frac{13}{14}, \frac{26}{19}, \frac{13}{9}$;

(c) .038, .3084, .369, .37, .375, 3.7.

4. (a) $\frac{39}{99}$, .376, $\frac{3}{8}$, .374, 37%;

(c) 1,260 tenths, 121%, $\frac{5}{4}$, $1\frac{17}{98}$, .125.

7.   (a) $\frac{9}{10}$, $\frac{7}{8}$, $\frac{4}{5}$, $\frac{4}{3}$, $\frac{3}{5}$, $\frac{5}{3}$;

    (c) 102%, 1.09, 1.1, $\frac{7}{8}$, 86%, $\frac{8}{7}$.

8.   (a) double the fraction;   (e) resulting fraction is larger when
    (b) double the fraction;   original fraction is proper; smaller
    (c) quarter the fraction;   when original fraction is improper;
    (d) triple the fraction;   (f) no change.

Problems Set 27, page 228

1.   (a) 120; (c) 45.2; (e) 24; (g) 150%; (i) 56; (k) $2\frac{1}{2}$%; (m) 200.
2. $.74.   3.   15%.   4. $463.20.
5. $99.00.   6. $94.50.   7. $0 — nothing.
8.   20% gain; $28\frac{4}{7}$% decrease.
9. $55,000.   10.   12 hits.   11.   5%.
12. $681.   13. $956.   14.   25%.
15.   36,500 books.

Problems Set 28, page 243

2.   (a) 6,336 in.; 528 ft; 176 yd; $\frac{1}{10}$ mile.
    (c) $\frac{14}{125}$ ton, $\frac{1}{10}$ long ton; 3,584 oz; 448,000 grains.
    (e) 8 months; 240 days; 5,760 hr; 345,600 min; 20,736,000 sec.
3.   (a) 4 yd 2 ft 4 in.;   (e) 3 gal 2 qt 1 pt;
    (c) 4 lb 12 oz;   (g) 3 hr 42 min 24 sec.
4.   12 ft 4 in.
5.   (a) 13 weeks 2 days 18 hr;
        35 weeks 5 days 0 hr;
        232 weeks 1 day 0 hr.
    (c) 10 gal 3 qt 1 pt;
        29 gal 0 qt 0 pt;
        188 gal 2 qt 0 pt.
6.   8 ft 8 in.
7.   528 in./sec.
8.   11 trips.
9.   (a)   .00423   myriameter
             .0423   kilometer
            .423   hectometer
          4.23   decameters
         42.3   meters
         423   decimeters
       4,230   centimeters
     42,300   millimeters
10.   (a) 1.61 miles; (b) 7.77 miles; (c) 6.84 km.
11.   (a) 1.06 qt; (b) 3.77 liters; (c) 2.12 pt.
12.   (a) .91 m; (b) 100 in.; (c) .39 in.
13.   134.43 liters.
14.   (a) 27 grams, 5 decigrams;
    (b) 1 gram, 7 decigrams, 3 centigrams, 6 milligrams;
    (c) 5 decigrams, 9 centigrams, 5 milligrams.

Problems Set 29, page 251

2. (a) tenth of inch ($\pm.05$ in.);
    (c) ounce ($\pm.5$ oz);
    (e) tenth of liter (or deciliter) ($\pm.5$ deciliter or ±5 centiliter);
    (h) minute ($\pm.5$ min or ±30 sec).

3. (a) first; since $\dfrac{\frac{1}{8}}{2} > \dfrac{\frac{1}{32}}{2}$;

    (b) first; since $\dfrac{\frac{1}{8}}{\text{dist.}} > \dfrac{\frac{1}{32}}{\text{dist.}}$.

4. (a) $22\frac{1}{2}$ in., $36\frac{1}{4}$ in., $27\frac{2}{7}$ in., $32\frac{3}{8}$ in., $46\frac{0}{16}$ in.;
    (c) 7 gal, 14 gal, 23 gal, 3 gal, 8 gal.

5. $3\frac{1}{2}$ in., 6 ft, 3.2 in., 3 yd 4 in., 7.2 miles.

6. (a) $22\frac{1}{2}$ in., $36\frac{1}{4}$ in., $32\frac{3}{8}$ in., $27\frac{2}{7}$ in., $46\frac{0}{16}$ in.;
    (c) 7 gal, 3 gal, 8 gal, 14 gal, 23 gal.

7. (a) 4; (c) 5; (e) 4; (g) 5; (i) 5; (k) 2.

8. (a) .66667; (c) .046875; (e) .02439.

9. (a) 4.63×10^8;   (g) 3.68×10^6;
    (c) 4.62×10^{-4};   (i) 7.2×10^{10}.
    (e) 2×10^0;

10. e, j, i, c, g, a, f, b, d, h.

11. c, i, j, e, g, a, f, b, d, h.

Problems Set 30, page 263

1. (a) 978; (b) 764.

2. (a) 1; (b) 4; (c) 7 hundred; (d) 375.

3. (a) 15o; (b) 141; (c) 17 thousand, or 17,ooo; (d) 10 ten-thousand, or 100,000.

4. (a) 13.3; (b) 4.4; (c) 41; (d) 1.7; (e) 3,920.

5. 254,ooo square rods.

6. $10o,ooo per month.

7. (a) 11 in.; (b) .010 in.; (c) 145.7 ft; (d) 2o miles.

8. 46.4 lb.   9.   25o cu ft.

10. 2,72o cars per week.

11. 324 lb.   12.   70o bags.

13. (a) 27o cm; (b) .39 in.

14. 2.3 million dollars.

15. $\frac{48}{60} = .77 \times 875 = 67$o Maryland bushels.

INDEX

275